OPERATIONS RESEARCH SOCIETY
OF AMERICA

Publications in Operations Research
Number 12

OPERATIONS RESEARCH
IN
SELLERS' COMPETITION

A Stochastic Microtheory

S. SANKAR SENGUPTA

MANAGEMENT SCIENCE CENTER
UNIVERSITY OF PENNSYLVANIA, PHILADELPHIA

JOHN WILEY & SONS, INC., NEW YORK · LONDON · SYDNEY

PUBLICATIONS IN OPERATIONS RESEARCH

Operations Research Society of America

Editor for Publications in Operations Research
DAVID B. HERTZ

No. 1. QUEUES, INVENTORIES AND MAINTENANCE
Philip M. Morse

No. 2. FINITE QUEUEING TABLES
L. G. Peck and R. N. Hazelwood

No. 3. EFFICIENCY IN GOVERNMENT THROUGH SYSTEMS ANALYSIS
Roland N. McKean

No. 4. A COMPREHENSIVE BIBLIOGRAPHY ON OPERATIONS RESEARCH
Operations Research Group, Case Institute

No. 5. PROGRESS IN OPERATIONS RESEARCH, VOLUME I
Edited by Russell L. Ackoff

No. 6. STATISTICAL MANAGEMENT OF INVENTORY SYSTEMS
Harvey M. Wagner

No. 7. PRICE, OUTPUT, AND INVENTORY POLICY
Edwin S. Mills

No. 8. A COMPREHENSIVE BIBLIOGRAPHY ON OPERATIONS RESEARCH, 1957–1958
Operations Research Group, Case Institute

No. 9. PROGRESS IN OPERATIONS RESEARCH, VOLUME II
David B. Hertz and Roger T. Eddison

No. 10. DECISION AND VALUE THEORY
Peter C. Fishburn

No. 11. HANDBOOK OF THE POISSON DISTRIBUTION
Frank A. Haight

No. 12. OPERATIONS RESEARCH IN SELLERS' COMPETITION:
A STOCHASTIC MICROTHEORY
S. Sankar Sengupta

No. 13. BAYESIAN DECISION PROBLEMS AND MARKOV CHAINS
James J. Martin, Jr.

PREFACE

This book attempts to answer the following question: given the form of competition and the organization of the market, how do different modes of action by individual business enterprises result in (a) certain patterns of relationship among observable market variables and (b) specific measures of uncertainty with which a firm's outcomes would appear to the firm itself. I have restricted the discussion to competition among sellers. The problems with which *Operations Research in Sellers' Competition* has been oriented are those of pricing, selling costs, management of production and inventories, and deciding when and how much to invest in fixed capital.

In spirit this book is normative; its purpose is to develop the structure of optimal decision rules for the problems mentioned above. The situations in which decisions have to be taken and variables have to be decided on are, of course, dependent on specific types of environmental setup; but the decisions in question are those taken by an *individual firm*. Thus the frame of analysis is one of microeconomics. To many this viewpoint may appear to be biased. Such bias, however, is not only natural to operations research, its roots also lie deep in the nature of the environment from which problems emerge and certain variables qualify as decision variables.

What, then, is special about *this* micro approach? Existing treatments in this category (particularly the more formal ones) tend to lose sight of the fact that models are fundamentally dependent on the institutional setup in which an organization functions. Part of this may be due to the extreme emphasis on normative analysis. To justify itself, however, a model must serve as a means of scanning the possible and probable responses (of the system of interest) to a course of action, *given the environment*. I have emphasized this almost *ad nauseum*. I have attempted to show how models—even of uncertainty—can be built from a careful consideration of the environment, that is, of the operational aspects of the situation in which uncertainty makes its appearance.

The orientation of this work is more analytical (hence, necessarily speculative) than empirical; it attempts to generate hypotheses about events before they occur. Nevertheless, all of it is applicable in the sense that the basic categories employed in the analysis are *observable*. When I have not been able to derive my hypotheses by strictly analytical methods, I have made extensive use of computer experiments. This is particularly true of the propositions that concern some aspects of the outcome of pure competition. In other contexts I have used the computer as a means of generating the data needed to illustrate (not verify) the abstract implications of my models.

The content of this book has its origin in the (now) classical theory of the firm on the one hand and probability theory on the other. I have maintained that the most fruitful approach is not to study competition as such but rather to analyze classes of competition. An essential step in this analysis is to uncover the "dimensions" of competition; that is the institutions (including the nature of the product, the distribution channels and trade practices, and information and communication) leading to the consummation of a transaction, the means or weapons of competition, and the outcomes affecting the interests of the individual sellers. In essence, this, too, is a "classical" outlook. The analysis, however, makes an important departure from the classical line of thinking. In the latter a major role is played by the *number* of sellers and by an individual seller's perception of his position in the market; these factors serve to characterize the parameters of a firm's sales anticipations. I have maintained, on the contrary, that the number of sellers is not the relevant issue. What is significant is how this number affects the processes by which buyers and sellers come into mutual contact and transactions take place. Similarly, I have de-emphasized "perception" and asserted that competition should be viewed as a set of acts rather than as a state of things or feelings. I assert that this is justified in the context of my principal concern, namely, an effective application of the analysis to decision-making at the micro level. It is on these grounds that I have freed myself from the burden of "determinate equilibrium" of the group (of sellers). It is no wonder, then, that conjectural variations, leader-follower relationships, bargaining, side payments, and similar words and concepts have no place in this analysis.

It also explains why I have stayed away from the framework of game theory.

The material in this book is organized in four parts. Part one is a review of the salient aspects of economic theory (of competition) from the viewpoint of methodology. I have attempted to remove some of the lacunae of problem formulation and to establish a uniform frame of reference with relatively few essential components. Chapters 4 to 6 demonstrate the use of this special frame of reference in the derivation of the static (i.e., pertaining to a single period) aspects of the probability distributions of sales of individual firms in oligopolistic competition. Problems of monopolistic competition in large and relatively small groups are also considered. These results are drawn on in Chapter 7, in which an attempt has been made to derive some qualitative propositions concerning relationships between price, profits, and market share. Chapter 8 is devoted to the analysis of the dynamic (i.e., multiperiod) decision situations. The results are used in Chapter 9 with a view toward throwing light on the general question of "apparent" collusion. Another class of dynamic models of sales probabilities is developed in Chapter 14 and applied in Chapter 15 to the problem of capacity expansion. Part three is concerned with static and dynamic models of probability distributions of prices in pure competition. Some attempt has been made in Chapter 12 to explain how price anticipations tend to be self-reinforcing in a purely competitive market.

Operations Research in Sellers' Competition is and should be regarded as an outline of a program rather than a set of results ripe for direct application. A book of this nature cannot have a conclusion, hence there is no concluding chapter. I am presenting it to my colleagues in the profession of operations research with the feeling that in its varied applications its approach will acquire a content far richer than I can now imagine.

To the English-speaking world and to the mathematicians I owe my sincere apologies: to the former because I was not born with that language and to the latter because I was not raised in their culture. I am painfully aware of the lack of uniformity of symbolism, and I may have left the impression of belaboring trivial matters.

I am deeply indebted to Professor Russell L. Ackoff whose generous encouragement was more than instrumental in the completion of this book. I have also drawn on the unpublished doctoral dissertations of my former pupils, Dilip K. Guha, Robert C. Hain, Jose Trevino, and Earl E. Bomberger, all of whom worked with me on a project initiated under my guidance at the Case Institute of Technology, Cleveland, Ohio. I owe the bulk of Chapters 4, 7, 8, and 9 to Dr. Guha and Dr. Hain, Chapter 13 to Dr. Trevino, Chapters 14 and 15 to Dr. Bomberger, and some derivations in Chapter 5 to Mr. P. R. Satyamurty. The model of speculative inventory holding in Chapter 12 owes its origin to my former colleague, Professor Gifford H. Symonds. All errors of form and content, of course, are mine. I must also thank Miss Constance Cini for the loving care with which she handled a clumsy manuscript.

S. SANKAR SENGUPTA

Philadelphia, Pennsylvania
February 1967

INTRODUCTION

The practicing economist often encounters a situation in which a firm has been experiencing fluctuations in sales in spite of maintaining a stable policy in regard to its prices or selling expenses. There is a class of more difficult problem situations in which the economist is called on to advise on pricing or selling efforts policy. These are not small problems; nor are the fortunes at stake small by any standards. The practitioner has to choose between the formalism of mathematical economics and the statistical estimation procedures of econometrics. The choice is difficult, to say the least.

The difficulty lies in what seems to me to be the following. Neither mathematical economics nor econometrics has aimed directly at the heart of the problem: how to develop models of probability distribution of events or relationships among appropriate variables? The typical style of treatment in mathematical economics is deterministic; neither the variables nor the relationships among them are seen from the viewpoint of uncertainty. Even in econometry models are formulated in terms of mean values or at best as implicit conditional expectations. The most we get from mathematical formalism and metric methods of economic theory is a set of quantitative relationships which is supposed to exist among the (random) data. No serious attempt has been made so far in the direction of concrete hypotheses of the nature of probability distributions of random terms or "disturbances." I contend that the problems of "specification of errors" which plague the econometrist cannot be treated as purely statistical. For instance, the whole issue of deciding whether the errors in some equations are autocorrelated rests on a deep and thorough understanding of the nature of forces that give rise to the data.

Instead of relegating randomness to the status of unobservable disturbances, I have addressed myself to its explicit recognition. In this sense the work presented here may be looked on as a bridge between formal and quantitative thinking in economics. I have made a systematic attempt to build models of randomness—that is, probability distributions—directly from a qualitative knowledge of the environment in which the observables are generated. I have chosen the field of sellers' competition as a proving ground for my approach, for this is a straightforward opportunity to consider a rich variety of environmental factors and accounts for the theme of this book: given a description of market institutions and modes of communication and contact, one can develop a model of the probability distribution of *sales*—when firms can, to a degree, set prices—or of *prices* when firms are price takers. If fluctuating levels of sales are experienced by a firm, even though its price policy has not changed, is it not more natural to consider the sales as values of a random variable and try to explain its probability structure? Why not employ some axiomatics in developing the distribution as functionally dependent on the price offered? In short, I raise this question: why not build models of the measures of *random* dependence of sales,

$$\Pr[\text{sales} \leq s; \ \text{price} = p] = \int_0^s f(x, p) \, dx$$

or

$$\Pr[\text{sales} \leq s; \ \text{price} = p, \text{selling efforts} = a] = \int_0^s g(x, p, a) \, dx,$$

on the firm's course of action such as the price set and/or selling costs incurred? To many of those who are as accustomed to received doctrines as myself, these questions may strike an unfamiliar note. For instance, some will be inclined to argue how or why all this is different from the "good old" price elasticity. Without being facetious, I claim that here is a case of "product differentiation."

Let me explain why. Suppose someone has estimated the price elasticity of sales (not demand) of a firm. First, in order to "sell" this to the sponsor, a *confidence interval* for the estimate must be furnished. But can it be calculated without a theory or a defensible speculation of the nature of the underlying random variable? Next, on a narrower level of technicality, what is the justification for treating either the sales or the price data as nonautocorrelated? To those who would still maintain that these are fine theoretical issues with little practical significance I have nothing to offer. I am presenting a method and a style of thinking to those who are often inclined to do something about these questions.

More needs to be said about the probability distributions (of sales or any other appropriate variable). In mathematical theory probability is a measure of a (measurable) function; the *existence* of a probability *is* the *measurability* of the function on a measurable sample space. Two deep problems are involved here. First, there is the statistical stability of the *empirical* probabilities or frequencies. An increase in the number of observations—if feasible—does not provide a solution unless the mathematical function satisfies the conditions of measurability (i.e., well behaved in some sense). This trivial remark is appropriate: the sense in which a random variable pertaining to a competitive situation can be said to be measurable—as seen from the viewpoint of probability theory—has a well-defined interpretation in terms of competitive environment and practices. That the stability of competitive environment and practices is at the root of the measurability (i.e., the condition for computing probabilities) of some outcomes of competition is the underlying theme of this book.

The second of the two problems raised is a little more complicated. Let me pose it as follows: given that a function has a probability (of attaining some magnitude), what determines that probability? To a mathematician this again is a trivial matter: the *structural properties* of the function are, of course, what determine the (probability) measure of the domain in which the function attains or does not exceed a given value. The particular function is always a matter of choice, but the domain or the argument variable on the one hand and the structure of the dependence of the function values on the argument on the other are due fundamentally to the *nature of the phenomena* under consideration and the processes that give rise to them. I have presented models of this dependence, together with the probability distributions, by making use of both common sense and "measure theoretic" constructions. In my view the latter are more direct and fundamental. I am not satisfied with a statement such as "*let $f(x, p) \, dx$ be the probability that sales lie between x and $x + dx$ when the price offered is p.*" I have tried to probe into the origins of $f(x, p)$ in the institutional setup of competition.

The same viewpoint is carried forward into the realm of dynamic analysis—that is, the analysis of situations in which the individual firm changes its pricing and/or selling-expense policy. The underlying setting is that of multiperiod rather than single-period decisions. In this context I have maintained that the essential problem is one of characterizing and interpreting the conditions in which conditional probabilities such as

$$\Pr [\text{sales} \leq s'; \ \text{price} = p \pm h \mid \text{sales} = s; \ \text{price} = p]$$

or

$$\Pr [\text{sales} \leq s'; \ \text{selling cost} = c \pm k \mid \text{sales} = s; \ \text{selling cost} = c]$$

may exist. From an analysis of the correlation between the sales at the two levels of price offered (and/or selling costs incurred) I have attempted to establish certain conditions that are equivalent to the existence of what Professor Fellner calls "coordination." Also, the magnitudes and the functional forms of the conditional probabilities and correlation functions are shown to be associated with the *actual* (not perceived) market strength of the firm. To the Bayesian reader the following should be abundantly clear: my derivations lead to a very important "prior," namely, the *type* of distribution function that can be modified in light of what the decision-making unit in the firm "feels" about competition. It is in the latter sense that I have left the door open for subjective elements to enter at an appropriate point: the *application* of the analysis. My approach does not furnish the numerical values of the moments of the distributions, because in the general case I look on the parameters as values of certain functions and because I take as my "input" only the broadest qualitative information about the structure of the market. The problem of estimation of the moments still remains the domain of the statistician who is now considerably better equipped with the frame in which the estimation and testing are to be performed.

In concluding this introduction I must point out that my principal aim has been one of making the classical microeconomic theory more operational with a view to making it applicable in decision-making situations. In the process I have abandoned some of the familiar elements of that theory as well as some of its more recent formulations. Incidentally, I have been able to show how in a wide class of situations the external observer may infer "collusion," although in fact there is none. I am not claiming originality for this book as a contribution to economics or mathematics. I do believe, however, that it provides a basis for reconsidering and enriching some of the analyses currently brought to bear on a firm's optimal course of action.

CONTENTS

PART ONE

1 SOME DIMENSIONS OF COMPETITION   1

1. Introduction, 1
2. Sellers' Action: The First Dimension, 2
3. Consumers' Choice: The Second Dimension, 4
4. Sellers' State of Mind: The Third Dimension, 4
5. A Modified Scheme, 7

2 THE CLASSICAL ORIENTATION   8

1. Equilibrium and Determinacy, 8
2. Conjectural Variations: Indeterminacy, 11
3. Leadership, 14
4. Summary, 16

3 THE PROBLEM OF FEWNESS REEXAMINED   17

1. An Objective Framework, 17
2. Purpose, Content, and Method, 18
3. Uncertainty in Sales, 20
4. Critique of the New Approach, 24

PART TWO

4 OLIGOPOLY: STATIC MODELS   **26**

1. Undifferentiated Oligopoly, 26
2. Differentiated Oligopoly, 32
3. The "Large Group": A Special Case, 37

**5 MONOPOLISTIC COMPETITION: MACROMODELS
AND MICROMODELS**   **41**

1. Multinomial Distribution of Sales, 41
2. A Micromodel: Bivariate Binomial Probabilities, 44
3. A Limiting Distribution: Bivariate Gaussian, 48

**6 MONOPOLISTIC COMPETITION: THE LARGE
GROUP CASE**   **52**

1. Interaction: Covariance of Sales, 53
2. A Digression: Models of Bias, 55
3. Summary: A Note on Skewness, 59

7 PRICE, PROFITS, AND MARKET SHARE   **62**

1. Undifferentiated Oligopoly: Profits and Market Share, 63
2. Tradeoffs between Profits and Market Share, 67
3. Differentiated Oligopoly, 70
4. Conflict of Objectives, 75

8 MULTIPERIOD PROBABILITY MODELS   **79**

1. Sales Transition Probabilities: Undifferentiated Oligopoly, 80
2. Sales Transition Probabilities: Differentiated Oligopoly, 87
3. Some Observations on the Markov Representation, 92
4. An Application: Analysis of Price Rigidity, 95

9 PRICES, PRODUCTION AND INVENTORIES   99

   1. Maximizing Short-Run Profits, 99
   2. The Structure of Decision Problem, 100
   3. The Structure of Optimal Decision Rule: Undifferentiated
      Oligopoly, 103
   4. Structure of Optimal Decisions: Differentiated Oligopoly, 108

10 A VERIFICATION   119

   1. The Nature of Verification, 119
   2. Simulation: Reproducing the (S, M, Y)-Complex of an
      Undifferentiated Oligopoly, 121
   3. Testing the Binomial Model and $\sigma(p)$, 125
   4. Reproducing the (S, M, Y)-Complex of a Differentiated
      Oligopoly, 128
   5. Testing the Poisson Hypothesis, 132

PART THREE

11 PURE COMPETITION: RANDOM PRICES   135

   1. Characteristics of Market Prices, 135
   2. Derivation of Price Probabilities, 137
   3. Joint Distribution of Price and Aggregate Quantity, 141
   4. An Induced Randomness, 148
   5. A Family of Dynamic Models, 150

12 REINFORCEMENT OF ANTICIPATIONS   158

   1. Anticipations: Formation and Revision, 158
   2. Speculative Inventory Holding, 160
   3. Summary of Observations, 163

**13 PURE COMPETITION: INVENTORY-PRODUCTION
DECISIONS**   170

   1. The Case of Known Price Transition Probabilities, 171
   2. Inventory Management with Price Forecasts, 175
   3. A Model of Random Withdrawals, 182

PART FOUR

14 SOME EXTENDED MODELS OF UNCERTAINTY   **188**

1. A Special Behavior Assumption, 188
2. Some Implications of the Renewal Model, 191
3. A Test of the Markov Transitions of Sales, 194

**15 AN APPLICATION: INVESTMENT DECISIONS
AND PRICE POLICY**   **202**

1. Some Primary Concepts, 202
2. An Application of the "Renewal" Model, 205

APPENDIX

**I AN ALTERNATIVE DERIVATION OF SALES
PROBABILITIES IN A DIFFERENTIATED OLIGOPOLY**   **213**

**II ON THE CONCAVITY OF AVERAGE
PROFITS FUNCTION**   **220**

REFERENCES   **223**

INDEX   **227**

OPERATIONS RESEARCH
IN
SELLERS' COMPETITION

PART ONE

Chapter 1

SOME DIMENSIONS
OF COMPETITION

Vastly different phenomena are conveniently summed up under "competition." Therefore, a systematic analysis must begin with a clear statement of the *dimensions* of competition. These include (a) the institutions, (b) the means employed, and (c) the outcomes of interest to the individuals and groups involved in an instance of competition. Some of the classical dimensions are retained while others are greatly modified; special attention is paid to the institutions that have direct influence upon the consummation of transactions.

1. INTRODUCTION

"Competition" is a word that has several interrelated but distinct connotations, but their common content is too vague and inclusive to make it definable in a simple fashion. Vastly different phenomena are conveniently summed up under "competition." The situation is no better even with such delimitation as competition among sellers. Machlup [40] makes the following observations:

"The various effects, good and evil, which have been ascribed to economic competition in general and to competition between sellers in particular could not possibly all be the effects of one and the same set of phenomena. It is sometimes useful to reverse the logical procedure and deduce from the alleged results the assumptions which an author must have made implicitly when he started from the condition of 'competition' among the sellers. Such an examination reveals that the competition that eliminates excessive profits is something else than the competition that makes a producer produce an output at which his marginal cost is equal to his selling price; that the competition which gives the purchaser more freedom of choice so that he is not subjected to the alternative of either

1

turning to one single purveyor or else doing without is not the same as the competition that weeds out the inefficient; that the competition which prevents different prices for the same commodity from prevailing at one time in a market is something else than the competition which forces a small firm to give up its independence; that the competition which leads to an increase in the advertising outlays in an industry is not the same as the competition which reduces the price differentials between different localities to the cost of transport, and those for different 'future' transactions to the cost of storage; that the competition which leads to continual improvements in the qualities of products is something else than the competition which makes earnings proportionate to efficiency."

These observations suggest that we should first attempt a clear demarcation of the institutions, the means employed, and the outcomes of whatever may be chosen to be called "competition." The outcomes, again, should be distinguished as those concerning the individual producer-seller, those concerning *the* group of sellers, and those concerning *other* groups or, even, the national economy. When enough distinctions have been drawn and the problem has been "well posed," there is a possibility, however, that the generalizing scientist may not find enough material to work with, for the study may have been reduced to the status of a detailed case study. Although such dangers always exist, we may nonetheless attempt a general *method* of analysis; this is the principal aim of this book.

2. SELLERS' ACTION: THE FIRST DIMENSION

2.1 The institutional basis of competition may be defined in a number of ways. However, an efficient way is to analyze what the competition is *about*. If two producers are producing the same product, the supplies of these products are certainly competing, even though the producers in question may not know each other. This is competition between goods of the same kind. Competition between goods need not be confined to those of the same kind, although very strong similarity between them brings about a high degree of substitutability, hence a strong measure of rivalry. In a very general sense even vastly dissimilar products compete among themselves for the consumer's dollar.

2.2 If products "compete" with one another in this general fashion, there is no room for "personal" competition among the sellers involved. Even the competition between very close substitutes may remain "impersonal," in spite of the fact that they may be sold in the same market. Suppose that the products are *perfect* substitutes, so that a buyer failing to buy from one seller will not lose anything by approaching the second seller and making his buy from him. If one of the sellers has regularly sold N units of the product and if now another N units of identical quality are offered for sale, the second batch of N units will "compete" with the first batch, whether the second batch is put up for sale by this seller or some other seller. In other words, even the increment of output of a producer-seller competes with his own original offerings.[1] Put another way, that goods compete with one another for entry into the consumers' system of preferences does not necessarily imply competition between the sellers.

2.3 It appears, then, that the key question is not what or who the competition is between; rather it is more closely concerned with what the competition is *for*. To be more precise, we should consider competition as an action or set of *actions* instead of a state of things or feeling. The actions referred to are those taken by sellers *to enhance the sales* of a given product.

There is a vast range of methods by which sellers attempt to increase their sales. A seller may reduce his selling price, improve the quality of his product, render some attendant services to the customers, publicize the quality and availability of his product and enhance the appeal of the product by advertising, improve and activate the channels through which his product is distributed, help his customers by free delivery and convenient credit terms, and so on. Although these methods are designed to increase the attractiveness of a seller's own offerings to the buyers, there are other devices—regardless of their legality or "fairness"—by which a seller obstructs or reduces the effectiveness of the offerings of his competitors. Such actions, again, may take a variety of forms: A seller may disparage the quality of his competitor's product, intimidate or inconvenience the buyers who have been habitual customers of his competitors, or obstruct the operations of the competitors by restricting their access to materials.

Among the methods that are designed to increase the attractiveness of a seller's own offerings to the buyers, two are basic: (a) reducing the price, directly or indirectly (for example, by allowing credit terms, free delivery, and so on) and (b) increasing the selling effort.[2] Precisely *how* these devices are employed depends on the institutional setup of the market in which the

[1] "In this sense competition between all products and competition between all parts of the output of any producer will exist regardless of whether there is only one seller or a large number of sellers in the market. The only difference is that not all sellers are equally conscious of this sort of competition," Machlup [40, p. 82].

[2] No distinction is made between advertising a given *product* and making improvements of the product itself. In making improvements the variation of quality necessarily involves additional costs. Such costs can always be absorbed into an equivalent addition to advertising outlays.

firm (seller) may be operating. The important dimension is the action of the seller. In Chapter 4 a detailed demonstration is given in which considerations of this kind play a crucial role: they determine the *kind of uncertainty* associated with the sales of an individual seller.

3. CONSUMERS' CHOICE: THE SECOND DIMENSION

The second important dimension is the institutional setup in which buyers choose among sellers and express their choices. Evidently, a good deal depends on the availability of information and on whether the buyers can bargain individually with individual sellers. Also, the existence or nonexistence of communication among the buyers themselves plays a role in shaping the uncertainty associated with the sales of an individual seller. The heart of the matter, in other words, is related to consumers' freedom of choice and the associated issue, namely, how they exercise it. Almost everyone would agree that the feeling that the consumers have a *range* of alternatives—large or small—and that they can compare the services of different sellers before deciding to choose one is an advantage that most consumers would not miss. It is also important to take into account the possible impact of distribution systems prevalent in an industry and other institutional setups that induce some measure of "laziness" on the part of some or all of the potential buyers. Also, it is equally important to realize that there are markets—especially the ones in which industrial raw materials or equipment are traded—in which the customers are likely to "compare the services" more actively than in others. In other words, the disposition and behavior of the *buyers* provide one dimension of sellers' competition. Models of competition must consider the mechanism—institutional and psychological—through which a buyer exercises his freedom to select his purchase from several sellers.[3]

4. SELLERS' STATE OF MIND: THE THIRD DIMENSION

4.1 A seller may *feel* that he is *competing* with an unknown and indefinite number of sellers selling the same or similar product. If he knows that no one of them has any special importance, each single seller may have the feeling that the "others would not care about what he does." This absence of real rivalry or rival-consciousness is the core of competition in a market of many sellers (polypoly). The individual seller is aware of

---

[3] From the viewpoint of traditional economic theory as well as of the theory to be developed in this monograph, this is only *one* sense of competition among sellers. This sense implies almost nothing about any *real* rivalry between the sellers or about their way of acting or about the sizes of their supply or their rates of profits.

his negligibly small share of the market and he thinks—and this thinking is reinforced by all that happens in the market—that none of his competitors would feel any appreciable outcome of his actions. Thus the seller will not *anticipate* any reactions from the rivals. Situations like this are also characterized as *pure* competition.[4] Purely competitive situations are conceivable in which the individual seller believes that he can secure more sales at the expense of others but that the others will hardly ever notice it.[5]

4.2 Sellers belonging to this category may again be subdivided into two groups: those who have unlimited sales opportunities but no choice of prices and those with limited sales outlets but *some* ability to choose the price. The first category consists of the price-*takers*. Sellers are price-takers because the single seller is "unimportant" and because the goods are so undistinguishable (by the sellers' labels) that an individual seller would lose all the sales opportunities if he tried to ask more than the going market price. Price, in other words, appears in the role of a parameter in the decisions of the single seller: the price is *given* to the seller and all he can do is to sell or not to sell. This is perfectly consistent with the fact that the seller *knows* that the market price will fall if more is offered for sales, for he has no reason to suppose that it is *his* relatively negligible supply that would depress the price. If nobody else tried to sell more at the same time, the price would *probably* not fall in spite of his sale, and if many others tried to sell more the price would fall even though he refrained from selling. Thus he concludes—and the developments in the market justify his belief—that he cannot influence the price: The price would be what it would be whether he sold little or much. The second category consists of the price-*makers*. In the kind of competition under consideration the sellers have a choice of possible selling prices. They have this choice because there are differences in the product offered which allow the seller to suppose that a segment of his customers prefer his product to similar products put out by his competitors. If the number of sellers offering closely "similar" products is still so large that the sellers

---

[4] Pure competition and Chamberlin's "monopolistic competition in the large group" require that no firm be large enough in relation to the market to be able to affect the value of the relevant market variables to the extent that any other firm could be influenced by that effect. Each firm knows that whether another firm violates an agreement does not depend on whether *it* violates, and this means that each firm has an interest in violating (Fellner [22, pp. 41–44]).

[5] If there are some K competitors in a product line and one of them, "stealing business from others," succeeds in raising his own sales by p percent, the loss of business to each of the rest will be p/K percent on the average. *If there is no reason* to expect a very uneven distribution of such loss among the others, the seller in question will not anticipate that his competitors will particularly take notice of his actions.

are not concerned about any other's reactions, the market position of the seller is characterized as one of monopolistic competition. When the degree of "differentiation" of the product is low, the individual seller knows that the volume of sales and the level of "his" price must be interdependent. Nevertheless, he also feels that his sales and prices will not appreciably affect the sales of other competitors. Thus these other competitors are not supposed to notice even if the seller in question secures more business at their expense.[6]

4.3 The *number* of sellers in a market *appears* to be the key factor that gives rise to the various kinds of "feelings"; but the number of sellers may get down to a level of fewness in which every seller realizes that any appreciable gain of customers necessarily implies an appreciable loss to the others. No seller can realistically suppose that his selling prices, selling efforts, and other means of enhancing business will go unnoticed and unopposed by the other sellers in the market. In other words, if an action is expected to call forth reaction and retaliation, these reactions and their consequences will evidently be taken into consideration *before* the action is taken. Such situations of fewness are characterized as "oligopoly."

"Oligopoly has in common with polypoly of differentiated products that the seller may have a choice of prices at which he might sell his goods. The difference lies in the 'mental process by which he chooses the selling price'. Sales expectations at the various possible contemplated prices are among the essential factors in the seller's decisions. The character of these sales expectations is fundamentally different under oligopoly, on the one hand, and differentiated polypoly (that is, Chamberlin's monopolistic competition in 'large groups') on the other. Under the latter the reflection 'How much more shall I be able to sell if I lower the price by five percent?' is concerned only with the buyers' reactions. Under oligopoly the same reflection is concerned *also* with the rivals' reactions: indeed, buyers' reactions cannot be guessed without a *simultaneous guess with regard* to the most probable reactions of the rivals (Machlup [40, p. 98])."

Sales expectations of an individual seller in differentiated polypoly are a falling function of the price offerings. This is also true of a seller in oligopoly, but there is a fundamental difference. In the first case the sloping demand curve "describes the seller's thoughts about the behavior

---

[6] This model of competition describes the "state of mind" of a seller who believes that his sales can be expanded only at a lower price (or with increased selling cost) but does not "believe" that a reduced price or increased sales effort will arouse particular reactions on the part of other sellers in the market. He thus feels that he has many competitors from whom he might gain or to whom he might lose some business, but that he has no *specific rivals* whose reactions he would have to heed (Machlup [40, p. 93]).

of his actual and potential customers"; in the second the oligopolist seller "expects that his selling price will *also* affect the policies of his rivals." [7]

4.4 To sum up. In the classical view sellers' competition is characterized by the three dimensions or descriptors: (a) the weapons employed—and potentially employable—by an individual seller to augment his own sales; (b) the manner in which buyers choose among sellers and express their choice; and (c) the number of sellers, taken in conjunction with the nature of market position of an individual seller. Element (c) plays the role in analysis of helping to characterize the "state of mind" of the seller which, in turn, characterizes the parameters of his sales anticipation.

5. A MODIFIED SCHEME

Of these three descriptors, the first one is retained in identical form and role in the analysis of this monograph. The second one is considerably modified and expanded to include the means and institutions by which the sellers and buyers approach one another and transactions are consummated. These relate to (a) the information available to the two sides of the market concerned and (b) the communication—if any—within and between the buyers and sellers.[8] In the present context it is sufficient to observe that a specification of the information-communication complex pertaining to a given situation serves to distinguish the intangible from the tangible—that is, observable and measurable—parameters that define the sales anticipations of the individual sellers. In a scheme of analysis freed from the burden of "determinate equilibria," there is no *need* to be concerned with the state of mind of the seller. Consequently, the third set of descriptors used in the traditional analyses is entirely dispensed with. Justification for this assertion will emerge after the orientation and content of the traditional theory (of a few sellers' competition) have been examined in the following chapter.

[7] In speculating by how much he might be able to increase his sales at a somewhat reduced price (or by increased selling effort), he asks himself first whether, when, and to what extent his rivals would follow suit or retaliate by other methods. How many new customers can be attracted and old customers retained depends not merely on the reduced price of the oligopolist but on the combined influence of *all* price changes: the primary—that is, his own—plus the induced, that is, his rivals' price changes. Indeed, if rivals were apt to cut their selling prices more radically than the seller who initiated the cut, the price reduction might bring him diminished sales (Machlup [40, p. 99]).

[8] The role played by these two factors—seldom explicitly considered and exploited in the traditional analyses—cannot be overemphasized. As will be seen later on, a detailed description of this element is essential to the development of a probability law for the sales of an individual firm.

Chapter 2

THE CLASSICAL ORIENTATION

A special motivation calls for the abandonment of the classical orientation of analysis in terms of (a) determinate equilibria and (b) conjectural variations and reaction functions. This motivation has its roots in the availability of information; but most important of all, the justification is sought in a need to have an analysis freed of the subjective attitudes of decision-makers.

1. EQUILIBRIUM AND DETERMINACY

1.1 The concept of *equilibrium* is an essential tool in the analyses of adjustments to changes in data confronting a group of producers (sellers) and buyers. Economic theory is used to explain how a change in data may affect prices and outputs. This is accomplished by assuming an initial position of equilibrium and then determining the final equilibrium position in accordance with the assumed changes in the data. Equilibrium is thus employed as a device to explain a movement.[1] A movement is conceptualized as an adaptation to a disequilibrating change. We postulate some balancing of forces in the initial position, and the movement elicited by the operation of the model is ascribed to a specific shock or external influence. In some types of analysis we *also* postulate a balancing of forces in the *new* position in order to ensure that the effects of the disequilibrating shock have fully worked out.

1.2 In all known types of economic analysis attempts are made to ensure the *determinateness* or uniqueness of equilibrium under given data. The main body of traditional value theory is concerned with an explanation

---

[1] In this broad sense we may observe a similarity with the fundamental method of analytical mechanics or kinetics: we measure the displacement of a system from a convenient origin which in many constructions is chosen as that of equilibrium itself, especially if it is stable.

of how unique equilibria are reached for price, output, and so on in particular kinds of markets under various attendant circumstances. The general method and reasoning consist of defining certain functional relationships on the basis of technology (i.e., engineering data) and tastes and preferences (i.e., utility functions) and then deriving a unique solution for price and output.[2] When a seller confronts a demand function but does not establish an *independent* supply function—and this is typical of situations in which the seller enjoys some measure of monopoly power—there is a unique equilibrium (of output) if the cost function of the supply side is known. It is then possible to select a point on the demand function which is optimal for the seller and, thus, the equilibrium is unique. Similarly, the equilibrium also is unique when a buyer faces a supply function without setting up an independent demand function, provided utility functions or their equivalents are defined. In these circumstances there exists a point on the supply function which is optimal from the viewpoint of the buyer. In the more restricted situation in which each market participant has both demand and supply functions (e.g., in pure competition or polypoly) the uniqueness of equilibrium is almost trivial.

1.3 It is remarkable, therefore, that we still look for determinateness in situations—such as those of competition among a few sellers—where demand functions or supply functions in the usual sense cannot be derived *exclusively* from the data pertaining to technology and tastes. Determinate equilibria cannot be established analytically for such markets.[3] This seems to be the chief reason why in the vast bulk of contemporary mathematical economics the problem of indeterminacy has been relegated to appendices and footnotes.[4] In the contemporary extensions of the classical theory[5] of competition among a few sellers and, especially, among two sellers an explicit attempt has been made to retain the use of classical notions and techniques in determining the *range of*

---

[2] In practice, we postulate that each seller sets up a supply function (or confronts a demand function or both), that each buyer sets up a demand function (or confronts a supply function or both), and that these functions are derivable from technology and utility functions which are taken for granted.

[3] The quantity that an oligopolist seller *can* sell at any given price depends on the prices charged by his competitors, which, in turn, are appreciably affected by what price *he* sets. Consequently, not only does the oligopolist fail to set up a supply function, but it is impossible to define for him a demand function from information pertaining to buyers' preferences alone.

[4] See, for example, Hicks [27, 28]. The game theoretic approaches (von Neumann-Morgenstern [59], Shubik [49]) are an important exception.

[5] This is typified by Cournot [16], Bertrand [9], Edgeworth [63], and Bowley [11]. Reference may be made to Machlup [40] for an excellent account of their models and assumptions.

indeterminacy. The upper and lower limits of indeterminacy are set in oligopoly (with or without product differentiation) by the cost and utility functions or some equivalent thereof. These limits are acceptable and attainable from the viewpoint of an individual oligopolist. This is as far as classical techniques can go in the analysis of competition among a few sellers. They fail because the core of oligopolistic competition is

"What I am willing to do depends on what I assume the other party's response will be and, at the same time, what the other party is willing to do depends on what he thinks my response will be" (Fellner [22, p. 13]).

The presence of conjectural interdependence, that is, the dependence of each seller's behavior on that of the other, increases the amount of *information* necessary for understanding or predicting the outcome of specific processes. The additional information cannot be obtained from methods by which production functions, cost functions, or consumer habits may be studied.

1.4 The attitude taken in this book to the triad of equilibrium-determinacy-information stems from an outright abandonment of the motivation of the classical equilibrium analysis. As is well known, that motivation has been one of explaining *simultaneously* the price and output of individual firms and of the industry. This explanation has been possible only because the firms in pure competition are not *really* competing: The actions of individual sellers are noninteresting. In economic environments in which there are actual and imagined interactions the search for a simultaneous determination of the output and price for the *industry* is of little practical interest to the individual firm. At the same time analytical methods fail to model the situation and pose the correct problem for analysis. In other words, we may attempt to justify a restriction of the analysis to the level of operations of an *individual firm* and to sharpen it by introducing other considerations whenever required. This has been the viewpoint of this book. Rather than searching for determinateness or determinate limits of variation, it attempts to *characterize the uncertainty of sales* of an individual firm associated with each contemplated price-offer. This can be done, as amply illustrated, exclusively on the basis of objective facts of the business environment. It is only in the manner in which a firm makes *use* of the probability distribution of its sales in arriving at its price-output decisions that room has been left to introduce the detailed considerations of "watching because others are watching me." This approach does away with the need for those aspects of conjectural variations that are purely subjective, both for the researcher and for the single firm. Other implications of this departure from the traditional approach will emerge in the following discussion of contemporary extensions of classical analysis. It is sufficient in the present context to observe that these suggested extensions also call for a kind of information that the gifted model-builder may assume as given but the empiricist will have a hard time obtaining.

2. CONJECTURAL VARIATIONS: INDETERMINACY

2.1 It has been emphasized that competition among a few sellers has the following characteristic: before an individual seller sets the level of his own decision variables (typically, the price and/or selling cost) he will conjecture the rivals' *variations* or countermoves in response to his own. Such conjecture has two aspects. First it may relate to the reaction from a *specific* rival or to the reaction from the *general* body of rivals. Second, the conjecture may relate to the level at which the competitors will probably set their decision variables in response to contemplated actions of their own. The first aspect essentially involves the entire issue of leader-follower and of symmetry or asymmetry of aspirations; this is taken up in the following section. For the purpose of the present discussion, then, it is assumed that the individual seller is cognizant of the possibility of reaction, regardless of who it may come from.

2.2 In the classical analyses of Cournot-Bertrand-Edgeworth it was assumed[6] that each seller believes or conjectures that the variations in the rival's determination of his (i.e., rival's) output or price in reaction to his own variations are zero. Relatively modern extensions of these models have considered nonzero conjectural variations.[7] Earlier attempts in this direction were relatively naïve. For two sellers profit-indifference contours were constructed to show the possible combinations of the sellers' decision variables (price or output as the case may be) that yield a given level of profits. These contours would then be used to determine the points of maximum profits for a seller adjusting his own variable to that of the rival or inducing his rival to adjust to his. (The juxtaposition of the resulting reaction curves therefore, would show whether a specific configuration of the two sellers were compatible; mutually incompatible configurations

---

[6] By so assuming, however; the substance of the problem was assumed away (Machlup [40]).

[7] One of the earliest attempts in this direction were due to Stackelberg [60], who constructed "reaction functions" to indicate the adjustments or variations one seller would make in response to those made by his competitor. The reaction curves and their intersection are useful in conceptualizing the process of gradual adjustment leading to equilibrium.

were characterized as occasions where the sellers would tend to "fight it out.")

2.3 After Stackelberg, attempts to remove the hypothesis of zero conjectural variations have consisted of introducing two distinct types of assumption:

1. "Each sellers' guesses about his rival's response depends on his own intuition and business moods" (Chamberlin [12, 13], Harrod [25]).

2. "Each seller's guess about his rival's response depends on the rival's actual pattern of reaction which the seller has learned to judge correctly" (Kahn [33], Stigler [54]).

The first type of behavior assumption would yield a determinate (in the sense described in the preceding section) solution whenever the analyst can completely specify, for each seller, the moods, judgments, and directions in which these are revised. More generally, we may develop an auxiliary theory for the formation and revision of individual sellers' conjectures about rivals' reactions[8] and incorporate such a theory in the main body of the analysis of oligopoly; thus we may retain all the determinacy we may care for. But such an attempt to "restore" determinacy would only be reminiscent of the classical view of mechanics. By insisting that the motion of an aggregate of N particles could be predicted from (a) the equations of motion of each individual particle and (b) dynamic constraints describing the interaction among the particles, the classical view was rendered trivial and noncomputable.

2.4 The second type of behavior assumption may be useful *if* the situation has been stable *and if* each seller had developed a more "mature" attitude. Each seller accepts and is happy with his own market position relative to the others. More about this·will be given in a discussion of leadership in a subsequent section. Fellner presents the most modern approach to the problem of interdeterminacy due to conjectural variations. In oligopolistic markets there is a *tendency* toward maximization of joint profits of the group[9] and toward the division of the maximized joint profits in accordance with the following factors: (a) long run consequence of "faring too well," that is, of violating accepted value judgments;

[8] Machlup observes that if the successive revisions are dictated by actual experience there is a good chance that any assumption concerning the development of sellers' conjectures will merge with the second kind of assumption (Machlup [40, p. 405]).
[9] The maximization of joint profits means that the bargaining ranges are determined by the traditional techniques of classical value theory in such a way that for each firm the upper limit is set by the possibility of obtaining for itself the entire maximized profit, whereas the lower limit is set at the zero-profits level.

(b) the immediate political consequences of a stalemate in the relations between the parties concerned; (c) the ability of the parties to take and inflict losses during possible stalemates, and (d) the unwillingness to yield in a range in which the other party is expected to yield if one of the parties fails to do so. Fellner [22] maintains that if the first three factors are appraised correctly for all parties from the outset, a permanent stalemate may occur only through a series of mutual errors. In other words, deviations from joint profit maximization are quite frequent in oligopoly owing to frequent conflicts between joint profit maximization and *acceptable* distribution of the maximum joint profits. As will be seen later on, Fellner's approach may be slightly modified to give a basis for the application of the theory of nonzero sum *n*-person games. What is more important in the present context, however, is the observation that any serious attempt to mathematize this hypothesis will run into the same kind of difficulties as would the more naïve notions of conjectural variations and reaction functions. In most empirical situations an individual seller does *not* have access to data pertaining to any of the four factors suggested by Fellner. It may be argued, however, that the hypothesis of joint profit maximization may be accorded the same status as that enjoyed by the hypothesis of utility maximization. In other words, oligopolists need not *in fact* so maximize; but the deductions from such a hypothesis should agree with facts, at least in a statistical sense. Again we may question the advantages of such mathematical construction to an individual seller. In the analysis to be presented no attempt is made to impute a rationality— tactit or explicit—to the aggregate behavior of the group. It is shown that such a view does *not* restrict the applicability of the rationality principle *within* a single firm. In closing the present section, it is emphasized that the approach of this monograph rests on the observation that the kind of information called for in Fellner's approach is singularly lacking. Although we could well agree that

"Part of the relevant information can be obtained only by observing the behavior of persons in a range in which their behavior depends on the assumed behavior of others and in which the actual behavior of others depends upon the assumed behavior of the first group" (Fellner [40, p. 14]),

we cannot help feeling that the possibility of such an observation will almost always be ruled out in practice. As shown in the models of the following chapter, the problem is further complicated by the characteristics of the institutional framework within which transactions are consummated. To sum up, then, we *treat the sales of an individual seller as a random variable;* this takes care of the entire dilemma of determinacy. The numerical characteristics of its probability distribution and the specific use of the distribution may be made to reflect the empirical counterpart of "feeling of being watched," the "conjectured variations," and other strategic considerations. Thus there is no room left in the analysis for subjective attitudes.

3. LEADERSHIP

3.1   The simplest and most extensive concept of leadership is composed of two elements:

"One, our observation that certain persons behave regularly and substantially in the same way that we observe in one who precedes them; the other, namely, our interpretive construction that the uniformity of behavior is deliberate in the sense that they observe the behavior of the 'leader' and follow his example" (Machlup [40, p. 491]).

A narrower concept of leadership may be defined by admitting two more attributes: the leader's knowledge (and expectation) that he is being (and will be) followed and some action of the leader designed to perpetuate the leadership (Machlup [40, pp. 491–492]). Regardless of a formal definition of leadership (which, in any event, must remain vague), the essential *problem* underlying the phenomenon of leadership is one of the *degree of coordination* between the policies of the competitors. Coordination may be complete, as in the case of syndicates and cartels, or it may be incomplete, that is, without organization and agreement, based only on "understanding"—including live and let live and business ethics considerations and resulting in concerted (or almost concerted) action. The underlying implication is that there is always an element of agreement about the manner in which economic power is to be shared. In other words, through experience and not mere "feeling," the individual seller had learned to trust his competitors to act in a certain way if they have done so consistently and uniformly over a long period in the past. A consistent pattern of conduct adhered to over a long period allows the competitors to *anticipate adherence* to the pattern:

"A long-continued uniformity of action, extended through a variety of situations amid changing circumstances can, therefore, be taken as a basis for inferring with a high degree of certainty the existence of *at least* an agreement to agree, that is, quasi-agreement" (Kaysen [35]).

3.2   In a duopoly the outcome of leadership is relatively simple. For example, in Cournot models (without product differentiation) with leadership, no firm acts on wrong assumptions. The follower correctly believes (and he is never betrayed) that the leader has adopted a policy of fixed output at a level he selects in complete knowledge of the follower's reaction function. Thus the leader is willing and able to indicate the output he will produce; the follower maximizes his profits with this knowledge. This, then, is the nature of duopoly equilibrium with leadership. As long as the leader is willing and able to make his own output a parameter from the follower's point of view, any change in the assumption that the follower will move along his (Cournot) reaction function will prove to be wrong. However, there is a break in the analysis when leadership considerations are introduced into *extensions* of Cournot models with product differentiation and many sellers, that is, differentiated oligopoly. The Cournot type reaction function of *each follower* is based on the supposition that all *his* rivals will produce a definite quantity regardless of what *he* does. In the present case such a supposition is correct *only* with respect to the leader.[10] Therefore, if each follower sets up his own reaction function (*à la* Cournot) and allows the leader to choose his output in light of these, then *each* follower will be acting on incorrect assumptions about every *other* follower. Thus any change in these assumptions "will prove that they were erroneous, and the pattern originally postulated will never be restored" (Fellner [22]). Much more important in analysis is the situation (such as those considered in Bertrand and Edgeworth type models of duopoly) in which *price* is the decision variable. In the classical tradition we would naturally look for price-reaction functions based on the notion that the price of the rival depends in some fashion on one's own price. If the product is undifferentiated, the introduction of conjectural variations of price will mean that an individual seller might not believe that his rival would stick to the (new) price. Thus the shapes of the price reaction functions are not predictable in theory. Even if they are intersecting (at positive prices) and the intersection point is stable, it is unlikely that the intersection will ever be reached. On the way to equilibrium the assumption about the rivals' behavior will prove to be incorrect. The situation with respect to leadership equilibrium—that is, the leader selecting a point on the reaction function of the follower—is relatively simple. If the follower knows

---

[10] When selecting a point on the reaction function of the follower, the leader does indeed operate with conjectural variations. This is not to say that the leader sets up his own reaction function. The concept of (nonzero) conjectural variations does not introduce anything new beyond what is involved in the leadership equilibrium derived from the Cournot problem proper in which all reaction functions are defined with zero conjectural variations. Reaction functions with conjectural variations do not acquire significance by virtue of the leadership problem. They acquire significance only if we attach importance to their intersection points (Fellner [22]). For a comprehensive discussion of the pitfalls associated with the last practice reference may be made to Fellner [22, pp. 73–74].

that the leader is choosing a point on his (follower's) reaction function, then he (the follower) will set up a reaction function indicating his price for alternative given (parameter) prices of his rivals. This is precisely the Bertrand assumption with zero conjectural variations.

4. SUMMARY

Some form of quasi-agreement (agreement to agree) is invariably associated with leadership equilibrium, for reaction functions expressing the follower's individual profit maximization (for alternative values of the leader's variables) have no significance if the leader deliberately refrains from selecting values for his own variables within the domain over which the function is defined. Also, reaction functions are acceptable to the leader if they give the followers no greater share of the total profits than corresponds to their relative bargaining strength. Thus leadership concept is not of special significance in analysis, unless it is placed in the context of quasi-agreement. The alternative to either leadership or reaction functions (with or without conjectural variations) is the hypothesis of joint profit maximization. It has already been noted that even for the purposes of classical analysis the concept of leadership is inadequate. Thus the development to follow in the next chapter ignores this method of analysis. The reaction function approach also is discarded, not only because the interest is not in its end product (i.e., determinate equilibrium) but also because the informational requirements implied in such con-structions are seldom met in practice. The hypothesis of joint profit maximization comes closest to the ideal requirements of analysis of oligopolistic competition. Here again the interest is not *primarily* in the industry and certainly not in the price-output relationships. Consequently, no use is made of any of the approaches mentioned. Nevertheless, as it will appear later on, the *notion* of quasi-agreement is retained in a special form.

Chapter 3

THE PROBLEM OF FEWNESS REEXAMINED

Competition among a few sellers is the principal theme of this book. The orientation given to its analysis stems from a distinction between the problems of interest to the social philosopher and legislator on the one hand and the businessman operating under conditions of "fewness" on the other. This distinction serves to draw the line between relevant and irrelevant issues, between acceptable or respectable and unacceptable or unfamiliar methods of analysis. The motivation of this chapter is to collect the comments made in the preceding chapters and sharply formulate a positive approach to and a workable method of analyzing the practical problems of "fewness" of sellers.

1. AN OBJECTIVE FRAMEWORK

1.1 When a few sellers constitute the industry and each seller is a price-maker, every seller's *planned* profit-maximizing price *depends* upon the (conjectured) prices of all other sellers. We may make hypotheses about the planning process and the dependence; leadership and reaction functions, with or without conjectural variations, are familiar examples in this regard. Although this is the *ex ante* situation, *ex post*, every seller's sales depend on all the prices. What is not known (and will never be observed) is the functional form of this dependence and the manner in which the dependence comes into existence. With organized contact among the sellers and with patterns of behavior well established on implicit or tacit agreement, the functional dependence in question becomes trivial.

1.2 It seems, then, that at the *ex ante* end of the analysis the object of research is the thinking, prejudices, temperaments, and shrewd knowledge possessed by the sellers (and communicated in confidence to the researcher). On the *ex post* side, too, it seems that we should be sleuths

17

looking for evidence of agreements to agree. It is true that the institutional setup acquires a significance not conceived of in that traditional battleground of economic theory, namely, "perfect" competition. However, this does not preclude the construction of a theory. This is especially so if it is recognized that the peculiarities of the problems are due to the kind of environment in which (oligopolist) businessmen operate. The distinguishing feature of a theory of oligopoly should lie in the "provision of a *framework* which will show the actions of a normal businessman under the specific conditions of an oligopolistic environment" [64]. This is the viewpoint adopted in this monograph; the success of the results presented here rests essentially on the inclusiveness and flexibility of the chosen framework.

1.3   The framework to be set up is to be completely objective. Also, it is to be sufficiently abstract so that one may specialize it to a specific situation. There are three components of the framework:

M: The organization of the market, that is, a description of the processes and institutions by which buyers and sellers come into contact and transactions are consummated.

Y: The information available to and acted on by the participants in the market, including the nature and content of communication among and between the buyers and sellers.

S: The individual firm's *experience* of the market and of the uncertainty in sales, including a specification of the decision variable at its disposal (such as price, selling costs, or both).

It is readily seen that we get a rich family of models as we look on each of the characteristics of the einvironment as a *variable*. It is also interesting to note how even simple modifications of the factors described in Y can significantly modify the firm's "understanding" of what the competition is about and whether it is with a particular rival or with an anonymous body of competitors. Furthermore, such modifications are likely to affect the degree of awareness of who it is competing with and how. The factors M and Y superimposed on S would completely specify the environment in which competition takes place: each specification of the (S, M, Y)-configuration leads to *a* model of competition, which is to say that *any* kind of competition can be completely characterized by its associated (S, M, Y)-complex.

2. PURPOSE, CONTENT, AND METHOD

2.1   Words like "analysis" and "theory" have been used in the preceding discussions without a specific connotation. It is only appropriate, then, to designate the purpose and content of the analysis. The purpose of the analysis is to answer questions of interest to an *individual* firm.

1. When[1] and by how much should a firm (in oligopolistic competition) change its price and/or selling costs?

2. What are the implications—in regard to the firm's sales and profits—of the policies indicated in answer to (1)?

3. What variations of policy would be admissible to the firm under which circumstances?

The answers[2] to these questions are developed in the form of *computable* decision rules, that is, rules of reacting to *observed* phenomena (signals). Special emphasis is laid on the derivation of the rules in a manner that will also indicate how they may be implemented. Thus the analysis is normative; it does not attempt to describe how sellers do act or what they think of competition. The purpose of the analysis is operational;[3] its economic content is based on the (S, M, Y)-configurations.

2.2 Because there is a great diversity[4] among firms with respect to the environment and motivation, it may well be asked whether an operationally oriented analysis would be worthwhile and whether it could at all be called a "theory." This raises some philosophical questions concerning the methods of any applied theory. The position taken may be summed up in the words of Machlup [40, pp. 422–423]:

"All we want to say is what *can* be validly said about a general *class* of phenomena. Where the phenomena become so unique that they no longer fit into any class, we may still be interested—as we may be in something equal or parallel—but our interest is no longer that of a generalizing scientist. The theory . . . must stop before it becomes too

---

[1] "When" is not to be understood as a specific instant of time; it should be understood as a configuration of *events* or *states* of the system.

[2] The generality with which the above questions are answered—hence the applicability of the theory—depends on the spirit in which the models are constructed and on the degree to which the models reflect the environment of competition.

[3] The major implication of being operational is that the sales process is considered only from the viewpoint of an individual firm.

[4] For example, achieving a target return on investment, expanding markets, rendering good services to customers, improving market share, gaining a reputation as a leader, maintaining a specified plant utilization, and so on. Machlup has indicated that profit maximization and security may be compatible in certain kinds of competition. Fellner, for example, suggests that the firm may try to maximize most probable profits "roughly derived from a universe of experience." He also suggests that there may be a desire to avoid cutthroat competition.

specific—that is, so specific that it applies only to unique cases—and even if it has not by that time arrived at complete determinacy."

Although we recognize the diversity of conditions and multiplicity of objectives of the firms, it is still possible to distil out the factors that are common to the firms selling under specific classes of environment. Such a view gives rise to an analysis that is not too general to be applicable nor too specific to be called an operational theory.

Usual analyses seem to place more emphasis on the *interpretation* of market phenomena with a view toward inferring the motivation of firms. In an operational theory, on the other hand, the emphasis in not on inferring the motivation. Two identical motivations may produce vastly different market phenomena, depending on how the market is organized, how transactions are consummated, what market information is available to buyers and sellers, and so on. Similarly, what a single firm *thinks* its rivals are doing is much less important than what the firm itself actually *does*. It is the things the firm does that contribute to the observed market phenomena (through a complex interaction with the decisions of other firms). Thus the emphasis in an operational theory is on a search for features of uniformity of both probabilistic and non-probabilistic relationships that characterize market events. The special characteristic of the theory presented in this monograph is that it tries to build models of uniformity *exclusively from the specifications* made about the environment. In this respect, then, there is much less need for introspection and for the analysis of the subjective attitudes of a firm.

3. UNCERTAINTY IN SALES

3.1 Consider the chain of events preceding a sale by a firm to a customer under conditions of fewness of sellers. Evidently, the M and Y specifications have important roles in shaping this chain. The customer, unless captive, is one of many whose arrival times and demand quantities are *unknown* to the firm. The fact of arrival is also uncertain because the customer may have been exposed to the selling efforts of other competitors (especially in the case of differentiated products). Typically, the firm in question will have no knowledge of this.

3.2 Also note that the mere arrival of an inquiring customer is not enough. The price offered by the firm in question is to be the lowest among those offered by the rivals that may have been approached by the customer. But, then, the firm does not know how many or which of the rivals have been approached. Neither would it know what prices they offered.[5] Thus the event in question appears to the firm to be a *random* one. The *probability* of occurrence of this event is a function of the selling efforts made by all the sellers involved. It is also a function of the prices offered by all the firms that the customer happens to have contacted. Finally, observe that even if the price offered by the firm in question happens to be the lowest a sale is not assured unless the offered price also happens to be at most equal to the maximum price the buyer is willing to pay, that is, his maximum demand-price. Typically, from the individual firm's viewpoint, the maximum demand-price of a customer is also random.

3.3　Enough has been said to indicate that there is an inherent randomness in the sales process: at the price at which a firm offers to sell a quantity the actual or observed sales are random. They are *random* in the sense that the outcome is not known before the actual occurrence of the event in question.[6] Such randomness is essentially due to the fact that the firm has only an imperfect knowledge of the interaction of price and quantity decisions of the competitors, on the one hand, and of the buyers, on the other hand. It is in the random response of sales volume to a price that we should look for the principal distinction between a firm in oligopoly and a firm in pure competition. In pure competition the firm is a price-taker and therefore experiences randomness in the *price;* in an

[5] In nearly all trades it is customary for the firms to have a comparable "price list," although the actual price or the *effective* price at which a transaction is consummated may be quite different from the listed price. The dollars knocked off the listed price may be actual, such as happens in a cash discount; they may also be virtual, in view of the attendant services, such as the terms of credit, free delivery, prompt supply, bulk discounts, and so on. Besides these there is the practice of giving allowances to wholesale distributors in some trades. In many instances, such allowances in essence are price supports or profit supports accorded to the wholesalers. All these deductions—actual and virtual—from customary prices are shrouded in secrecy. They also provide the principal inspiration to the viewpoint adopted in this monograph.

[6] There is a related but sufficiently distinct concept of randomness, namely, that due to the impossibility of an accurate measurement by an instrument. Although important in the natural sciences, this view of randomness will not be considered appropriate to the kind of situations discussed here. From a strictly mathematical viewpoint, however, there is no difference between these two notions.

In either case the situation is the following: there is a quantity z uniquely dependent on a variable w, such that $z = f(w)$; but, given a value z', there may be indefinitely many values of w giving rise to this assigned value. In these circumstances the only meaningful characterization of the *set* $S = \{w \mid z' = f(w)\}$ is in terms of the measure of S relative to the domain D of the definition of $f(.)$. This measure is the probability of the event that $f(w)$ takes on a value z':

$$\Pr\left[f(w) = z'\right] = \text{meas } \{w \mid z' = f(w)\}.$$

oligopoly, on the other hand, the randomness is associated with the *quantity sold*. The central theme of this book is to show that models of stochastic dependence of the quantity sold on the price offered (and/or selling costs in product differentiation) can be constructed exclusively on the basis of the specifications about the (S, M, Y)-complex. Finer structural characteristics of the models can also be obtained to the extent that the specifications are stated in detail. Such models furnish a simple and efficient summary of total impact and implication of the market and competition environments of a firm. They are completely free of endless "speculations" about customer and competitor characteristics; they can be constructed from recorded observations. A remarkable feature of this approach is that it yields models of probability distribution functions of sales; the firm's own decision variables appear as *parameters* of these functions.

3.4 An important consequence of this approach is that the traditional demand functions are replaced by probability distribution functions of sales volume. The ideas leading to this treatment of "demand" may be conveniently summed up in the following observations:

"If the demand at a specified price is represented by a dot on a graph, the implication is that the quantity of demand is a definite magnitude. This assumes that the potential customers at this price divide themselves into two groups; those who will buy and those who will not. If demand is taken to mean the quantity wanted at a given *moment*, such a twofold division is possible. But when demand is made to refer to a period of time, a threefold, rather than twofold, division is more appropriate. There are some who during the period will buy at the specified price and who know that they will buy at that price. Then, there are still others who do not honestly know whether they will or will not buy at the specified price during the period" (Eiteman [65, p. 61]).

Now, if sufficient observations can be accumulated on a random event, it is well known that we can always—except, perhaps, in pathological cases—construct *empirical* probability distributions for the event in question. This opens up the possibility of representing such demand-price relationship in purely statistical terms. The statistical version may be visualized as follows. Let p denote the price offered and let $X(p)$ indicate the random quantity of sales at that price. Then it is asserted in the statistical version that there is a probability

$$\Pr\left[a < X(p) \leq b\right] = \int_a^b f(x, p) \, dx \qquad (3.1)$$

parametrized by the price quoted. Similarly, in product differentiation we would have

$$\Pr\left[a < X(p) \leq b\right] = \int_a^b g(x, p, c)\, dx, \qquad (3.2)$$

c being a measure of the selling efforts. The essential point here is that the demand (i.e., anticipated sales) at a certain price is probabilistically dependent on the price offered. This is true also of the *aggregate* demand in pure competition (or, of the individual firm's revenue from a given output) or of an individual firm's demand in monopoly or monopolistic competition. The question is whether this also applies as a description of demand from the viewpoint of an oligopolistic firm.

3.5 The economist's view of the demand curve of an oligopolist—and the one that comes closest to the one adopted in this book—may be summed up as follows:

"There is no such thing as oligopoly demand curve, or even a demand curve that can be said to be typical of oligopoly positions. A demand curve relates quantities *saleable* to price charged, but it says neither in whose mind this relation exists nor what are the considerations by which the relationship has been established. In particular, it does not say—even if we knew that the relationship in question did exist in the mind of an individual seller imagining his selling opportunities—whether the seller assumes that his competitors will change their selling prices if he first changes his; indeed, it does not say whether or not the seller gives any thought to such possibilities, that is, whether or not he is an oligopolist.

"Thus, no geometric finesse can reveal what type of mentality and attitude we assume the seller to have. If we assume that he is an oligopolist, we have to say so, for we cannot show it by the kind of curve we draw. On the other hand, assuming a particular oligopolistic seller actually to relate in his mind the quantities he might sell with the prices he might charge, taking full account of the price changes with which his competitors might react to his own price changes, the curve depicting these price-quantity relationships may have *all sorts of shapes* . . . and some parts of the curve may be good only for a one-way movement . . . for price reductions but not for price increases" (Machlup [40, p. 355]).

The viewpoint cited is correct, but it is *incomplete* as a foundation for an operational theory. The author seems to have in mind a curve, namely, that of the expected demand curve, a curve showing the dependence of the *expected* demand upon price. In oligopolistic situations it is obviously not enough to consider the mathematical expectation of sales at a contemplated price; one *also* requires the *probability distribution* of demand (sales) corresponding to different prices.

4. CRITIQUE OF THE NEW APPROACH

4.1   In the preceding section it was asserted that except in "pathological" instances, we can obtain the *empirical* probability distribution of sales[7] in which price or some other decision variable of the firm will appear in the role of a parameter. It should be observed, however, that empirical distributions are but realizations of theoretical distributions or probability measures. These latter measures must exist in order that the computation and use of the empirical distributions may be justified. Such existence calls for the stability of the patterns of behavior, that is, of *some* degree of quasi-agreement. The point made in terms of *stable measurable stochastic processes*, $X(p)$, $p' \leq p \leq p''$, may be put in an heuristic fashion: If there is no quasi-agreement, the empirical data will appear to be "too rough and erratic" to allow for any empirical probability reasonably stable under sampling fluctuations. In short, the *mathematical assumption that the stochastic sales process is measurable is a reflection of an assumption about the real world, namely, that there is quasi-agreement.* If the empirical distributions have, in other words, a small sampling error, then there is *prima facie* evidence of quasi-agreement; each one in the industry has learned to read the message and to respond in a mature and responsible manner. The mathematical counterpart of this statement would be, "The process is stochastically stable and measurable." Thus, the probability distributions of sales may be made to serve as a convenient closet in which sufficient room may be left for nonquantitative considerations such as "leadership" and "quasi-agreements." (As shown in Chapter 7, it is in the analysis of correlations between the random variable $X(p)$ and $X(p')$ that the practical implications of a departure from a firm's current price policy may be examined.)

4.2   What room will be left for the *psychological attitudes* toward competition and for considerations of business *shrewdness* and moves and countermoves? The answer is to come in the following two chapters; the substance of the answer may be stated here in simple language. Suppose that an empirical distribution has been computed from past records of effective prices offered and quantities sold by a firm. Also, suppose that the decision-making body is about to consider a revision of the current price policy and that it has the empirical distribution as "something tangible to go by." Evidently, then, the decision-makers have the choice

---

[7] In practical terms, the procedure would consist of (a) fitting smooth probability distributions to the sales data corresponding to relatively small ranges of variation of the effective price and (b) estimating the functional dependence of the moments—usually the mean and variance—of the distribution on the effective price.

of accepting the implications of the distribution as it stands or of rejecting it and waiting for additional data or accepting the distribution *only* as a guidepost and tempering its implications in light of whatever specific knowledge or hunch they may have. It is true that there is no room for these factors in a (mathematical) *pure theory* that seeks to "explain" the movement of prices and output for an oligopolistic industry. But in a less ambitious *operational theory* an express provision has thus been made for giving the decision-makers a material guide on which refinements can be made, if necessary, in light of "judgment." In the practice of modern statistical decision theory, the empirical distribution can be modified in light of "business intuition" and "mood" to yield the "prior" probabilities of outcomes of a proposed policy. Even if the probability distribution is not put to its final use, it can certainly serve as a sounding board, a device that may be used in diagnosing how much coordination may be expected from the *other* sellers. The idea of employing a probability distribution of sales (especially demand) is not new in operations research; indeed, the theory of inventory management is replete with examples of such distributions [1, 2, 24, 30, 61]. What is characteristically lacking in most[8] of these treatments is an attempt to build up the distribution from a consideration of the *environments and institutions in which sales occur.*

[8] There are some exceptions, for example, in which models have been constructed in which the decision variables are especially made to influence some probability distributions that are subsequently used to calculate the expected values of certain outcomes (Howard [31], Bass [5], Telser [56], Silver [51]). But even these treatments introduce the probability distribution in an *ad hoc* manner. In the Markov models of Howard (*loc. cit.*) and Telser (*loc. cit.*) the transition probabilities are explicitly assumed to have density functions parametrized by the decision variables. This deficiency, however, has been remedied—albeit in an *ad hoc* fashion—in Silver (*loc. cit.*). Finally, it should be observed that in all these models one has to make assumptions about the previous action by the buyer and about the transition probabilities of the buyers who did not purchase from the firm in the past and will not purchase from it.

PART TWO

Chapter 4

OLIGOPOLY: STATIC MODELS

Under certain assumptions regarding the principal descriptors of competition—the (S, M, Y)-complex of Chapter 3—an attempt has been made to apply deductive methods in developing probability distributions of sales of an individual firm. In the model of an *undifferentiated* oligopoly (Section 1) the sales process is essentially one of bidding; for this model, it is shown that in the absence of communication the probability distribution of sales of an individual firm is binomial, with the probability of "success" a function of the price quoted by the firm. In the model of oligopoly with *differentiated* products (Section 2) the firm has two decision variables; the price to quote and the level of selling efforts to undertake. It is shown that in the absence of communication a firm's sales have a Poisson distribution with mean-value a function of the price quoted and the sales efforts undertaken.

A simple variation of this model (Section 3) considers the situation in which the firms reach the final buyers through a chain of franchised wholesalers and retailers. It is shown that an individual wholesaler's sales have the Gamma distribution; the parameters depend upon the number of retailers and upon the differential profit margin accorded by the wholesaler.

The random variable in each of these models is the volume of sales of an individual firm; the purpose of analysis is the derivation only of the general distribution properties of this random variable. Deductive methods employed here and later on are obviously inadequate for developing hypotheses about the *numerical* values of the moments of the distributions.

1. UNDIFFERENTIATED OLIGOPOLY

A situation is considered in which the market is oligopolistic and the individual firm does not know precisely who it is competing with and what price-policies are being pursued by the competitor(s). The firm's decision variable is the price p to ask during a given period.

It is shown that with proper specification of information and communication patterns the probability that the firm will sell r units ($r = 1$, 2, ..., n) in n contacts is

$$g(r; p) = \binom{n}{r}[f(p)]^r[1 - f(p)]^{n-r},$$

$f(p)$ being the expected market share or the probability of "success" in a contact.

1.1 Consider a market, with a few sellers, in which the individual firm's primary decision variable is the price to ask. Also consider the following specialization of M, the descriptors of market organization:

M:1 Each buyer directly approaches each seller for a price quotation. Each seller then quotes a price—the asking price—at which he intends to sell if the buyer accepts the quotation.

M:2 Neither the buyers nor the sellers resort to renegotiation.

M:3 Each buyer has a maximum demand price. Each buyer concludes a transaction with the firm whose asking price bears the largest deficit from his demand price.[1]

About the structure of information and the organization of communication within and between the two sides of the market, consider the following specialization:

Y:1 There is no communication among the sellers in respect of the prices asked, or in respect of the prices at which sales were made in the preceding periods.

Y:2 The buyers do not communicate among themselves (or to any seller) their maximum demand prices, neither do they communicate among themselves the prices asked by different sellers.

An important role is frequently played by the presence or absence of the trade practice of allowing quantity discounts. In the first of the two submodels to be developed it is supposed that the buyers are *not* distinguished by the number of units they seek to buy. Thus an inquiry for k units from a single buyer will be looked on as a case of k contacts, *each for one unit* of the product.

Consider a randomly selected contact in which a firm (seller) asks a price p. Let $P_1, P_2, \ldots, P_{N-1}$ be the selling quotations of the other $N - 1$ firms. Because of Y:1, these are unknown to the firm in question.

[1] This behavior assumption may be alternatively conceived of as one of maximization of consumer's surplus. It appears to be sufficiently realistic in the case of commercial buyers, especially in the market of machinery and equipment. Any "sluggishness" or similar characteristics of customers may be incorporated in the model without difficulty.

Suppose P^* is the demand price of the inquiring buyer. Then

Pr [a sale occurs in a random contact]

$$= \Pr [P_1 > p, \ldots, P_{N-1} > p; \; P^* \geq p].$$

Because the variables $P_1, \ldots, P_{N-1}$ are not observable by the firm, let there be a subjective distribution of these variables, with the density function $\Phi(\bar{p}) = \Phi(P_1, P_2, \ldots, P_{N-1})$. Similarly, let $\Psi(P^*)$ denote the density of the subjective distribution of the demand price P^*. The above probability, therefore, is seen to be given by the following:

Pr [a sale occurs in a random contact]

$$= \left[\int_{p+}^{\infty} \cdots \int_{p+}^{\infty} \Phi(u_1, \ldots, u_{N-1}) \, du \, \cdots \, du_{N-1} \right] \int_{p+}^{\infty} \Psi(u) \, du \equiv \sigma(p).$$

Thus we obtain the following expression for the probability that r $(r = 1, 2, \ldots, n)$ units will be sold in n contacts made by the firm:

$$\Pr [\text{sale} = r \text{ units in } n \text{ contacts}] = g(r; n) = \binom{n}{r} [\sigma(p)]^r [1 - \sigma(p)]^{n-r}.$$

$$(4.1)$$

It will be shown that the subjective probability distributions can be replaced by their *empirical equivalents*, so the $\sigma(p)$ may be interpreted as an empirically observable function.

Suppose, on the other hand, that there is a practice of allowing *quantity discounts*, so that buyers are treated differentially according as they come with a smaller or larger number of units of demand. For the sake of definiteness consider a population of customers of size n and regard it as divided into m classes, depending on the number of units demanded. Thus let d_k $(k = 1, 2, \ldots, m)$ and n_k $(k = 1, 2, \ldots, m)$ denote the number of units demanded by a customer belonging to the kth class and the number of customers in the kth class, respectively. Thus $n = \sum_{k=1}^{m} n_k$. Furthermore, let q_k $(k = 1, 2, \ldots, m)$ denote the probability that a customer belongs to the kth class. Because the classes are mutually exclusive and exhaustive, we have $\sum_{k=1}^{m} q_k = 1$. If $p_{(k)}$ denotes the price offered by the seller to the kth class of customers, $(k = 1, 2, \ldots, m)$, then

Pr [a sale occurs in a random contact with a buyer of class k]

$$= \int_{p_{(k)}+}^{\infty} \cdots \int_{p_{(k)}+}^{\infty} \Phi_{(k)}(u_1, \ldots, u_{n-1}) \, du_1 \cdots du_{N-1} \int_{p_{(k)}+}^{\infty} \Psi_{(k)}(u) \, du \equiv \sigma_k.$$

The derivation of this probability is the same as in the preceding paragraph, except for the fact that the density functions $\Phi(.)$ and $\Psi(.)$ are now specific to the classes of customers. Because the classes are independent and do not communicate or act together, the probability that $d = \sum_{k=1}^{m} r_k\, d_k$ units are sold by the firm to a group of n customers partitioned into m classes is calculated as

$$Z \times \sum_{d=\Sigma r_k d_k} \binom{n_1}{r_1} [(\sigma_1)]^{r_1}[(1 - \sigma_1)]^{n_1 - r_1} \cdots \binom{n_m}{r_m}(\sigma_m)^{r_m}(1 - \sigma_m)^{n_m - r_m}, \quad (4.2)$$

where Z is defined as

$$Z = \frac{n!}{(n_1)!\,(n_2)! \cdots (n_m)!}\,(q_1)^{n_1} \cdots (q_m)^{n_m}. \quad (4.3)$$

We *could* introduce a probability distribution of n itself; this point is not pursued further for the expressions (4.2) and (4.3) are not amenable to further simplification. Numerical evaluation is the only means available for computing these expressions.

1.3 It is important to observe that the formula (4.1) has been derived from two subjective elements, namely, $\Phi(\bar{p})$ and $\Psi(P^*)$. It is appropriate, then, to determine whether these can be replaced by some quantities that are computable from observations. To this end, note that if the outcome of ith contact is Z_i:

$$Z_i = \begin{cases} 1, & \text{if a sale is consummated,} \\ 0, & \text{otherwise.} \end{cases}$$

Then, $\sigma \equiv \sigma(p) = \Pr[Z_i = 1] = E(Z_i)$. Suppose now that an identical price p is asked for in k contacts in a period and that $q(\le k)$ of them are successful. Such an event has the likelihood

$$g(q, p) = \binom{k}{q}(\sigma)^q(1 - \sigma)^{k-q}.$$

The maximum likelihood estimate $\hat{\sigma}$ of σ is given by the nontrivial solution of $(d/d\sigma)[\ln g(q, p)] = 0$, that is, by

$$\hat{\sigma} = \frac{q}{k}, \quad (4.4)$$

which is precisely the *empirical market share* of the seller because of the price asked. But $q = \sum_{i=1}^{k} Z_i$ implies that $E(q) = \sum_{i=1}^{k} E(Z_i) = k\sigma$. Since

k is a constant, it follows that

$$E\left(\frac{q}{k}\right) = E(\hat{\sigma}) = \sigma,$$

a familiar property of maximum likelihood estimates.

1.4   Now, since the prices asked by the competitors are not known (see Y:1), the *deterministic or explanatory component* of the firm's market share $\hat{\sigma}$ will be regarded as *dependent on its own price-offers only*. In other words, we would seek a representation of $\hat{\sigma}$ as

$$\hat{\sigma} = F(p, u) = f(p) \cdot u$$

$$0 \leq f(p) < 1, \qquad (0 < p < \infty), \qquad E(u) = 1, \qquad \text{Var}(u) = w^2, \quad (4.5)$$

such that one would have

$$E(\hat{\sigma}) = E[f(p) \cdot u] = f(p). \tag{4.6}$$

This enables the *substitution* $\sigma = f(p)$ in formula (4.1), whenever the price offered by the firm in *known to be* p.[2] Thus formula (4.1) reads

$$g(r; n) = \binom{n}{r}[f(p)]^r[1 - f(p)]^{n-r}. \tag{4.7}$$

In concluding this section it is observed that the method of explicit probabilization eliminates the need to estimate the partial (functional) dependence of a firm's sales on the (concurrently offered, but not observable) prices of the rivals. The ignorance and uncertainty about these are subsumed under the random dependence of sales on the price asked. To sum up: the sales probability σ has been represented as the mathematical expectation of a random variable, namely, $\hat{\sigma} = f(p)u$.

1.5   It may be worthwhile to examine the contribution of Shubik [48] to the analysis of "demand, as seen by an individual seller" in an undifferentiated oligopoly. Shubik introduces the concept of *contingent demand* in the following way: "Suppose that a group of firms is selling a homogeneous product and that each firm is capable of supplying the market by itself. Then, if a firm has a price lower than all the others, it faces the complete market demand; for a price higher than any other

---

[2] In an extensive simulation of the conditions M:1 to 3 and Y:1 and 2 and the market convention (see Chapter 10), $f(p)$ could be estimated as a function of the following form: $f(p) = a/[1 + b\,e^{cp^2}]$ for $p' < p < p''$, with $0 < a < 1, b > 0, c > 0$. The parameters and the domain of definition of $f(.)$ would evidently vary according to the firm. This confirms the usual notion of market share declining with increasing price offers.

Contingent Demand Curve:
Price Independent Variable

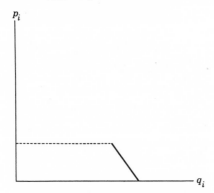

Figure 1 The all-or-none case: If the firm's price is the least, it faces the whole market demand; otherwise, it has no demand.

firm it has no demand." The contingent demand curve is shown in Figure 1.

Shubik also considers the case in which the firms are selling a homogeneous product but the capacities of the firms are limited: they may be unable or unwilling to supply more than a certain amount at the price they are prepared to charge. The contingent demand (with the price as the independent variable) may take on the form shown in Figure 2. "Each

Contingent Demand Curve:
Price Independent Variable

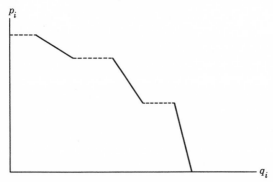

Figure 2 The "saturation" case: each discontinuity occurs at a price charge by an opponent whose production does not saturate the remaining market.

discontinuity occurs at a price charged by an opponent whose production does not saturate the market remaining at that time." Although it is perfectly legitimate to maintain that the nature of demand of a single competitor follows one of the two patterns presented above, there is no mechanism by which we can *determine* the contingent demand. In order to do this, we have to know the prices and quantities to be offered by the competitors in a period. But in most forms of oligopoly this is not feasible. As an "assumption" introduced for methodological reasons, it is unrealistic because there is no communication between the sellers. In short, it is *not* possible to construct a deterministic demand function for a firm. It appears that the best we can do is to turn to probabilistic representation of the functional relationship between prices and sales opportunities. Together with the assumption that the past pattern of behavior of the rivals will continue,[3] the function $\Phi(\bar{p})$ takes on an important role in the framework of analysis. $\sigma(p)$, which defines the probability that the offered price p is minimum, takes care (on the average) of all possible price changes of the competitors, including the retaliation and deliberate advances of prices through intentional limitation of supply. The outcome of all the price changes of the competitors relative to the price p offered by the firm *is* the market share obtained in a period. It is this that forms the empirical basis for estimating the functional form of $\sigma(p)$. Thus it has been possible to find a probability model of demand, as seen by an individual firm in an undifferentiated oligopoly. The model is based on the convention (assumption) that the behavior of the competitors, as observed in the past, will substantially continue into the period in question.

2. DIFFERENTIATED OLIGOPOLY

A situation is considered in which the market is oligopolistic and the product is differentiated. The individual firm's decision variables are (a) the price p to ask and (b) the selling cost c to incur in a given period.

---

[3] This is more in the nature of a convention and therefore it is likely that one school of thought may find it "perfectly natural," whereas another may take strong exception. It should be emphasized that the assumption does *not* imply that one can "extrapolate." The assumption *does* imply, however, that certain relevant probability measures remain stable such that one can construct empirical distributions from past observations. This was substantially the argument of Chapter 3, Section 4. To deny the existence of such empirically stable probability structure is to deny the possibility of *any* analysis and, thus, open the door to unquantifiable speculation. Put another way, the assumption really implies that although the sales volume is random, its probability measure will not undergo unpredictable changes over a short time. It is not merely a mathematical convention; it is a reflection of the existence of coordination or of implicit trust.

With specifications substantially the same as in Section 1, it is shown that if the buyers have roughly equal preferences for the product of the sellers they approach, then the probability that S units will be sold when the unit price asked is p and unit selling cost is c is given by

$$\Phi(S; p, c) = e^{-A(c,p)} \frac{[A(c, p)]^S}{S!}$$

where $A(c, p)$ is of the form, $\mu(p)\lambda(c)$. $A(c, p)$ plays essentially the same role as that of $f(p)$ in Section 1.

2.1   Consider a market, with relatively few sellers (compared to the number of buyers), in which the individual firm's decision variables are two: (a) the price to be asked and (b) the amount of selling costs to incur. Also, consider the following specialization of M:

M:1   Sellers advertise only the characteristics of their products; price information is not made available through advertising.

M:2   There are no intermediaries or dealers, so buyers approach the sellers directly. Individual buyers do not bargain, nor do they necessarily approach *every* seller.[4]

M:3   Every buyer has his own maximum demand price P^*, and the buyers do compare the price-offerings, but only of those firms they approach.

Next, consider the following specifications with respect to the availability of information and the pattern of communication within and between the buyers and sellers:

Y:1   Buyers do not communicate their P^*'s either among themselves or with the sellers they approach.

Y:2   Sellers do not communicate with respect to their prices (that is, price quotations) and selling costs. Also, no records of the price quotations and selling costs of the previous periods are made available among the competitors.

Finally, consider the following specifications of the seller's experience of competition:

S:1   Competition is over sales, that is, over the money spent by the customers.

S:2   Every seller knows from experience that the power to make prices is not absolute, not even when supplemented by selling effort.

---

[4] This follows from the fact that the product is differentiated. It does not matter whether the products are "really" different or whether they are "made to appear different." The effect is the same: consumers have different degrees of preference for the products (brands).

The specifications are still incomplete in that they do not provide enough information in regard to the operations of the firm. In the first place, we have to know whether the firm is quoting an identical price to every customer arriving with an inquiry. Second, we have to know if the production is to be made on order. Finally, we should recognize that different individuals (customers) may arrive with different sizes of potential orders; in other words, it is important to know how the firm is disposed toward the treatment of an inquiry for k $(= 1, 2, \ldots)$ units of the product. Therefore some additional working assumptions have to be introduced:

W:1 The seller quotes an identical price to every unit of inquiry[5] that arrives during a planning period.

W:2 A customer arriving with k units of inquiry is treated by the seller as k customers, each arriving with one unit of inquiry.

W:3 The sellers all produce on order, so that there is no inventory holding.

W:4 The product-differentiation is of such a nature that the buyers have *roughly equal* preferences for the products of all the sellers *they approach*.

The specifications and working assumptions introduced above will now be employed in a systematic manner with a view toward arriving at the probability distribution of sales of an individual seller.

2.2 Let p be the price of the firm and let $q(j)$ denote the maximum demand price of the jth customer for the product of the firm in question. Suppose that the jth customer approaches r of the other firms (the number and identification of which are not known to the firm) and let

$$\bar{q}(j) = \{q_1(j), \ldots, q_r(j)\}$$

denote the customer's maximum demand prices for the product of these other firms. Let

$$\bar{p} = \{p_1, \ldots, p_r\}$$

denote the price quotations of the other firms. It is possible to suppose that the customer decides to buy according to some criterion, say,

$$\text{(a) } \min[p - q(j), p_1 - q_1(j), \ldots, p_r - q_r(j)],$$

or

$$\text{(b) } \min[p/q(j), p/q_1(j), \ldots, p_r/q_r(j)].$$

---

[5] A distinction must be made between a unit of inquiry and a unit of demand. A "unit of *inquiry*" refers to the volume of business for which a customer approaches a seller and asks for a price quotation. This is done in conformity with the specifications of S, M, and Y. A "unit of *demand*," or a unit of sale, on the other hand, refers to a volume of business a seller receives *after* acceptance of the offer. In short, a unit of demand is a unit of inquiry that *materializes* as a sale at the price quoted.

But, according to Y:1 to 2, the elements of $\bar{p}$, $q(j)$ or $\bar{q}(j)$ are in effect random variables from the viewpoint of the firm. Now, consider M:2 and W:4 in conjunction; thus the seller with the lowest price will obtain the sales. In other words, the likelihood of a sale by the firm to a randomly arriving inquiry depends upon the likelihood of two events:

$$E_1: p < \min (p_1, \ldots, p_r), \qquad E_2: p \leq q(j).$$

But the seller does not know the prices offered by other sellers, nor does he know which of the firms were approached by the customer. Thus the events E_1 and E_2 are independent. The likelihood of E_1 is $L(p)$:

$$L(p) = \Pr [p < p_1, \ldots, p < p_r]$$

$$= \int_{p^+}^{\infty} \cdots \int_{p^+}^{\infty} f_1(p_1, \ldots, p_r) \, dp \cdots dp_r,$$

$f_1(p_1, \ldots, p_r)$ being the density of the joint distribution of the competitors' prices. Let $f_2(q) = f_2[q(j)]$ denote the probability density of the maximum demand price for a given customer. The likelihood of a sale in a randomly chosen contact is $\mu_s(p)$:

$$\mu_s(p) = \Pr [E_1] \Pr [E_2]$$

$$= \left(\int_{p^+}^{\infty} \cdots \int_{p^+}^{\infty} f_1(p_1, \ldots, p_r) \, dp_r \cdots dp_r \right) \left(\int_{p}^{\infty} f_2(q) \, dq \right). \quad (4.8)$$

2.3 Neither of the two probabilities appearing in this expression is objectively defined. This, as we shall now see, does not present any special difficulty because they can be replaced by their *empirical counterparts*. Observe, first, that the buyers have been assumed to be anonymous units of demand. Consequently, the likelihood $\mu_s(p)$ is to be averaged or smoothed over the *ensemble of customers;* such an average would represent probability of acceptance, $\mu(p)$, $0 < \mu(p) < 1$. Next, according to the working assumptions of the model, each unit of inquiry is free to reject a quotation and go elsewhere or to accept the quotation and place the order with the seller in question. Thus the Pr [S units are sold in ν inquiries] is given by Pr [$S; \nu, p$]:

$$\Pr [S; \nu, p] = \binom{\nu}{S} [\mu(p)]^S [1 - \mu(p)]^{\nu - S}. \quad (4.9)$$

Note, however, that ν itself is a *random* variable. What *can* be said about the probability distribution of ν? If the choices of the individual customers are mutually independent and the number of inquiries is not too small (in suitably defined units of time), a simple model for the distribution of ν is the Poisson process. The parameter of this process is the average number λ of units of inquiry per period (which may, for example, be chosen to coincide with the planning period). Thus

$$\Pr\left[\nu = n\right] = \frac{\exp\left(-\lambda\right)\lambda^n}{n!}. \tag{4.10}$$

The "arrival rate" λ depends, among other things, on the intensity of the selling efforts of *all* the firms. A simple and obvious measure of this intensity is the rate of spending c per unit of sale. The firm in question, however, does not know these rates nor does it know how its own (potential) sales are influenced by the unit selling costs incurred by its rivals. Thus $\lambda = \lambda(c)$ is itself a statistical quantity; the outcome of a given intensity of selling effort per unit is to elicit only an *expected number* of arrivals of customers per unit of time. In other words, $\lambda = \lambda(c)$ is to be understood, again, as a mean-value. To sum up,

$\Pr\left[\text{sales} = S; \text{quoted price} = p, \text{unit selling cost} = c\right]$

$$= \sum_{n=0}^{\infty} \Pr\left[S; n, p\right] \Pr\left[n; c\right]$$

$$= \sum_{n=0}^{\infty} \binom{n}{s} [\mu(p)]^S [1 - \mu(p)]^{n-S} e^{-\lambda(c)} \frac{[\lambda(c)]^n}{n!}$$

$$= e^{-\lambda(c)\mu(p)} \frac{[\lambda(c)\,\mu(p)]^S}{S!} \equiv e^{-A(c,p)} \frac{[A(c,p)]^S}{S!}, \tag{4.11}$$

where $A(c, p) = \lambda(c)\mu(p)$, the average rate of sales with a price quoted at p and unit selling cost c. An alternative derivation of the probability distribution (4.11) is presented in Appendix I, in which a simple measure-theoretic construction shows how one may develop a dynamic version of (4.11).

2.4 For the sake of definiteness, the following working assumptions are made about the functions $\mu(p)$ and $\mu(c)$:

$$-\infty < \left(\frac{d\mu}{dp}\right)_{p \geq 0} < 0; \tag{4.12}$$

$$0 < \lim_{p \to 0} \mu(p) = \alpha < \infty \quad \lim_{p \to \infty} \mu(p) = 0, \qquad \lim_{p \to \infty} p\mu(p) = 0,$$

$$\lim_{p \to \infty} \frac{d\mu}{dp} = 0; \tag{4.13}$$

$$0 < \left(\frac{d\lambda}{dc}\right)_{c \geq 0} < \infty \tag{4.14}$$

$$0 < \lim_{c \to 0} \lambda(c) = \beta < \infty, \quad 0 < \lim_{c \to \infty} \lambda(c) = \nu < \infty, \quad \lim_{c \to \infty} \frac{d\lambda}{dc} = 0. \tag{4.15}$$

On account of these assumptions, it is immediately verified that the function $A(c, p)$ will possess the following properties:

$$-\infty < \left(\frac{\partial A}{\partial p}\right)_{p\geq 0} < 0, \quad 0 < \left(\frac{\partial A}{\partial c}\right)_{c\geq 0} < \infty, \tag{4.16}$$

$$0 < \lim_{p\to 0} A(p, c) = \alpha\lambda(c) < \infty, \ \lim_{p\to\infty} A(p, c) = 0, \tag{4.17}$$

$$0 < \lim_{c\to 0} A(p, c) = \beta\mu(p) < \infty, \ 0 < \lim_{c\to\infty} A(p, c) = \nu\mu(p) < \infty. \tag{4.18}$$

A few brief observations of the implications of (4.16) to (4.18) are in order; as will be seen immediately, these represent some natural restriction on the shape of the function $A(p, c)$; (4.16) implies that the average sales decrease as price increases and increase as the selling expenses (per unit of sales) increase. This coincides with the concept of a demand curve in classical economic theory. The conditions (4.17) assert that the average sales would become large—although not infinite—as price quoted reaches zero (the product is given away), whereas average sales would approach zero as the price quoted tends to increase. The condition (4.18) on the selling expenses implies that the average sales would reach *some* constant or nearly constant level as c approaches zero.

3. THE "LARGE GROUP": A SPECIAL CASE

The purpose of this section is to analyze a situation of product differentiation with not too few sellers. The particular model to follow is, in effect, a version of what Chamberlain has called the "large group" case of monopolistic competition. There is an added feature, namely, that the product is *distributed through wholesale and retail outlets.* The speciality of the situation is in the fact that selling costs are presumably directed toward the final buyers, while the price policy pursued by (the wholesalers of) the firm would have more immediate impact on the distribution channel. This speciality is reflected in the fact that the probability distribution of the sales of an individual firm (wholesaler) is essentially different from the one derived in Section 2. In particular, it is shown that the probability of s units of sale (in excess of some "normal" level) by a firm's wholesaler to a class of retailers is of the form

$$F(s) = \frac{[g(\mu')]^n}{\Gamma(n)} \int_0^s y^{n-1} e^{-g(\mu')y} \, dy;$$

$g(\mu')$ is a monotone decreasing function of the excess μ' of (a) the maximum markups accorded to this class by all the competing wholesalers in the region over (b) the profit margin provided by the firm's wholesaler to this class. The parameter n is to be interpreted as the number of retailers in the class or the number of time-periods over which s has been observed. The general model for monopolistic competition in the large group is discussed in Chapter 6.

3.1 Consider a situation in which manufacturers (of a consumer product that is purchased high frequency) deal exclusively with the wholesalers, who, in turn, reach the consumers through retailers. In particular, consider the following trade practice and market organization:

M:1 The wholesalers have no franchise; in other words, a manufacturer can at any time transfer business from one wholesaler to another.

M:2 The product is fair-traded, but fair-trade practice is not rigorously enforced.

M:3 A wholesaler is assigned a certain geographical area in which, typically, there is a large number of retailers; this number is relatively stable over a period of time.

In other words, a wholesaler of a brand is the local monopolist in regard to the supply of that brand; he can and does accord varying profit margins or "markups" to the retailers.[6] Equivalently, as seen by a retailer, there is a spectrum of profit margins provided by the wholesalers of the rival brands.

3.2 Next, consider the following specifications about the nature and content of information available to the market participants:

Y:1 Manufacturers advertise their products with a view toward promoting consumer interest in their respective brands. The information contained in the advertising may pertain to quality, superiority of the brand, social status associated with the consumption of the brand, and so on. Not much *additional* information of this kind can be conveyed to the consumers, especially if the brand has been in existence for a long time and has gained consumer acceptance.

Y:2 Retailers do not communicate among themselves on the prices at which they conclude transactions with the wholesalers.

Y:3 Each wholesaler is aware of the *range* of the profit margins or markups provided by the wholesalers to the retailers in the given geographical unit. In other words, a wholesaler has an *estimate* of the upper and lower bounds on the markups provided to the retailers. These bounds are reasonably stable, although the exact level of a rival wholesaler's selling price is not known.

---

[6] Thus the wholesalers may find it profitable to divide the customers—that is, the retailers—into classes, according to their average (or, perhaps, model) offtakes, and follow a uniform price policy with regard to the markups accorded to each class.

The specification Y:2 implies that the wholesaler can maintain some *discrimination* among the classes of retailers. The significance of the specification Y:1 may be understood as follows: Additional advertising and similar selling efforts, unless done on a massive scale and with considerable ingenuity, will not carry much additional information or appeal to the consumer. It is natural, therefore, to conclude that the response of an individual brand's sales to variations in its own advertising (per unit of the product) will be approximately a *constant* over some appropriately defined *interval* of advertising variations.[7] The implications of Y:3 are obvious: It is the lack of exact knowledge of the margins accorded by the wholesalers of the rival brands that imparts randomness or uncertainty to the sale of a wholesaler.

3.3 It is important to examine the consequences of M:3 even when fair-trading is not rigorously practiced. Regardless of the diversity of their practices, the retailers are equally capable of making their purchases from the wholesalers at "good" prices. In other words, the offtakes by the retailers are expected to be sensitive to the markups provided by the wholesalers: They would prefer to purchase as large a fraction of their demand as possible from the wholesaler who offers the greatest profit margin. In the short run, however, the retailers must purchase a certain minimum amount of *each* brand in order to satisfy that portion of the (expected) demand which cannot be satisfied with the inventory of some alternative brand, although the brand in question may be offering a greater margin.

3.4 The preceding considerations furnish a clue to the analysis that follows. In order to avoid needless details, mention is made only of *a* given class of retailers; aggregation over all the classes of retailers is a matter of routine calculations. Define the following:

a: The minimum purchase by a class of retailers.
z: The profit margin provided by the wholesaler to this class.
Z: The maximum of the markups accorded to this class by *all* the wholesalers in the geographical region in question.

In view of the preceding comments about the retailers' behavior, it follows that they are more likely to purchase (from a wholesaler) in excess of the minimum quantity *if* the markup offered by the wholesaler in question is closer to the maximum markup *available* in the market. In

---

[7] In other words, if S denotes the volume of sales, and α denotes the advertising outlay per unit of the product, then for $a \leq \alpha \pm d\alpha \leq b$ the ratio, $(dS/S)/(|d\alpha|/\alpha)$, is a constant. In view of this consideration, it is possible to have a model of sales in which the advertising outlays do not appear explicitly.

other words, if μ' denotes the excess of Z over z , then, from the viewpoint of the wholesaler, the probability amplitude of a sale of s units (in excess of a units) will have the following property:

$$\Pr [\text{sales} = s; \ \mu' = h] > \Pr [\text{sales} = s; \ \mu' = h^*] \quad \text{for} \quad h^* > h. \quad (4.19)$$

If the volume of sales (in excess of the amount a) is denoted by the random variables S, this property may be realized by any probability distribution function in the form of

$$F(s) = \Pr [S \leq s] = \frac{[g(\mu')]^n}{\Gamma(n)} \int_0^s y^{n-1} e^{-g(\mu')y} dy, \quad (4.20)$$

the function $g(\mu')$ being a monotone decreasing function of μ', for positive values of μ', that is, of $Z - z$; n, may be interpreted either as the number of retailers in the class or as the number of time periods over which an observation is made. In other words, *given* a level of μ', the probability amplitude of sales increases and then diminishes as s increases indefinitely. The model (4.20) reappears in Chapter 6, Section 2, where it is derived from more fundamental considerations and more rigorously.

Chapter 5

MONOPOLISTIC COMPETITION: MACROMODELS AND MICROMODELS

The macroanalysis of monopolistic competition takes the viewpoint of an ideal observer with complete information and attempts to explain the *joint probabilities of sales of all the firms* in the industry. The microanalysis, on the other hand, focuses attention on the uncertainty of sales as seen from the viewpoint of an individual firm. Such uncertainties are, in part, due to the lack of prior knowledge about the competitors' reactions. The purpose of this chapter is to develop the theme that *in a framework of probabilistic representation of outcomes of competition there is no need for an explicit consideration of the interaction among the firms*. An attempt is also made to show that if there is some measure of implicit "coordination"—and, hence, some measure of stability in the pattern of interactions—it is possible to analyze the effects of a *variation* of the selling efforts of one firm relative to the rest of the industry.

The principal contribution of this chapter is a direct measure-theoretic derivation of a multinomial distribution (Section 1) of the sales of a (finite) number of firms in an environment of monopolistic competition. The probability corresponding to an individual firm depends upon the share of its own selling efforts to the aggregate or industrywide selling efforts. The macromodel is modified (Sections 2 and 3) to yield a micromodel of the probable effects of a variation in the relative selling efforts of an individual firm. The outcome of the analysis is bivariate binomial distribution in which the conditional probabilities depend upon the variation in the relative selling efforts.

1. MULTINOMIAL DISTRIBUTION OF SALES

The purpose of this section is to develop the joint distribution of the sales of several (but finite number of) firms in an industry in which the "product" is differentiated by brands and the prices of all the brands are in a narrow range close to one another. The associated notion of the market is to be interpreted in a somewhat narrow sense, so as to eliminate the problems due to transportation costs and nonhomogeniety of geographical regions. The special case is considered in which the buyers are scattered and for too many relative to the number of sellers.

1.1 Suppose there are m brands and a nonrandom number N ($< \infty$) of customers in a given market; also suppose that N is considerably larger than n. For the sake of convenience, it may be assumed that there are as many firms as brands. Let ω denote the proportion of selling efforts (measured, for instance, in dollars) of any single firm to the aggregate selling effort of all the firms in the industry during an arbitrary but fixed length of time. Evidently, $0 \leq \omega \leq 1$; define Ω: ($\omega: 0 \leq \omega \leq 1$). Any firm can be characterized by its location in Ω. Consider, in particular, a partition of Ω into m disjoint intervals

$$S_1: 0 \leq \omega \leq \alpha_1, \quad S_2: \alpha_1 < \omega \leq \alpha_2, \ldots, S_m: \alpha_{m-1} < \omega \leq 1 \quad (5.1)$$

each interval corresponding to a firm.

1.2 In the type of markets considered here the buyers are scattered and are far too many in relation to the numbers of sellers. Thus there is no bargaining among individual buyers and sellers. Also, the buyers are unorganized, so that the *choices of any two buyers are mutually independent.* It is necessary, therefore, to have a mathematical construction which will reflect this aspect of the market structure. Let

$$T_\alpha(\omega) = T_{\alpha_1 \ldots, \alpha_{m-1}}(\omega) = \begin{cases} \dfrac{\omega}{\alpha_1}, & 0 \leq \omega \leq \alpha_1, \\[2mm] \dfrac{\omega - \alpha_s}{\alpha_{s+1} - \alpha_s}, & \begin{matrix} \alpha_s < \omega \leq \alpha_{e+1}, \\ (s = 1, 2, \cdots, m-2) \end{matrix} \\[2mm] \dfrac{\omega - \alpha_{m-1}}{1 - \alpha_{m-1}}, & \alpha_m < \omega \leq 1, \end{cases} \quad (5.2)$$

and define the functions E_k,

$$E_1(\omega) = s, \; \alpha_{s-1} < \omega \leq \alpha_s \; (s = 1, 2, \ldots, m; \alpha_0 = 0, \alpha_m = 1)$$
$$E_k(\omega) = E_{k-1}[T_\alpha(\omega)], \qquad (k = 2, 3, \ldots, N), \quad (5.3)$$

which represent the choices by individual customers. Now, observe that

$$\Pr\,[E_k(\omega) = s] = \alpha_s - \alpha_{s-1} \equiv p_s$$
$$(s = 1, 2, \ldots, m \; ; k = 1, 2, \ldots, N), \quad (5.4)$$

with the convention that $\alpha_0 = 0$ and $\alpha_m = 1$; also, from (5.2) and (5.3), we may verify that

$$\Pr\left[E_k(\omega) = s \mid E_{k-1}(\omega) = s^*\right] = \Pr\left[E_k(\omega) = s\right]. \tag{5.5}$$

Thus the functions $\{E_k(\omega), k = 1, \ldots, N\}$ are a sequence of identically distributed, mutually *independent* measurable functions (random variables) with measures given by (5.4).[1] In other words, the functions E_k denote the individual customer's choice, and the quantities p_k denote the associated probabilities.

1.3   A partition of the N customers into m brands can now be represented as

$$g_N(\omega) = \sum_{k=1}^{N} E_k(\omega). \tag{5.6}$$

Let $g_N(\omega)$ have a realization, namely, $\sum_{s=1}^{m} s j_s = 1$. The probability of this "event" is the measure $\mu(.)$ of the Ω-interval on which $g_N(\omega) = j$:

$$\Pr\left[g_N(\omega) = j\right] = \mu_N = \mu[\omega : g_N(\omega) = j]. \tag{5.7}$$

Because μ_N is the *mathematical expectation* of the set-function $I(j)$ defined as

$$I(j) = \begin{cases} 1, & g_N(\omega) = j, \\ 0, & g_N(\omega) \neq j, \end{cases} \tag{5.8}$$

and since the set function has a representation as an integral,

$$I(j) = \frac{1}{2\pi} \int_0^{2\pi} \exp\left\{ix[g_N(\omega) - j]\right\} dx, \qquad (i = \sqrt{-1}), \tag{5.9}$$

therefore it may be verified that

$$\mu_N = \int_0^1 \left(\frac{1}{2\pi} \int_0^{2\pi} \exp\left\{ix[g_N(\omega) - j]\right\} dx\right) d\omega$$

$$= \frac{1}{2\pi} \int_0^{2\pi} e^{-ixj} \left(\int_0^1 \exp\left[ix\sum_{k=1}^{N} E_k(\omega)\right] d\omega\right) dx.$$

---

[1] From a purely mathematical point of view the functions $E_k(\omega)$ are the mutually orthogonal coefficients in the m-ary representation of ω:

$$\omega = \sum_{k=1}^{\infty} E_k(\omega) m^{-k},$$

where, for all k, $E_k(\omega)$ takes on the value of 1 with probability $p_k = 1/m$ and the value of zero with probability $1 - 1/m$.

The integral in the parenthesis is a Lebesgue integral which is to be evaluated by considering the possible values of $E_k(\omega)$, multiplying the corresponding values of the integrand by the measure of the Ω-interval on which these values are taken on, and finally summing over the terms so obtained. Thus, noting that $\alpha_j - \alpha_{j-1} = p_j$, it may be seen that

$$\int_0^1 \exp\left[ix \sum_{k=1}^N E_k(\omega) \right] d\omega = (p_1 e^{ix} + \cdots + p_m e^{imx})^N, \qquad (5.10)$$

the exponentiation being due to the fact that the $E_k(\omega)$ are independent and identically distributed random variables. Hence the expression (5.7) is evaluated as

$$\mu_N = \frac{1}{2\pi} \int_0^{2\pi} e^{-ijx} \left(\sum_{j=1}^m p_j e^{ijx} \right)^N dx$$

$$= \frac{1}{2\pi} \int_0^{2\pi} e^{-ijx} \sum_{j_1, j_2, \ldots, j_m} \binom{N}{j_1, j_2, \ldots, j_m} (p_1)^{j_1} \cdots (p_m)^{j_m}$$

$$\times \exp\left[\sum_{s=1}^m ixsj_s \right] dx = \binom{N}{j_1, j_2, \ldots, j_m} (p_1)^{j_1} \cdots (p_m)^{j_m}, \qquad (5.11)$$

where, by construction, $\sum_{s=1}^m p_s = 1$. Equation (5.11) gives the probability of a situation in which an aggregate of N customers is partitioned as j_i $(i = 1, 2, \ldots, m)$ customers for the ith brand. This is seen to be a multinomial distribution. It should be observed that if the predominant customer habit is to buy one unit at a time, then (5.11) is also the probability distribution of the sale of individual brands. With this interpretation, (5.11) has the following significance. The *relative positions of the firms in the scale of aggregate selling efforts may be employed as estimators of the sales probabilities under a multinomial distribution.*

2. A MICROMODEL: BIVARIATE BINOMIAL PROBABILITIES

With the implicit assumption that the competitive behavior is stable enough to allow the computation of relevant probabilities, it is possible to examine the probable effects of a variation in the (relative) selling efforts of an individual firm. In conformity with the representation set up in the previous section, such a variation may be looked upon as a jump from one subinterval of Ω to another.

2.1 It has been observed in Section 1 that the sales probability of a firm is dependent on its own selling efforts relative to that of the industry. This suggests that in order to analyze the impact of a variation of the firm's own selling efforts we need two elementary choice-functions; one, $\Phi(\omega)$, for the situation *before* the variation and the other, $\Psi(\omega)$, for the situation *after* the variation:

$$\Phi(\omega) = \begin{cases} 1, & 0 \le \omega \le \alpha, \\ 0, & \omega > \alpha, \end{cases} \qquad \Psi(\omega) = \begin{cases} 1, & 0 \le \omega \le \beta, \\ 0, & \omega > \beta. \end{cases} \tag{5.12}$$

Depending on the quality of selling efforts and the customer characteristics. there are certain conditional probabilities μ_{ij}:

$$\mu_{ij} = \mu[\omega : \Psi(\omega) = j \mid \Phi(\omega) = i], \qquad i, j = 0, 1. \tag{5.13}$$

(Such probabilities are empirically determinable. For the remainder of the discussion they are assumed to be known.) It should be observed that the $\Phi(\omega)$ and $\Psi(\omega)$ are not independent; their mutual dependence is reflected in the following equation:

$$(1 - \beta, \beta) = (1 - \alpha, \alpha)\begin{pmatrix} \mu_{00} & \mu_{01} \\ \mu_{10} & \mu_{11} \end{pmatrix}. \tag{5.14}$$

With the quantities defined in (5.12) and (5.13), the stage is now set for the derivation of the *joint distribution* of sales of a given firm *before and after* a change in the relative amount of its selling efforts. Define the following transformations on Ω,

$$T_\alpha(\omega) = \begin{cases} \dfrac{\omega}{\alpha}, & 0 \le \omega \le \alpha, \\[2mm] \dfrac{\omega - \alpha}{1 - \alpha} & \alpha < \omega \le 1, \end{cases}$$

$$T_\beta(\omega) = \begin{cases} \dfrac{\omega}{\beta}, & 0 \le \omega \le \beta, \\[2mm] \dfrac{\omega - \beta}{1 - \beta} & \beta < \omega \le 1, \end{cases} \tag{5.15}$$

and introduce two sequences, each of mutually independent functions constructed as follows:

$$\begin{aligned} \Phi_1(\omega) &= \Phi(\omega), & \Phi_k(\omega) &= \Phi_{k-1}[T_\alpha(\omega)], \\ \Psi_1(\omega) &= \Psi(\omega), & \Psi_k(\omega) &= \Psi_{k-1}[T_\beta(\omega)], \end{aligned} \qquad k = 2, 3, \ldots, n, \tag{5.16}$$

n being the number of contacts. Note that by this construction the $\Phi_k(\omega)$ and $\Psi_k(\omega)$ represent the mutually *independent choices* by the n customers. Suppose that n contacts are made *both* before and after the variation. Then the corresponding level of *sales* (of the firm) can be represented as the sums of the elementary choice functions $\Phi_k(\omega)$ and $\Psi_k(\omega)$:

$$X(\omega) = \sum_{k=1}^{n} \Phi_k(\omega), \qquad Y(\omega) = \sum_{k=1}^{n} \Psi_k(\omega). \qquad (5.17)$$

The following probability is of immediate interest:

$$\Pr\left[X(\omega) = x, \; Y(\omega) = y\right] = \mu[\omega : X(\omega) = x, \; Y(\omega) = y]. \qquad (5.18)$$

2.2 This probability is the mathematical expectation of the set-function $I_{x \wedge y}$:

$$I_{x \wedge y} = \begin{cases} 1, & \text{if} \quad X(\omega) = x \quad and \quad Y(\omega) = y, \\ 0, & \text{otherwise.} \end{cases}$$

A convenient representation of this set-function is the following integral

$$I_{x \wedge y} = \frac{1}{(2\pi)^2} \int_0^{2\pi} \int_0^{2\pi} \exp\left\{i\xi[X(\omega) - x] + i\eta[Y(\omega) - y]\right\} d\xi \, d\eta \qquad (5.19)$$

Therefore the probability we would proceed to develop is

$$\mu_n = \int_0^1 I_{x \wedge y} \, d\omega = \frac{1}{(2\pi)^2} \int_0^{2\pi} \int_0^{2\pi} \exp\left(-i\xi x - i\eta y\right) d\xi \, d\eta$$

$$\times \int_0^1 \exp\left[i\xi X(\omega) + i\eta Y(\omega)\right] d\omega, \qquad (5.20)$$

where the interchange of order of integration follows from Fubini's theorem. Substituting from (5.17) and taking into account (5.12), (5.13), and the mutual independence of the $\Phi_k(\omega)$ and $\Psi_k(\omega)$ *inter alia*, it may be seen that

$$\int_0^1 \exp\left[i\xi X(\omega) + i\eta Y(\omega)\right] d\omega$$

$$= \int_0^1 \exp\left[i\xi \sum_{k=1}^{n} \Phi_k(\omega) + i\eta \sum_{k=1}^{n} \Psi_k(\omega)\right] d\omega$$

$$= \prod_{k=1}^{n} [(1 - \alpha)(\mu_{00} + \mu_{01}e^{i\eta}) + \alpha e^{i\xi}(\mu_{10} + \mu_{11}e^{i\eta})]$$

$$= [(1 - \alpha)(\mu_{00} + \mu_{01}e^{i\eta}) + \alpha e^{i\xi}(\mu_{10} + \mu_{11}e^{i\eta})]^n$$

$$\equiv H(\xi, \eta), \qquad (5.21)$$

the last step following from the constructions that ensure the *identical distribution* of the $\Phi_k(\omega)$'s and the $\Psi_k(\omega)$'s. By substituting (5.21) into

(5.20), we have

$$\mu_n = \frac{1}{(2\pi)^2} \int_0^{2\pi} \int_0^{2\pi} e^{-i\xi x - i\eta y} H(\xi, \eta) \, d\xi \, d\eta$$

$$= \frac{1}{(2\pi)^2} \int_0^{2\pi} \left[\int_0^{2\pi} e^{-i\xi x - i\eta y} H(\xi, \eta) \, d\xi \right] d\eta$$

$$= \sum_{k=0}^{\min(x,y)} \binom{n}{n-x-y+k, \, y-k, \, x-k, \, k}$$

$$\times (\mu_{00})^{n-x-y+k}(\mu_{01})^{y-k}(\mu_{10})^{x-k}(\mu_{11})^{k}(1-\alpha)^{n-x}(\alpha)^{x} \qquad (5.22)$$

$$= \sum_{k=0}^{\min(x,y)} \binom{n}{x}\alpha^x(1-\alpha)^{n-x}\binom{n-x}{y-k}\binom{x}{k}$$

$$\times (\mu_{00})^{n-x-y+k}(\mu_{01})^{y-k}(\mu_{10})^{x-k}(\mu_{11})^{k}, \qquad (5.23)$$

which follows on integrating first with respect to ξ and then with respect to η. Equation (5.23) gives the probability that in n contacts there will be x units of sales before and y units of sales after the variation in the relative amount of selling efforts of the firm. It is a joint binomial distribution in which the sales before and after the variation are not independent. The pattern and magnitude of their dependence is determined by the conditional probabilities μ_{ij} $(i, j = 0, 1)$.

2.3 We may now examine the following question: *What happens if the firm does not make a relative variation?* According to the preceding development, a zero relative variation has the following representation, namely,

$$\mu_{00} = 1 = \mu_{11}, \qquad \mu_{01} = 0 = \mu_{10}, \qquad (5.24)$$

which again implies that $\alpha = \beta$ [see (5.14)]; hence $H(\xi, \eta)$ in (5.22) takes on the form $H(\xi, \eta) = [(1-\alpha) + \alpha e^{i(\xi+\eta)}]^n$. This can be expanded as

$$H(\xi, \eta) = \sum_{k=0}^{n} \binom{n}{k}[\alpha e^{i(\xi+\eta)}]^k(1-\alpha)^{n-k};$$

hence from (5.22) it follows that

$$\mu_n = \binom{n}{k}\alpha^k(1-\alpha)^{n-k}. \qquad (5.25)$$

In other words, if the firm does not change its (relative) level of selling efforts, the probability distribution of its sales—in particular, the probability of "success" in n contacts—is likely, with probability one, to remain unchanged. This probability is seen to depend upon the position of the firm in the industry's scale of selling efforts. More interesting interpretations are taken up in the following section where the limiting case of (5.23) is explored.

3. A LIMITING DISTRIBUTION: BIVARIATE GAUSSIAN

The purpose of this section is to show that the bivariate binomial distribution (5.23) goes over, in the limit as $n \to \infty$, to the bivariate Gaussian distribution. The properties of this limiting distribution are examined. The principal results relate to the predictability of the probable consequences of large variations in the firm's selling efforts.

3.1   Recall from Section 2 that each $\Phi_k(\omega)$ and $\Psi_k(\omega)$ has identical mean values, namely, α and β, respectively. Centering around these mean values and normalizing, define

$$v_k(\omega) = \frac{\Phi_k(\omega) - \alpha}{\sqrt{n\alpha(1 - \alpha)}} = \begin{cases} + \dfrac{\sqrt{1 - \alpha}}{\sqrt{\alpha n}}, & 0 \leq \omega \leq \alpha, \\[3mm] - \dfrac{\sqrt{\alpha}}{\sqrt{n(1 - \alpha)}}, & \alpha < \omega \leq 1; \end{cases} \tag{5.26}$$

$$\delta_k(\omega) = \frac{\Psi_k(\omega) - \beta}{\sqrt{n\beta(1 - \beta)}} = \begin{cases} + \dfrac{\sqrt{1 - \beta}}{\sqrt{\beta n}}, & 0 \leq \omega \leq \beta, \\[3mm] - \dfrac{\sqrt{\beta}}{\sqrt{n(1 - \beta)}}, & \beta < \omega \leq 1. \end{cases} \tag{5.27}$$

Consider the sums of such normalized functions, namely,

$$U_n(\omega) = \sum_{k=1}^{n} v_k(\omega), \qquad V_n(\omega) = \sum_{k=1}^{n} \delta_k(\omega), \tag{5.28}$$

and consider the problem of determining the probability that $x_1 < U_n(\omega) < x_2$ and $y_1 < V_n(\omega) < y_2$, that is, $\mu_n = \mu[\omega : x_1 < V_n(\omega) < x_2, y_1 < V_n(\omega) < y_2]$. The first step is to define the set function

$$g(x, y) = \begin{cases} 1, & \text{if } x_1 < x < x_2 \text{ and } y_1 < y < y_2, \\ 0, & \text{otherwise,} \end{cases}$$

which has a Fourier integral representation [53]

$$g(x, y) = (2\pi)^{-2} \int\limits_{-\infty}^{\infty} \int\limits_{-\infty}^{\infty} g(u, v) \exp\left[i\xi(u - x) + i\eta(v - y) \right] du \, dv \, d\xi \, d\eta.$$

Hence μ_n, the mathematical expectation of $g(x, y)$, is seen to be

$$\mu_n = \int_0^1 g[\sum \nu_k(\omega), \sum \delta_k(\omega)] \, d\omega$$

$$= (2\pi)^{-2} \int_0^1 \left\{ \iiiint_{-\infty}^{\infty} g(u, v) \exp(i\xi u + i\eta v) \, du \, dv \, d\xi \, d\eta \right.$$

$$\left. \times \exp[-i\xi \sum \nu_k(\omega) - i\eta \sum \delta_k(\omega)] \right\} d\omega$$

$$= (2\pi)^{-2} \iiiint_{-\infty}^{\infty} g(u, v) \exp(i\xi u + i\eta v) \, du \, dv \, d\xi \, d\eta$$

$$\times \left[\int_0^1 \exp[-i\xi \sum \nu_k(\omega) - i\eta \sum \delta_k(\omega)] \, d\omega \right]. \quad (5.29)$$

Again, noting that the $\nu_k(\omega)$ and $\delta_k(\omega)$ are each a family of independent *identically* distributed random variables, the inner integral in (5.29) is seen to be $F_n(\xi, \eta)$:

$$F_n(\xi, \eta) = \int_0^1 \exp\left[-i\xi \sum_{k=1}^n \nu_k(\omega) - i\eta \sum_{k=1}^n \delta_k(\omega) \right] d\omega$$

$$= \left[(1 - \alpha) \exp\left(\frac{-i\xi\sqrt{\alpha}}{\sqrt{n(1 - \alpha)}} \right) \left\{ \mu_{10} \exp\left(\frac{i\eta\sqrt{\beta}}{\sqrt{n(1 - \beta)}} \right) \right. \right.$$

$$\left. + \mu_{01} \exp\left(\frac{-i\eta\sqrt{1 - \beta}}{\sqrt{n\beta}} \right) \right\} + \alpha \exp\left(\frac{-i\xi\sqrt{1 - \alpha}}{\sqrt{n\alpha}} \right)$$

$$\times \left. \left\{ \mu_{10} \exp\left(\frac{i\eta\sqrt{\beta}}{\sqrt{n(1 - \beta)}} \right) + \mu_{11} \exp\left(\frac{-i\eta\sqrt{1 - \beta}}{\sqrt{n\beta}} \right) \right\} \right]^n. \quad (5.30)$$

Expanding (5.30) in power-series around $\xi = 0$ and $\eta = 0$, and retaining terms of the orders up to ξ^2, η^2 and $\xi\eta$, it is seen that

$$F_n(\xi, \eta) = \left[1 - \frac{1}{2n} (\xi^2 + \eta^2 + 2\xi\eta\rho) \right]^n, \quad (5.31)$$

where ρ is defined as

$$\rho = \frac{1}{\lambda_1 \lambda_2} [\mu_{00}(1 - \alpha) - \lambda_1^2 \alpha \mu_{10} - (1 - \alpha)\lambda_2^2 \mu_{01} + (\lambda_1 \lambda_2)^2 \alpha \mu_{11}], \quad (5.32)$$

$$\left(\lambda_1 \equiv \frac{\sqrt{1 - \alpha}}{\sqrt{\alpha}}, \qquad \lambda_2 \equiv \frac{\sqrt{1 - \beta}}{\sqrt{\beta}} \right).$$

By substituting (5.31) into (5.29), we have

$$\mu_n = \frac{1}{(2\pi)^2} \int\limits_{-\infty}^{\infty}\int\limits_{-\infty}^{\infty} \int\int g(u, v) e^{i\xi u + i\eta v}\, du\, dv F_n(\xi, \eta)\, d\xi\, d\eta. \qquad (5.33)$$

Following a procedure due to Kac [32] which, in effect, legitimizes the limiting operation under the integral sign in (5.33), it is seen that

$$\Pr\left[x_1 < U(\omega) < x_2, y_1 < V(\omega) < y_2\right]$$

$$= \lim_{n\to\infty}\mu_n = \frac{1}{2\pi} \int_{x_1}^{x_2}\int_{y_1}^{y_2} \exp\left[-\frac{1}{2}\frac{u^2 + v^2 - 2uv\rho}{1 - \rho^2}\right]\frac{du\, dv}{\sqrt{1 - \rho^2}}. \qquad (5.34)$$

Thus, in the limit, as the number of contacts grows sufficiently large, the *aggregate* sale (each component of which is appropriately centered and normalized) tends to be a bivariate Gaussian distribution with correlation coefficient ρ.

3.2 It is fruitful to reexamine the question posed in Section 2. Suppose that the firm has been pursuing a certain policy in regard to the (relative) selling efforts over some length of time, and suppose that the policy is continued in a subsequent period. This means that

$$\mu_{00} = 1 = \mu_{11}, \qquad \mu_{01} = 0 = \mu_{10}$$

which implies that $\alpha = \beta$. From (5.32) it is easy to verify that, in this case, $\rho = 1$. The significance of this result follows from an examination of the expectation and variance of $V(\omega)$, under the condition that $U(\omega) = x$. Thus,

$$E[V(\omega) \mid U(\omega) = x]$$

$$= E[V(\omega)] + \rho\frac{\sqrt{\text{Var}\,[V(\omega)]}}{\sqrt{\text{Var}\,[U(\omega)]}}(x - E[U(\omega)]) = \rho x; \qquad (5.35)$$

$$\text{Var}\,[V(\omega) \mid U(\omega) = x] = \text{Var}\,[V(\omega)] \cdot (1 - \rho^2) = 1 - \rho^2.$$

Thus, when $\rho = 1$ the entire probability "mass" of the conditional distribution becomes concentrated at one point, namely, x, the sales under the "old" policy. Here is a case of perfect predictability. But how does ρ depend upon the variation in the relative amount of selling efforts? Let $\beta = \alpha + h$ in (5.32). Then,

$$\rho = (\mu_{11} - \mu_{01})\frac{\sqrt{\alpha(1 - \alpha)}}{\sqrt{(\alpha + h)(1 - \alpha - h)}}.$$

Differentiation with respect to h gives

$$\frac{d\rho}{dh} = -\frac{1}{2}(\mu_{11} - \mu_{01})\sqrt{\alpha(1-\alpha)}\left[\frac{1 - 2(\alpha + h)}{(\alpha + h)(1 - \alpha - h)}\right]^{3/2}$$

$$\equiv -\frac{1}{2}(\mu_{11} - \mu_{01})G(\alpha, h). \tag{5.36}$$

For $\frac{1}{2} - \alpha > h > 0$, the quantity $G(\alpha, h)$ is positive. Hence, for h restricted in this range, $d\rho/dh$ is positive or negative according as μ_{11} is greater than or less than μ_{01}. Thus the elementary conditional probabilities μ_{ij} appear as the principal factors influencing the shape of correlation coefficient. Finally, observe that if the entries in each column of (μ_{ij}) were to be equal then, from (5.32), it follows that $\rho = 0$ and, hence, that the sales before and after the variation are mutually independently distributed. In other words, the sales level following on a variation of relative selling costs cannot be predicted from past data.

Chapter 6

MONOPOLISTIC COMPETITION: THE LARGE GROUP CASE

The purpose of this chapter is to examine more explicitly the class of situations that answer the description of Chamberlin's "large group" case of monopolistic competition. This case has certain special features that call for some modifications of the techniques employed in Chapters 4 and 5.

More specifically, the setup to be considered is one in which (a) the product is differentiated, (b) the price *and* selling cost are the decision variables of the individual firms, (c) the "perception" of competition is stable, and (d) there is free competition among the buyers. In specializing these general descriptors of the environment and behavior, it will be additionally assumed that (e) neither the buyers nor the sellers communicate *inter alia*, and that (f) there is no bargaining between individual buyers and sellers.

The models presented in this chapter apply to a wide class of empirical market situations in which the buyers are not households and, consequently, the typical unit of *sale* consists of more than one unit of the product, although in practice there may be some measure of bargaining between the trader-customer and the prime supplier. A significant class of situations that conform reasonably closely to the above assumptions consists of the retail distribution channels in consumer products, especially those that are purchased frequently and whose cost per item is rather small. Even with product differentiation and the associated practice of incurring selling costs, markets of this type are much more sensitive to price differentials. This, for example, may be evident in the widespread practice of "promotions," in which a massive advertising campaign is accompanied by reductions in price to the customers and/or the retail channels. The sensitiveness of the markets in question is therefore expected to be qualitatively different from those considered in Chapter 4 and is reflected in the nature of the sales probability function derived in the present chapter.

1. INTERACTION: COVARIANCE OF SALES

In the "large group" case it is more likely that the firms will seek out the customers. Thus the total number of contacts made by a firm is seen to play an important role; this is brought out in (6.1). When the product is relatively strongly differentiated, it becomes appropriate to refer to joint probabilities of sales of all the firms; these probabilities are represented in (6.2).

1.1 It is to be observed that on account of the operating characteristics (a), (b), (e), and (f) of the market the outcome of a price policy is random. Also, on account of (a), (b), and (e), an individual firm has an *expected* market share (which is "normal" in the usual sense), say, σ, $(0 < \sigma < 1)$. Now, if the demand is always for one unit of the product, the aggregate number (N) of potential buyers is also the potential number of units that may be sold. But, product differentiation, maintained through selling costs, has the following consequence: as seen from the viewpoint of an individual firm, the N potential buyers are essentially divided into two groups, namely, those who *are* and those who *are not* potential customers of the firm in question. On account of (c), however, this implies that the expected number in the former category is $N\sigma$. Under the general conditions of "large group"—and especially if the differentiation is relatively weak—it is *more* likely that firms seek customers, so that the *total number of contacts is the decision variable* of the individual firm.[1] Suppose, then, that the firm in question makes n contacts ($n = 0, 1, \ldots, N$) while a given price policy is pursued. Usual combinational reasoning shows that

Pr [number of customers $= x$]

$$= \binom{N\sigma}{x} \binom{N - N\sigma}{n - x} \div \binom{N}{n}, \qquad x = 0, 1, \ldots, N. \qquad (6.1)$$

Because it was assumed that each customer could be identified with a unit of demand (as, for example, in the case of durable consumer products), the above probability is also the probability that the number of units sold is x.

1.2 A recurrent issue in the discussion of monopolistic competition centers around the nature of interdependence among the sales of individual firms, although it is not clear whether the "sales" refer to the actual or

---

[1] This may also be the trade practice in many empirical situations. On the other hand, if the products are "strongly" differentiated—in the sense that their mutual substitutability is relatively low—it is likely that the potential buyers will seek out the sellers they are interested in. From the viewpoint of the individual firm, then, the *number* of customers arriving during an interval of time is a chance variable.

potential magnitudes. It is interesting, therefore, to examine how the phenomenon of interdependence may be represented and understood in the above analytical scheme. Indeed, the viewpoint that the sales of individual firms are to be regarded as random variables does, in a somewhat limited sense, take account of their interdependence. To proceed deeper into the problem, consider the case in which the number r of sellers is not large enough to satisfy Chamberlin's definition of "large groups." In such cases we would expect the product to be rather strongly differentiated. Let the number of potential customers of the ith firm be $N\sigma_i$, $0 \leq \sigma_i < 1$, $i = 1, 2, \ldots, r$; $\sum \sigma_i = 1$. In a short period of time it may be supposed that the factors governing the inclination or readiness of the buyers will remain substantially unchanged. This implies that in that time there are r mutually exclusive classes of potential buyers. Let X_i denote the sales to the ith class of buyers, so that

$$X_r = n - \sum_{i=1}^{r-1} X_i,$$

n being the aggregate sales by the entire group of firms. The joint distribution of sales

$$x_1, x_2, \ldots, x_{r-1} \quad \text{and} \quad x_r = n - \sum_{i=1}^{r-1} x_i$$

is thus given by

$$\binom{N\sigma_1}{x_1}\binom{N\sigma_2}{x_2} \cdots \binom{N\sigma_r}{x_r} \div \binom{N}{n}. \tag{6.2}$$

For a *given* size N of the aggregate market, this is the *joint probability density of the market shares of the r firms*. It may be verified that the covariance of the sales of any two firms is

$$\text{Cov}\,(X_i, X_j) = K_{ij} = -n\sigma_i\sigma_j\,(N-n)(N-1)^{-1}, \tag{6.3}$$

and the coefficient of correlations is

$$R_{ij} = -\frac{-\sqrt{\sigma_i\sigma_j}}{\sqrt{(1-\sigma_i)(1-\sigma_j)}}. \tag{6.4}$$

Now, observe that for all $N > n > 1$, the covariance K_{ij} is *negative* and remains negative for all $n < N$. In order to appreciate this aspect of interdependence of the sales of any two firms, let us observe that

$$\left(\frac{\partial K_{ij}}{\partial n}\right)_{n=n''} > \left(\frac{\partial K_{ij}}{\partial n}\right)_{n=n'} \quad \text{if} \quad n'' > n',$$

that is to say, as n increases, $\partial K_{ij}/\partial n$ increases from larger to smaller negative magnitudes. *With a relatively small number of firms, this is to be expected: As the aggregate number of contacts by the group increases, the interdependence of sales*—as reflected in the size and sign of the covariance—*begins to increase.* Also, we may observe that

$$\frac{\partial K_{ij}}{\partial N} = -n(n-1)(N-1)^{-2}\sigma_i\sigma_j < 0,$$

hence

$$\left(\frac{\partial K_{ij}}{\partial N}\right)_{N=N''} > \left(\frac{\partial K_{ij}}{\partial N}\right)_{N=N'} \quad \text{if} \quad N'' > N'.$$

As N grows larger, $\partial K_{ij}/\partial N$ tends to zero. This may be interpreted to mean that the *"feeling" of conflict gradually disappears as the size of the aggregate (potential) market tends to expand.*[2]

2. A DIGRESSION: MODELS OF BIAS

Although a digression from the principal theme of the preceding discussion, the present section makes use of the same kind of analysis and representation as was presented in Chapter 5. It demonstrates how the microstructure of the transaction-generating process naturally leads from certain elementary probabilities to the probability of a more complex event such as the *waiting time for a market share*. The elementary probabilities to be introduced here correspond to those for the outcome of tossing a "biased" coin and, thus, establish the model of Chapter 4, Section 1 on a measure-theoretic basis.

2.1 Consider the operating characteristics described in the preceding section and suppose that the firm adheres to a given price policy during a given period. Let σ denote the *expected market share normally enjoyed by the firm* and let $\Sigma:0 \leq \sigma \leq 1$ denote the unit interval. Define the following function on Σ:

$$\Phi(\sigma) = \begin{cases} \dfrac{\sigma}{\alpha}, & 0 \leq \sigma \leq \alpha, \\ \dfrac{\sigma - \alpha}{1 - \alpha}, & \alpha < \sigma \leq 1, \end{cases} \tag{6.5}$$

where α represents the *actual* market share scored by the firm. Also define the set-function $\Psi(.)$:

$$\Psi(\sigma) = \begin{cases} 0, & \text{if} \quad 0 \leq \sigma \leq \alpha, \\ 1, & \text{if} \quad \alpha < \sigma \leq 1. \end{cases} \tag{6.6}$$

[2] Although plausible, statements like these are not empirically verifiable unless a framework of experimentation is set up in which the experimenter accords himself the status of a "super" observer.

Consider the succession of functions obtained by an application of Ψ defined as follows:

$$\Psi_1(\sigma) = \Psi'(\sigma),$$

$$\Psi_2(\sigma) = \Psi'(\Phi(\sigma)) = \begin{cases} 0, & 0 \leq \Psi'(\sigma) \leq \alpha, \\ 1, & \alpha < \Psi'(\sigma) \leq 1, \end{cases} \tag{6.7}$$

$$= \begin{cases} 0, & 0 \leq \sigma \leq \alpha^2, \quad \text{or} \quad \alpha \leq \sigma \leq 2\alpha - \alpha^2, \\ 1, & \alpha^2 \leq \sigma \leq \alpha, \quad \text{or} \quad 2\alpha - \alpha^2 < \sigma \leq 1, \end{cases}$$

$$\cdot \quad \cdot \quad \cdot \quad \cdot \quad \cdot \quad \cdot \quad \cdot \quad \cdot \quad \cdot \quad \cdot$$

$$\Psi_n(\sigma) = \Psi_{n-1}[\Phi(\sigma)], \qquad n = 2, 3, \ldots.$$

Introducing the function $\mu(.)$ to denote the length of the Σ-set over which an appropriate event is defined, it may be verified that

$$\mu[\sigma:\Psi_2(\sigma) = 0] = \mu[\sigma:\Psi_2(\sigma) = 0 \,|\, \Psi_1(\sigma) = 1] = \alpha,$$

$$\mu[\sigma:\Psi_2(\sigma) = 1] = \mu[\sigma:\Psi_2(\sigma) = 1 \,|\, \Psi_1(\sigma) = 0] = 1 - \alpha,$$

hence that $\Psi_1(\sigma)$ and $\Psi_2(\sigma)$ are statistically independent. Now, consider the random variable $g_s(\sigma)$,

$$g_s(\sigma) = \sum_{k=1}^{s} \Psi_k(\sigma). \tag{6.8}$$

From the definition of the $\Psi_k(\sigma)$, it follows that $g_s(\sigma)$ is a natural representation of the total number of "successes" in s trials. The probability of interest is

$$\Pr[g_s(\sigma) = x] = \mu_s[\sigma:g_s(\sigma) = x].$$

Let

$$I(x) = \frac{1}{2\pi} \int_0^{2\pi} e^{iu[g_s(\sigma)-x]} \, du = \begin{cases} 1, & g_s(\sigma) = x \\ 0, & g_s(\sigma) \neq x \end{cases}.$$

Now, $\mu_s(.)$ is the mathematical expectation of $I(x)$; Thus

$$\mu_s = \int_0^1 I(x) \, d\sigma = \int_0^1 \frac{1}{2\pi} \int_0^{2\pi} e^{iu[g_s(\sigma)-x]} \, du \, d\sigma$$

$$= \frac{1}{2\pi} \int_0^{2\pi} e^{-iux} \, du \int_0^1 e^{iug_s(\sigma)} \, d\sigma; \tag{6.9}$$

but, because

$$\int_0^1 e^{iug_s(\sigma)} \, d\sigma = \int_0^1 e^{iu\Sigma\Psi_k(\sigma)} = [\alpha + (1 - \alpha)e^{iu}]^s,$$

(6.9) is evaluated as

$$\mu_s = (2\pi)^{-1} \int_0^{2\pi} [\alpha + (1 - \alpha)e^{iu}]^s e^{-iux} \, du$$

$$= \sum_{k=0}^{s} \binom{s}{k} \alpha^k (1 - \alpha)^{s-k} \frac{1}{2\pi} \int_0^{2\pi} e^{iu(s-k)-iux} \, du \qquad (6.10)$$

$$= \binom{s}{x} \alpha^x (1 - \alpha)^{s-x}.$$

Note that (6.10) is a generalization of the binomial model presented in Chapter 4, Section 1, where α was considered a function of the price quoted by the firm.

2.2 Suppose, now, that the event of interest is the *time to wait for one unit of sale*. In other words, in $s + 1$ "trials," the first s trials have the outcome "no sales" and the $(s + 1)$st trial has the outcome "sales." The probability of the first event is $\mu_s = \mu[\sigma : g_s(\sigma) = 0] = (1 - \alpha)^s$. Hence the probability of the event defined above is $(1 - \alpha)^s \alpha$. Now, s may be conceived of as the "waiting" time before a unit of sale occurs. Thus let each trial take a time dy so that s trials take $s \, dy$ units of time. Let dy tend to zero in such a way that $s \, dy$ tends to take on a fixed value, y. Let, also, $\alpha = \lambda \, dy$. Then

$$\lim_{dy \to 0} (1 - \alpha)^s \alpha = \lim_{dy \to 0} (1 - \lambda \, dy)^{y/dy} \lambda \, dy$$

$$= \lambda e^{-\lambda y} \, dy \qquad (6.11)$$

yields the probability of the time required to generate a market share.

2.3 At this stage it should be observed that the probability model of sales of an individual firm in the "large group" case is not directly applicable. This deficiency may be removed if the problem of randomness in the firm's sales is posed in the reverse. Thus it will be fruitful to derive the probability distribution of the *number of contacts required to* obtain s units of sale, the underlying institutional setup being the same as in Section 1.[3] Define the events E and F as follows:

E: [sale $= s - 1$ units in $x - 1$ contacts],

F: [sale $= 1$ unit in the xth contact $\mid E$].

Then it follows that

Pr [number of contacts X needed to make s units of sale $= x$]
$= $ Pr $[E]$ Pr $[F]$.

[3] This includes, in particular, the assumption that each "customer" is equivalent to a unit of sales. Thus s units of sales and s units of buying customers are equivalent in the developments to follow.

But the conditioning by the event E does not influence the probability of occurrence of one unit of sale in the xth contact; hence

$$\text{Pr } [F] = \text{Pr } [\text{sale} = 1 \text{ unit in the } x\text{th contact}]$$
$$= \sigma$$

Note, however, that the outcome of a contact is independent of that of any other contact and that the probability of "success" in each contact is σ. Hence

$$\text{Pr } [E] = \binom{x-1}{s-1}(\sigma)^{s-1}(1 - \sigma)^{x-s}$$

and the required probability is seen to be

$$\begin{aligned}
\text{Pr } [X = x] &= \binom{x-1}{s-1}(\sigma)^{s-1}(1 - \sigma)^{x-s}\sigma \\
&= \binom{x-1}{s-1}(\sigma)^{s}(1 - \sigma)^{x-s}.
\end{aligned} \tag{6.12}$$

Clearly, this is a testable conclusion and, if validated, becomes a practically useful step in the evaluation of the effectiveness of selling efforts of a firm. The expression (6.12) may be interpreted in terms of the usual accounting practice and data. An expedient means of doing this is to look upon an occurrence of a sale (that is, consummation of a transaction) as an *event in time*. This viewpoint calls for a reinterpretation of (a) the "event" of interest and (b) the market share σ, which was also taken to mean the probability of "success" in an arbitrarily selected contact in the market. The event in question now is the waiting time for scoring exactly s units of sale. Similarly, the market share is to mean the market share per unit of time. More specifically, it is assumed that $\sigma = \lambda h + 0(h)$, h being a suitably defined unit of time. Thus, if $[0, t]$ and $[t, t + h]$ are two disjoint intervals of time and if the events A and B are defined as $A:[s - 1$ units sold in t/h time units]; $B:[s$th unit sold in $h]$, then the *probability of waiting time* is the probability of joint occurrence of A and B. But B is independent of A, therefore, the required probability is Pr $[A]$ Pr $[B]$. The computation follows from (6.6) by replacing x by t/h, and σ by λh:

$$\begin{aligned}
F(t) &= \text{Pr } [\text{time to wait for } s \text{ units of sale} = t] \\
&= \binom{t/h - 1}{s - 1}(\lambda h)^{s}(1 - \lambda h)^{t/h-s} + 0(h^2),
\end{aligned} \tag{6.13}$$

Employing the kind of reasoning that was used to derive (6.11), one may observe that the limiting probability is

$$f(t)\, dt = \frac{\lambda^s}{\Gamma(s - 1)}\, t^{s-1}e^{-\lambda t}dt, \qquad t \geq 0. \tag{6.14}$$

If the event of interest is the *time to wait for one unit of sale*, one sets $s = 1$ in (6.14); this gives the exponential density of waiting time:

$$f(t, \lambda) = \lambda e^{-\lambda t}, \qquad t \geq 0. \tag{6.15}$$

3. SUMMARY: A NOTE ON SKEWNESS

The main purpose of this section is to sum up the various models of monopolistic competition. In addition, an attempt will be made to explain a commonly occurring phenomenon: skewness in the distribution of the firm's sales. This is to be distinguished from the skew distribution of customers according to size of demand. The latter phenomenon shares certain aspects of the "vocabulary" problem of linguistics and can be analyzed by known method of statistical linguistics.

3.1 It was shown in Chapter 5, Section 1, that when the prices of the various brands vary only in a small range, the *joint* probabilities of sales of the r firms are given by the multinomial distribution

$$p(x_1, \ldots, x_r) = \frac{n!}{(n_1)! \cdots (n_r)!} (p_1)^{n_1} \cdots (p_r)^{n_r}$$

where

$$n_r = n - \sum_{k=1}^{r-1} n_k \quad \text{and} \quad p_r = 1 - \sum_{k=1}^{r-1} p_k.$$

It may be verified by direct computation that the joint distribution of sales of any s $(s < r)$ firms is also multinomial, with the same pattern of dependence of the p_k on the relative positions of the firms in the industry-wide selling efforts. Similarly, it may be verified that the *conditional* probability of sales of the $(r - 1)$st firm, given the sales of the $r - 2$ others, is

$$\binom{n'}{x_{r-1}} (p')^{x_{r-1}} (1 - p')^{n' - x_{r-1}},$$

where $n' = n - x_1 - \cdots - x_{r-2}$ and $p' = (p_{r-1})/(p_{r-1} + p_r)$. No explicit consideration was given to such conditional distributions which rest upon the implicit assumption that the sales of the other firms can be *observed*. A second macromodel has been developed for monopolistic competition among a group of sellers who are not many in number. The derivation follows from two notions: first, an identification of the "normal" market share σ of a firm with its probability of "success" in a given contact; second, on account of a strong degree of product differentiation, the aggregate demand is likely to be strongly polarized between the firms.

Thus follows the hypergeometric (joint) distribution of sales $x_1, x_2, \ldots, x_r$ of the r firms:

$$\binom{n\sigma_1}{x_1} \cdots \binom{n\sigma_r}{x_r} \div \binom{N}{n},$$

with

$$x_r = n - \sum_{k=1}^{r-1} x_k \quad \text{and} \quad \sigma_r = 1 - \sum_{k=1}^{r-1} \sigma_k.$$

The "interaction" among the firms was represented by the covariance of sales. In the multinomial model for the "large group" case, one has

$$\text{Var}\,(x_i) = n\sigma_i(1 - \sigma_i), \qquad \text{Cov}\,(x_i, x_j) = -n\sigma_i\sigma_j,$$

while in the hypergeometric model for the "small group" case it is seen that

$$\text{Var}\,(x_i) = n\sigma_i(1 - \sigma_i)\frac{N - n}{N - 1}, \qquad \text{Cov}\,(x_i x_j) = -n\sigma_i\sigma_j\frac{N - n}{N - 1}.$$

Thus, the dispersion of the sales of individual firms as well as the covariance between the sales of any two firms are multiplied by a factor of $(N - n)/(N - 1)$ which lies between 0 and 1 for $1 < n < N$.

3.2   At the micro level the analysis was not based upon models of conditional distributions. Instead, attention was focused exclusively on the data available to the firm. In the context of the "large group" this led to the formulation of a special problem: the predictability of the outcome of a *variation* in the firm's own selling efforts relative to that of the industry. The analysis was made on the basis of a bivariate binomial distribution Chapter 5, Section 19.3); "bivariate" considerations were introduced for the purpose of representing the sales or market-share situations before and after the variation. For the "small group" case of strong differentiation of products the probability distribution of the firm's sales was seen to be

$$\binom{N\sigma}{x}\binom{N - N\sigma}{n - x} \div \binom{N}{n}, \qquad x = 0, 1, \ldots, N,$$

which is a specialization of the hypergeometric distribution derived for the macromodel. The model of a "biased" coin provides the formal bridge between the micromodels and macromodels based upon (a) expected market-shares, on the one hand, and (b) the abstractly defined "probability" of success, on the other hand.

It is interesting at this stage to attempt an explanation of a very familiar phenomenon observed at the micro level. This concerns the skewness of the distribution of sales by an individual firm in a wide variety of competitive situations. The special feature of this skewness is the presence of a long tail to the right. It is difficult to set up a sufficiently general scheme of axioms to explain skewness in all possible circumstances; therefore, an attempt may be made to provide several models each capable of explaining the lack of symmetry in a distribution. An immediate explanation of skewness in the "large group" case may be sought in the fact that the multinomial distribution

$$p(x_1, \ldots, x_r) = \frac{n!}{(n_1)! \cdots (n_r)!} (p_1)^{n_1} \cdots (p_r)^{n_r}$$

tends to the χ^2-distribution as $n \to \infty$. The distribution of an individual firm's sales will therefore tend to a χ^2-distribution with a suitably modified degree of freedom.

A less trivial explanation may be provided as follows. For processes in which the impacts of independent chance forces are *additive*, one makes use of the well-known principle that the distribution of sums of independent, identically distributed chance variables tends to the Gaussian. There are chance-determined processes in which each "elementary" chance cause gives an impulse to change the magnitude of the sales. In such cases, the variable in question depends upon the immediately preceding one and, thus, there is an element of "order"; the element of order which merges with pure chance is the influence of the immediately preceding event upon the following one. Suppose, in addition, that the effect of an impulse is proportional to the strength of the impulse and the magnitude of the variables (sales) at the instant of the impulse is applied. Note that these hypotheses are inclusive enough to describe sufficiently general forms of competition. From precisely these hypotheses it follows that the *ratios* of equal amounts in excess or defect from a central value (for example, the mean-value) are Gaussian. In other words, the *logarithms* of sales are likely to have a Gaussian distribution.

Chapter 7

PRICE, PROFITS,
AND MARKET SHARE

The purpose of this and the following chapter is to indicate some applications of the basic models developed in Chapter 4. It may be recalled that in each of these models the firm's sales were represented as random variables with probability distributions parametrized by the price quoted by it. Thus the net profits and other measures of performance emerge as random variables with their distribution functions dependent on the price policy. It is interesting therefore to examine the nature of dependence of expected profits on the price policy and, in particular, to inquire into the nature of price policy that may support the expected profits in a certain interval or band. Such questions are systematically explored in the opening sections of this chapter. Out of a solution to these more obvious questions arises the possibility of examining possible *tradeoffs between profits and market share at different levels of prices quoted.* Similar tradeoffs are also examined for the case in which, in addition to price policy, variations of selling costs play an important role in the strategic actions of the firms.

Implicit in these discussions and illustrative derivations is the assumption that the price-planning period is reasonably long and that no variations are practiced *during* such a period. This is a rather severe assumption; its removal calls for a different kind of probability model which, in some sense, is an extension of the basic models of Chapter 4. In the absence of a better name, these extensions covering more than one planning period have been called "dynamic," although time is not allowed to enter these representations in an explicit manner. In Chapter 8 some dynamic versions of the models of Chapter 4 are examined; in Chapter 9 applications are considered with special reference to production-inventory planning, on the one hand, and pricing on the other.

1. UNDIFFERENTIATED OLIGOPOLY: PROFITS AND MARKET SHARE

The aim of this section is to examine some *qualitative* relationships between price, profits, and market share of a firm in an undifferentiated oligopoly. To simplify the analysis two working assumptions are introduced: (a) the firm produces only on orders and (b) the physical plant capacity is much in excess of that required to support the production (that is, demand) associated with the optimizing price. Thus problems of inventory management and of making decisions about capacity expansion do *not* enter the present discussion. With certain plausible assumptions about the behavior of market share as a function of the price quoted, it is shown that there exists at least one *range* of prices capable of supporting (a) an expected level of net profits short of the absolute maximum *and* (b) a stable expected level of market share.

1.1   Let the total cost of producing r units be denoted by $c(r)$, a monotonically increasing function of r. Then, according to Chapter 4, Section 1, the expected net profits are

$$\bar{\pi} = \sum_{r=0}^{n} [pr - c(r)]g(r; n, p)$$

$$= \sum_{r=0}^{n} [pr - c(r)]\binom{n}{r}[\sigma(p)]^{r}[1 - \sigma(p)]^{n-r},$$

(7.1)

where according to Chapter 4, Section 6, $\sigma(p)$ can be replaced by $f(p)$ for a known value of p. The right member of (7.1) is the difference between (a) R, the expected sales revenue, that is, p. $\sum_{r=0}^{\infty} rg(r; n, p) = pn\sigma(p)$, and (b) Q, the expected costs, that is, $E[c(r)]$,

$$Q = E[c(r)] = \sum_{r=0}^{n} c(r)\binom{n}{r}\sigma^{r}(1 - \sigma)^{n-r}.$$

In order to examine the dependence of R on the price quoted p, it will be necessary to introduce a few assumptions about the nature of the market share function $\sigma(p)$. In particular, it will be assumed that

$$\frac{d\sigma}{dp} < 0, \quad \text{for} \quad 0 \le p < \infty,$$

(7.2)

$$\sigma(0) > 0, \lim_{p \to \infty} [x\sigma(x)]_{x=p} = 0,$$

(7.3)

$$\lim_{p \to \infty} [\sigma(x)]_{x=p} = 0, \qquad \lim_{p \to \infty} \frac{d\sigma}{dp} = 0,$$

(7.4)

and that $\sigma(p) + p(d\sigma/dp) = 0$ has only one finite positive root p^*. Now observe that

$$\frac{dR}{dp} = n\sigma + pn\frac{d\sigma}{dp}. \tag{7.5}$$

Combining (7.5) with (7.3), we see that $[dR/dp]_{p=0} = n\sigma(0) > 0$. Also note that

$$[R(p)]_{p=0} = [pn\sigma]_{p=0} = 0, \qquad \lim_{p \to \infty} R(p) = \lim_{p \to \infty} pn\sigma(p) = 0.$$

Hence, because of (7.4), it follows that R has a *unique maximum* at $p = p^*$, such that

$$\frac{dR}{dp} \begin{cases} > 0, & \text{for} \quad p < p^*, \\ < 0, & \text{for} \quad p > p^*. \end{cases} \tag{7.6}$$

Next, consider the dependence of Q on p. Note that

$$\frac{dQ}{dp} = \sum_{r=0}^{n} c(r)\frac{d}{dp}[g(r;p)],$$

$$\frac{dg(r;p)}{dp} = \binom{n}{r}(r - n\sigma)\sigma^{r-1}(1 - \sigma)^{n-r-1}\frac{d\sigma}{dp}. \tag{7.7}$$

But, because of (7.2), $d\sigma/dp$ is negative; hence, dg/dp will be negative, too, if $r > n\sigma$. Let $r_0 = [n\sigma(p)]$, the largest integer contained in $n\sigma(p)$; then, $r - n\sigma(p) > 0$ for $r > r_0$. Thus:

$$\frac{dg(r;p)}{dp} \begin{cases} > 0, & \text{for} \quad r \leq r_0, \\ < 0, & \text{for} \quad r > r_0. \end{cases} \tag{7.8}$$

Also, because $\sum_{r=0}^{n} g(r;p) = 1$, it follows that $\sum_{r=0}^{n} [dg(r;p)]/dp = 0$. Hence

$$\sum_{r=0}^{r_0} \frac{dg(r;p)}{dp} = -\sum_{r=r_0+1}^{n} \frac{dg(r;p)}{dp}. \tag{7.9}$$

Writing dQ/dp in the form

$$\frac{dQ}{dp} = \sum_{r=0}^{r_0} c(r)\frac{dg(r;p)}{dp} + \sum_{r=r_0+1}^{n} c(r)\frac{dg(r;p)}{dp}, \tag{7.10}$$

observing that $c(r)$ is monotone increasing in r, and employing (7.9), we see that the first term on the right member of (7.10) has the following upper bound, namely,

$$\sum_{r=0}^{r_0} c(r) \frac{dg(r; p)}{dp} < - \sum_{r=r_0+1}^{n} c(r) \frac{dg(r; p)}{dp}. \qquad (7.11)$$

Thus the right member of (7.10) is negative and, for $0 \leq p < \infty$, it follows that $dQ/dp < 0$. Also, $\lim_{p \to \infty} dQ/dp = 0$, because of (7.3). It has been shown that if the market-share function $\sigma(p)$ satisfies the assumptions (7.2) to (7.4) *there exists a finite* level of quotations p such that marginal expected cost dQ/dp remains negative for all quotations below that level and vanishes asymptotically beyond it.

1.2   If an addition to the assumptions (7.2) to (7.4) one makes the assumption that $d\bar{\pi}/dp = 0$ has exactly one positive root, $p^{**} < \infty$, then the expected net profits $\bar{\pi}$ is seen to attain a unique maximum at $p = p^{**}$; also, it is not difficult to see that $p^{**} > p^*$. It may be observed (from Figure 1) that in order to maintain an expected profit $\bar{\pi}$ in excess of some predesignated level $\bar{\pi}_0$, the price has to be in the interval $p' \leq p \leq p''$. Because $d\sigma/dp \leq 0$ for any finite nonnegative price,

$$\sigma(p'') \leq \sigma(p) \leq \sigma(p'), \qquad p' \leq p \leq p''.$$

In other words, the expected market share also lies in a certain interval (Figure 1). Even without the assumption that $d\bar{\pi}/dp = 0$ has only one finite positive root, a few interesting conclusions of a general nature may be attempted. Note, first, that $d\bar{\pi}/dp$ remains positive at least up to $p = p^*$. Now, consider the case in which $d\bar{\pi}/dp$ does not change sign for $p > p^*$. Evidently, at zero price, $(R - Q)_{p=0}$ is a large negative quantity. Also,

$$\lim_{p \to \infty} \bar{\pi} = \lim_{p \to \infty} [R(p) - Q(p)] = \lim_{p \to \infty} R(p) - \lim_{p \to \infty} Q(p) = -c(0) > -A.$$

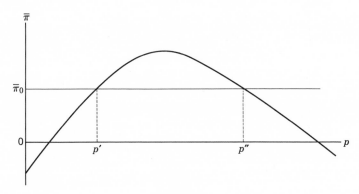

Figure 1

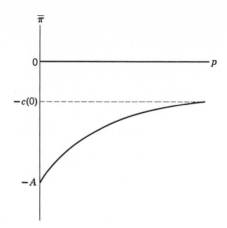

Figure 2

Hence $\bar{\pi}$ gradually increases from a large negative magnitude ($-A$ in Figure 2) to $-c(0)$, implying that $\bar{\pi} < 0$ for *all* levels of price. But no business can be expected to continue if the expected profits are negative for all levels of price offerings; this case therefore, may, be excluded from further consideration. It is ordinarily true, however, that for *some* interval or range of price the expected profits will be positive. Thus in a practical situation $d\bar{\pi}/dp$ *does* change sign for $p > p^*$. It may happen, however, that $d\bar{\pi}/dp = 0$ has more than one positive root (Figure 3). In such cases it is possible to obtain more than one maximum so that there may exist more than one range of price that can support an expected net profit $\bar{\pi}_0$. To sum up, it has been shown that with a plausible behavior of

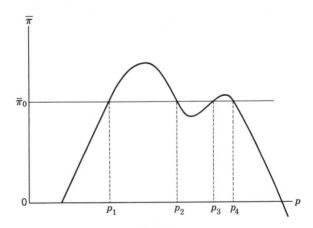

Figure 3

the market share function (such as (7.2) to (7.4)), there exists *at least one* price range which (a) supports an expected net profit $\bar{\pi}_0$ less than the absolute maximum and (b) secures a stable expected market share. In other words, the expected net profits and the expected market share during a planning period are mutually related through the price offered during the period.

2. TRADEOFFS BETWEEN PROFITS AND MARKET SHARE

The analysis of Section 1 was motivated by the consideration that profits and market share are likely to be competing criteria of performance from the viewpoint of the decision-making unit. It was seen that one could conceive of a "tradeoff" between the profits and market share. The tradeoff is emphasized because existing means of analyses do not consider the circumstances in which a switch from one objective to another may be called for. This *plurality of objectives* will play a key role in the discussion to follow.

Derivation of decision rules is the principal theme of this section. Since market share and profits are both random, it is important to define the precise sense in which maximization process is to be interpreted. Here arises the *essential nonuniqueness of the optimization problem*: It is possible to formulate the optimization problem in a number of ways.

Three formulations will be examined: (a) the seller aims simultaneously at maintaining net profits *and* market share in some "desired" *ranges*, (b) the seller aims at maximizing the expected net profits, subject to the condition that some market share aspiration shall be fulfilled, and (c) the seller aims at maximizing the expected net profits, subject to a chance constraint on the market share. The three formulations are by no means complete and exhaustive. However, they have been inspired by the practical consideration that the decision-making unit within the firm may not be aware of the full implications of maximizing either one of the criteria without constraints on the other.

2.1 Suppose that the seller is interested in maintaining profits and market share in some range, say,

$$\sigma_1 \leq \sigma \leq \sigma_2, \qquad \pi_1 \leq \pi \leq \pi_2 \qquad [\pi \equiv pr - c(r)], \qquad (7.12)$$

where π and σ both refer to a *given* level of sales r. From the development of the preceding section it may be verified that starting with a definite level of the price quotation p we can determine an interval of r *required* to maintain the net profits in the desired interval. However, the associated interval $[\sigma^*, \sigma^{**}]$ of market share due to this interval of r-values may not coincide with the desired interval $[\sigma_1, \sigma_2]$. For the discussion to follow the interval $[\sigma_1, \sigma_2]$ is said to be *consistent* whenever the following holds:

$$[\sigma^*, \sigma^{**}] \subseteq [\sigma_1, \sigma_2] \tag{7.13}$$

Thus it is important to examine how an interval of r-values may be derived from a given magnitude of quotations p. The principal device is the probability distribution $g(r; n, p)$, which is used in the following manner: from the set of values of p that give *consistent* intervals of profits and market share, choose a value p_x and compute the corresponding interval of r, say, $r_{1x} \leq r \leq r_{2x}$. Thus

$$\Pr[\pi_1 \leq \pi \leq \pi_2, \sigma_1 \leq \sigma \leq \sigma_2]$$

$$= P(p_x) = \sum_{r_{1x}}^{r_{2x}} g(r; n, p_x) = \sum_{r_{1x}}^{r_{2x}} \binom{n}{r} [\sigma(p_x)]^r [1 - \sigma(p_x)]^{n-r}. \tag{7.14}$$

Let $p_1, p_2, \ldots, p_k$ be the values of p that can support consistent intervals of profits and market share. The price to be quoted is the index x ($x = 1, 2, \ldots, k]$, such that

$$P(p_x) = \sup_k [P(p_1), \ldots, P(p_k)]. \tag{7.15}$$

In other words, the *optimal price p_x maximizes the probability of securing the desired ranges of profits and market share*. Because the values of p that ensure the fulfilment of the consistency requirement will constitute an interval, it follows that the optimal decision will have the following simple structure:

> Determine the appropriate interval of price quotations that satisfies the assigned objectives, and select that value of quotations p which gives the maximum probability given by the formula (7.14).

2.2 Next, consider the problem of choosing a price quotation p such that the expected profit $\bar{\pi} = \bar{\pi}(p)$ will attain a maximum and, simultaneously, some satisfying constraint on the market share will be met:

$$\text{maximize } \bar{\pi}(p) = \sum_r [pr - c(r)] \binom{n}{r} [f(p)]^r [1 - f(p)]^{n-r} \tag{7.16}$$

with respect to variations in p in $\mathcal{R} = [p : f(p) > f_0]$.[1] The technique of solving this problem is to exploit the role of f_0 as a parameter. Thus, for each value of f_0, we obtain an upper limit of price, $p = p(f_0)$, such that $f(p) > f_0$ for $p \in I : [0 \leq p \leq p(f_0)]$. If the interval I contains the profit-maximizing price p^{**}, then the expected net profits $\bar{\pi}$ does attain a maximum at $p = p^{**}$. If, on the other hand, the interval I does not contain the

---

[1] It should be recalled from Chapter 4 that the expected value of market share σ is $f(p)$. Also note the explicit assumption that $\bar{\pi}'(p) = 0$ has a unique solution with some finite positive price. This, together with the stipulation (7.2) to (7.4), always ensures a unique maximum at $p = p^{**}$.

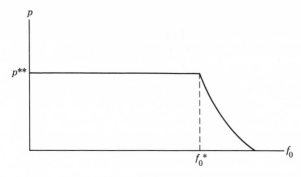

Figure 4

value p^{**}, then $\bar{\pi}$ attains its maximum at $p = p(f_0)$; but because $p(f_0)$ is a *decreasing* function (see Figure 4) of f_0 the optimizing level of quotations for different levels of f_0 will have the characteristic shape shown in Figure 4.

2.3 Finally, consider the problem of maximizing (7.16) subject to a "chance constraint" [14, 15] on the market share, that is,

$$\Pr\left[\hat{\sigma} \geq \sigma_0\right] \geq \alpha. \tag{7.17}$$

Let r_0 be a value of r, such that $\sigma_0 = r_0/n$. Then, corresponding to a price set at p, the probability that $\hat{\sigma} > \sigma_0$ is given by

$$\Pr\left[\hat{\sigma} > \sigma_0\right] = \sum_{r=r_0}^{n} \binom{n}{r} [f(p)]^r [1 - f(p)]^{n-r}, \tag{7.18}$$

but because $f(p)$ is a decreasing function of p (7.18) should also be a decreasing function of p. Thus, corresponding to a fixed σ_0 and a fixed α, it is seen that the chance-constraint (7.17) is satisfied by *any* price in the interval $J = [p: 0 \leq p \leq p(\sigma_0, \alpha)]$ whose upper bound $p(\sigma_0, \alpha)$ is a decreasing function of both σ_0 and α. As long as the profit-maximizing price p^{**} is included in the interval J, it maximizes (7.16) subject to (7.17); otherwise, the optimal price is $p(\sigma_0, \alpha)$. If, on the other hand, α is fixed as a certain value, the solution will have the structure shown in Figure 5; it is

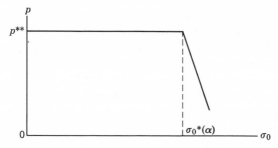

Figure 5

of the same nature as that in which a constraint was placed on the expected market share. In the latter case, there is only one critical value of f_0, say, $f_0 = f_0^*$, such that p^{**} is the profit-maximizing price whenever $f_0 \leq f_0^*$. However, in the problem with a constraint like (7.17) p^{**} is the solution whenever $\sigma_0 \leq \sigma_0^*(\alpha)$ for a given α. Again $\sigma_0^*(\alpha)$ is a decreasing function of α. The slopes of the solution curves beyond f_0^* (in Figure 4) and beyond $\sigma_0^*(\alpha)$ (in Figure 5) will obviously be different.

2.4   In concluding this inquiry it is interesting to examine the behavior of the variance of $\hat{\sigma}$, the *estimate* of the firm's market share:

$$\text{Var}\,(\hat{\sigma}) = f(p)[1 - f(p)]/n.$$

Since $0 < f(p) < 1$, therefore, $f(p)[1 - f(p)]$ cannot exceed 0.25. Hence, $\text{Var}\,(\hat{\sigma})$ tends to zero as n, the aggregate industry demand, tends to infinity. In that event, a change in the setting of α will *not* materially affect the functional dependence of the optimizing price $p^*(\sigma_0)$ on the market share *aspiration* level σ_0. Indeed, it may be seen from numerical examples that $p^*(\sigma_0)$ becomes almost identical with the function $p^*(f_0)$. However, since the effects of past retaliations from the competitors are built into $f(p)$, the conclusions reached so far remain valid so long as the price *variation* contemplated in the present planning period is small relative to the *levels* of past prices. If, however, the proposed price variation is far out of line with the ones the industry has been accustomed to, then, it is very unlikely that $f(p)$ will remain unchanged. Hence the statements made about the tradeoffs between market share and profit goals will cease to be valid. This is also true of the case in which something happens in the period of interest that radically changes the disposition of the competitors and, thus, changes their modes of reaction. In such cases the discussion of tradeoffs between goals becomes irrelevant and unrealistic.

3. DIFFERENTIATED OLIGOPOLY

The structure of optimal single-period decisions under conditions of a differentiated oligopoly is the theme of this and the following section. Working assumptions about the cost function introduced in Section 1 will be retained, as will the assumptions (4.12) to (4.15) about $\lambda(c)$ and $\mu(p)$. The dependence of the expected costs and revenues upon the function $A(c, p) = \mu(p) \cdot \lambda(c)$ makes the formalism a little more clumsy. The interested is, reader however, referred to the Appendix II, in which the concavity of the average net profits function is examined in detail and certain conditions are introduced in order to ensure the existence of a maximum. The principal question to be investigated is that of the *existence of a unique maximum* of $R - Q$ above a preassigned level which, in practical situations may be interpreted as a satisfying constraint. In the discussion to follow, the optimal price is obtained as a function of selling cost; next, the optimal selling cost is expressed as a function of the price and, finally, by combining these two functional dependencies, an attempt will be made to define admissible regions in the (p, c)-space on which certain tradeoffs between variations of price and selling costs will be characterized.

3.1 Let it be recalled from Chapter 4, Section 2, that the random net profits π were defined as $\pi = pS - K(S) - cS$, where $K(S)$ is the function relating the aggregate production costs to the level of sales, S.[2] From Chapter 4, Section 10, it is seen that the expected value of π is

$$E[\pi(p, c)] = \sum_{s=0}^{\infty} [pS - K(S) - cS] \, g(S; p, c)$$

$$= p \, A(p, c) - c \, A(p, c) - E[K(S)].$$

Defining

$$R = pA(p, c) = p\lambda(c) \, \mu(p), \qquad Q = c \, A(p, c) + E[K(S)],$$

one may write

$$\bar{\pi}(p, c) = E[\pi(p, c)] = R - Q.$$

As in the preceding discussion, it is expressly assumed that the expected gross revenue function has a unique maximum at a finite positive price; that is, when there exists a $p^* < \infty$, such that for $\lambda(c) \neq 0$, the following holds:

$$\lambda(c) \left[\mu(p) + p \, \frac{d\mu(p)}{dp} \right]_{p^*} = 0. \tag{7.19}$$

It is also assumed that cost function $K(S)$ is monotone increasing in S:

$$K(S) > K(S') \quad \text{for} \quad S > S'. \tag{7.20}$$

3.2 For a given c the necessary condition for R to be stationary under variation of p is

$$\frac{\partial R}{\partial p} = \lambda(c) \left[p \, \frac{d\mu}{dp} + \mu(p) \right] = 0 \tag{7.21}$$

[2] Implicit in this definition of net profits is the assumption that the price-planning period is long enough for the price and selling cost policy to take complete effect within the period. In reality, however, there is some "spilling over" of the effects of one period's policy into the following period(s), and this possibility cannot be ignored when the planning period is short and coincides, for example, with the more conventional units of time, such as the month or quarter.

which, according to (7.19) has a unique root p^*. Also, because of (4.13) and the positivity of $\lambda(c)$, it is clear that $\partial R/\partial p$ is to be positive for non-negative p, not exceeding p^*, and negative beyond p^*. This conclusion follows from the consideration that

$$\lim_{p \to \infty} \frac{\partial R}{\partial p} = \lim_{p \to \infty} \lambda(c) \left[\mu(p) + p \frac{d\mu}{dp} \right] < 0.$$

A further application of (4.13) gives the following:

$$\lim_{p \to \infty} R(p, c) = \lambda(c) \lim_{p \to \infty} p\mu(p) = 0.$$

Thus, one may conclude that under the condition (7.19) and (4.13) for every value of c, the expected revenue $R(p, c)$ has (7.22) a maximum at $p = p^*$, and

$$\left(\frac{\partial R}{\partial p} \right)_{p \geq 0} \begin{cases} \text{is positive for } p < p^*, \\ \text{is negative for } p > p^*. \end{cases} \tag{7.23}$$

Next, consider the expected cost Q as a function of p and c:

$$Q = c\, A(p, c) + E[K(S)]$$

$$= c\mu(p)\lambda(c) + \sum_{s=0}^{\infty} K(S)\, g(S; p, c).$$

Define the marginal cost of the sth unit as $M(s, s - 1) = K(s) - K(s - 1)$; this is strictly positive on account of (7.20). Also, define

$$L = \sum_{s=1}^{\infty} M(s, s - 1)e^{-A(p,c)} \frac{A(p, c)^{s-1}}{(s - 1)!}, \tag{7.24}$$

so that one may express $\partial Q/\partial p$ as

$$\frac{\partial Q}{\partial p} = \lambda(c)(L + c) \frac{d\mu}{dp}. \tag{7.25}$$

Because L, c, and $\lambda(c)$ are all positive and on account of (4.12), it may now be seen that $(\partial Q/\partial p)_{p \geq 0} < 0$. Furthermore, taking (4.13) in conjunction with (7.25), one has $\lim_{p \to \infty} (\partial Q/\partial p)$ tending to zero.

Thus, we may conclude that if $\mu(p)$ satisfies the conditions of Chapter 4, Section 11.1 and 11.2, then there is a finite price p_0 (7.26) such that for every *given* level of c one has

$$\frac{\partial Q}{\partial p} \begin{cases} \text{negative for } p < p_0, \\ \text{tending to zero for } p \text{ increasing beyond } p_0. \end{cases}$$

The proposition (7.26) implies, among other things, that for $p = p^*$, the quantity, $-\partial Q/\partial p$, is positive.

3.3 In light of the preceding derivations, one may write $\partial\bar{\pi}/\partial p$ as

$$\frac{\partial\bar{\pi}}{\partial p} = \frac{\partial}{\partial p}[R - Q] = (p - L - c)\frac{\partial}{\partial p}A(p, c) + A(p, c).$$

So, combining the propositions (7.22) and (7.26), it may be seen that $\partial\bar{\pi}/\partial p$ is positive for $p < p^*$ and may become negative for $p > p^*$. Thus, if in addition to the assumptions introduced in the preceding, it is also assumed that $\partial\bar{\pi}/\partial p$ vanishes for a $p^{**} > 0$, then, for every given value of c, the expected net profits $\bar{\pi}$ has a unique maximum at $p = p^{**}$. But it was observed that $-\partial Q/\partial p$ is positive for $p = p^*$. Hence the p^{**} (whenever it exists) must be larger than p^*. Also, note that if $\bar{\pi}$ has a unique maximum, say $\bar{\pi}(p^{**}, c)$, then, corresponding to any level of expected profits $\bar{\pi}_0$ in the interval $0 \leq \bar{\pi}_0 \leq \bar{\pi}(p^{**}, c)$, there must exist two values of p, say, p_1 and p_2, such that $\bar{\pi} > \bar{\pi}_0$ for $p_1 \leq p \leq p_2$. Since $d\mu/dp$ is negative, one must also have $A(p_1, c) \geq A(p, c) \geq A(p_2, c)$ for $p_1 \leq p \leq p_2$.

> Thus, it follows that if $\mu(p)$ satisfies the conditions (4.12) and (4.13) the condition (7.19), and in addition, $\partial\bar{\pi}/\partial p = 0$ has exactly one finite positive root, then, for *any* magnitude of c, there is an *interval* of price quotations such that the expected (7.27) net profit is greater than some designated base profit and the expected level of sales is in the interval $A(p_1, c) \geq A(p, c) \geq A(p_2, c)$.

Some characteristics of the relationship between selling expenses and profits may now be examined. Observe, first, that on account of (4.14), one may write

$$\frac{\partial R}{\partial c} = p\mu(p)\frac{d\lambda}{dc} > 0 \tag{7.28}$$

and, on account of (4.15)

$$\lim_{c\to\infty}\frac{\partial R}{\partial c} = p\mu(p), \qquad \lim_{c\to\infty}\frac{d\lambda}{dc} = 0 \tag{7.29}$$

Next, consider the partial derivative[3] of Q with respect to c:

$$\frac{\partial Q}{\partial c} = \frac{\partial}{\partial c}E[K(S)] + c\frac{\partial A}{\partial c} + A(p, c)$$

$$= \mu(p)(L + c)\frac{d\lambda}{dc} + A(p, c). \tag{7.30}$$

[3] There is a term, namely, $\partial A/\partial c$ that appears in this derivative. It is analogous to the "cost of variation" concept introduced by Scitovsky [47, 250–251]. His definition of a variation with respect to selling cost—as discussed in this monograph—refers to that change in selling cost which is sufficient to change sales by one unit; in other words, this variation cost can be approximated by $1/(\partial A/\partial c)$.

On account of the definition of L, the probability function $g(S; p, c)$, and the condition (4.14), all the terms on the right member of (7.30) are positive; thus $\partial Q / \partial c > 0$. Again, by the condition (4.15) one observes that

$$\lim_{c \to \infty} \frac{\partial Q}{\partial c} = \lim_{c \to \infty} \mu(p)\left[(L + c)\frac{d\lambda}{dc} + \lambda(c)\right] = \gamma\mu(p).$$

Thus under assumptions (4.14) and (4.15) there exists a finite level of selling expenses c_0 such that for *any* price quotation p, $\partial Q / \partial c$ is positive for all selling costs *less than* (7.31) c_0 and tends to $\gamma\mu(p)$ as the selling costs tend to exceed the level c_0.

3.4 In light of the above analysis of the expected revenue and expected cost, one may now consider the dependence of the expected net profits on selling efforts c and the price quotation p. It should be observed that

$$\frac{\partial\bar{\pi}}{\partial c} = \frac{\partial R}{\partial c} - \frac{\partial Q}{\partial c}$$

$$= \mu(p)(p - L - c)\frac{d\lambda}{dc} - A(p, c) \qquad (7.32)$$

$$= (p - L - c)\frac{\partial A}{\partial c} - A(p, c).$$

The sign of $\partial\bar{\pi}/\partial c$ is seen to depend on the relative magnitudes of $\partial R/\partial c$ and $\partial Q/\partial c$; but it was also seen that $\partial R/\partial c$ is positive and tends to zero, whereas $\partial Q/\partial c$ is negative and tends to $-\gamma\mu(p)$ as c tends to increase indefinitely; thus $\partial\bar{\pi}/\partial c$ tends to $-\gamma\mu(p)$ as $c \to \infty$. The sign $(\partial\bar{\pi}/\partial c)_{c=0}$ again depends on the signs of $\partial R/\partial c$ and $\partial Q/\partial c$. The following may be stated about the existence of a unique optimum of $\bar{\pi}$ with respect to variations of selling cost:

If, in addition to (4.14) and (4.15), the following conditions, namely,

$$\lim_{c \to 0} \frac{\partial R}{\partial c} > \lim_{c \to 0} \frac{\partial Q}{\partial c} ; \qquad \left(\frac{\partial\bar{\pi}}{\partial c}\right)_{c^{**}>0} = 0, \qquad (7.33)$$

are satisfied, then for *every* $p > 0$ the expected net profit $\bar{\pi}$ has a unique maximum (at c^{**}) with respect to variations of selling costs.

It is important to observe that if the selling efforts are "saturated" the $d\lambda/dc$ is likely to have the following characteristics, namely,

$$\frac{d\lambda}{dc}\begin{cases} > 0 & \text{for} \quad 0 \leq c \leq c^*, \\ = 0 & \text{for} \quad c = c^*, \\ < 0 & \text{for} \quad c > c^*, \end{cases} \qquad (7.34)$$

which are fundamentally different from those postulated in (4.14) and (4.15). The property (7.34) implies that $\partial R/\partial c = 0$ for *some* finite level of c. Because p and $\mu(p)$ are always positive, it follows from (7.28) that $\partial R/\partial c$ will have the same sign as $\lambda(c)$. The condition (7.34), combined with (7.31), imply that $\partial \bar{\pi}/\partial c$ may be positive for $c < c^*$ and negative for $c \geq c^*$. Consequently, under these circumstances, a unique maximum of $\bar{\pi}$ *can* exist for $c^{**} < c^*$. In conclusion, it should be observed that whenever, for a given price quotation p, there is unique root $c = c^*$ for $\partial \bar{\pi}/\partial c = 0$, one may make a statement analogous to (7.27), namely,

> If $\lambda(c)$ satisfies the conditions (4.14) and (4.15) and if, in addition, $\partial \bar{\pi}/\partial c = 0$ has a unique finite root, then there exists an *interval* of selling costs $c_1 < c < c_2$ such that (a) the expected net profit is greater than some floor level
>
> $$\bar{\pi}_* < \bar{\pi}(p)_{\max}, \tag{7.35}$$
>
> and (b) the expected volume of sales is likewise in some interval
>
> $$A(p, c_1) \leq A(p, c) \leq A(p, c_2).$$

The propositions (7.21) and (7.35) bring out the full implications of conditional optimization of $\bar{\pi}(p, c)$.

4. CONFLICT OF OBJECTIVES

The purpose of this section is to apply the analysis of Section 3 to the decision-making situations within a firm; its organization is similar to that of Section 2, although a number of details will be omitted. More specifically, multiplicity of and possible conflicts between profits and market share or sales objectives constitute the main theme of this section. The following configurations of objectives are considered:

1. The firm likes to have $\Pr [\pi_1 < \pi \leq \pi_2] > P_1$ and, at the same time, $\Pr [S_1 < S \leq S_2] > P_2$.

2. The firm likes to maximize expected net profits $\bar{\pi}$, subject to some constraint on the expected *volume* of sales.

3. The firm would like to maximize expected net profits, $\bar{\pi}$, subject to the condition that $\Pr [S_1 < S \leq S_2] \geq P$.

Since the firm has two decision variables (price and selling expenses), one may examine the tradeoffs [39] between these variables at various levels of expected net profits.

4.1 Consider the decision situation of the first kind. Computation of the probability distribution of $\pi(p, c)$ is vastly simplified if the Poisson probability function $g(S; p, c)$ can be suitably approximated.[4] It is well known [21], for instance, that for large values of $A(p, c)$ one can make use of the following approximation:

$$g(S; p, c) = e^{-A(p,c)} \frac{[A(p, c)]^S}{S!}$$

$$\rightarrow G(S; p, c) = \frac{1}{\sqrt{2\pi A(p, c)}} \exp \left\{ \frac{- [S - A(p, c)]^2}{2A(p, c)} \right\} dS. \qquad (7.36)$$

(The nature of this approximation should be carefully noted: on the intervals of values of p and c over which the magnitude of $A(p, c)$ is small, the approximation will not be good.) Now, if

$$z = \pi(S) = (p - c) S - K(S) \qquad (7.37)$$

is a strictly monotomic function of sales (S), then, under fairly "mild" conditions [62], the probability density function of z may be determined as

$$h(z; p, c) = G[\pi^{-1}(z); p, c] \frac{d\pi^{-1}(z)}{dz} \qquad (7.38)$$

Hence, with a given quotation p and selling expense c, the probability constraint on profits may be written as

$$\Pr [\pi_1 < \text{net profits} \leq \pi_2] = \int_{\pi_1}^{\pi_2} h(z; p, c) \, dz \geq P_1 \qquad (7.39)$$

and from (7.35), the probability constraint on sales may be written as

$$\Pr [S_1 < \text{sales} \leq S_2] = \int_{S_1}^{S_2} G(S; p, c) \, dS \geq P_2. \qquad (7.40)$$

Any pair of values of p and c that satisfy (7.39 and 7.40) would be a feasible policy. Given a complete specification of the cost function $K(S)$, it is possible to derive qualitative properties of the space of feasible solutions.

4.2 Next, consider a decision situation of the second type, that is, one in which

$$\bar{\pi}(p, c) = (p - c) A(p, c) - E(K(S)]$$

---

[4] It is possible to do away with approximation methods and to treat the distribution of profits in a more direct manner. This consists of determining, for a given pair of values of p and c, all the intervals of values of sales S that will support profits in the desired range and then summing up the probabilities of occurrence of such intervals of S-values.

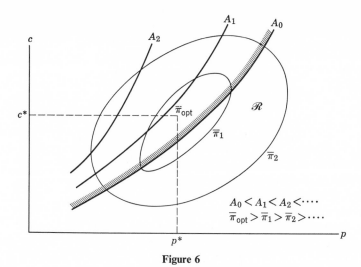

Figure 6

is to be maximized, subject to the constraint that

$$E[S] \equiv A(p, c) \geq A_0.$$

A simple means of visualizing the solution is to draw, in the (p, c)-plane, a set of contours or level-curves of $\bar{\pi}(p, c)$ and $A(p, c) = \mu(p) \lambda(c)$. This is illustrated in Figure 6. For given levels of expected net profits and expected sales volume, the contours indicate sets of marginal rates of substitution between price and selling expense. Thus, one can examine —on each contour—the degree to which a change in the price must be compensated for by a change in the selling expense in order to maintain a given level of expected net profits or sales volume. The region $\mathscr{R}$ is the admissible region in which $A(p, c) \geq A_0$. An inspection of the contours also indicates that if the point of maximum profits does not lie in $\mathscr{R}$ then

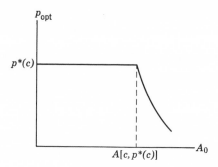

Figure 7

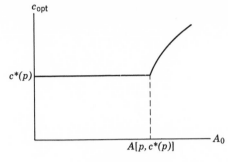

Figure 8

it would be a point where the A_0-curve is *tangent* to one of the $\bar{\pi}$-curves. It is also seen from the contours that p is a decreasing function and c is an increasing function of A_0. Therefore for any level of selling expense c, the dependence of the optimal price p_{opt} on A_0 may be represented as in Figure 7; similarly, for any price p the dependence of the optimal selling expense c_{opt} on A_0 may be represented as in Figure 8.

Chapter **8**

MULTIPERIOD PROBABILITY
MODELS

Models of the sales probabilities of individual firms were developed to
exhibit the explicit dependence of these probabilities on the policy variables
of the individual firms—price, in the case of an undifferentiated, and price
and selling expense, in the case of a differentiated oligopoly. The models
have an explicit reference to a *given epoch* of price policy and selling
expense policy; they are *single-period* models ("period" being understood
as the duration of a given price or selling expense policy).

The probability functions, therefore, should be interpreted with caution.
In general, there is *no* assurance that the sales experience before and after
a change in price or selling expense be statistically dependent or independent. Put another way: the only valid use which the probability
functions may be put to is in computing the mean values and variances
of sales before a change in policy is implemented.

The purpose of the present chapter is to consider *multiperiod* versions of
the single-period models. Its orientation is largely "classical" in that it
is developed with a view toward obtaining probabilistic representation—
and, in some instances, explanation—of some of the salient observable
features of competition among a few. Its content is to examine the
conditional probability of sales due to a change of policy, given the sales
under the current policy. In spirit, it is an attempt to construct a theory of
stochastic sales processes by a model of a *sequence* of random sales. The
concept of a sequence is rooted firmly in business practice: a firm does not
set its price or selling expense policy *de novo*—there is a price; the firm
decides only upon the magnitude and direction of a *change*. Thus the
sequence of sales is seen as indexed by the level of price quoted. But unlike
"time," which is the customary parameter in the mathematical theory of
stochastic processes, price can vary in both directions. Hence, the sales
process needs to be defined in two senses.

1. SALES TRANSITION PROBABILITIES: UNDIFFERENTIATED OLIGOPOLY

A multiperiod model of sales probability of a single firm is developed for the case of an undifferentiated oligopoly. The key notion is that of a conditional probability distribution. It is shown that if the mean and second moment of this distribution possess certain limit properties, then one can generate a Markov representation of the sales process. One representation is of the form

$$dS(p) = \begin{cases} \Phi_1(p)_{dp} + s_1(p)\, dY(p), & \text{for increase in price,} \\ -\Phi_2(p)_{dp} + s_2(p)\, dY(p), & \text{for reduction in price,} \end{cases}$$

where $dS(p)$ denotes the change in sales, and $dY(p)$ represents an interval-valued stochastic process whose increments $dY(p)$ are mutually independent Gaussian random variables. Explicit forms are obtained for the transition probabilities of sales under a variation of price quotations; the transition probabilities are parametrized by the variation of quotations. Of general interest are the results which permit a representation of rigidity of competition and of "kinked" demand.

1.1 Without loss of generality, the following assumptions will be made about the aggregate industry demand and about the shape of the *expected* market share function $f(p)$:

C:1 The aggregate industry demand n is large and approximately of the same order of magnitude in each decision period of the firm in question.

C:2 All the derivatives of $f(p)$ are bounded and, in particular, $|hf'(p)/f(p)| < 1$ whenever the change $|h|$ in price is less than a small positive number.

Assumption C:1 is introduced primarily with a view toward simplifying the mathematical manipulations. The first part of C:1 justifies the approximation of

$$g(r; p) = \binom{n}{r} [f(p)]^r [1 - f(p)]^{n-r}$$

by

$$g(r; p) = \{2\pi n f(p)[1 - f(p)]\}^{-\frac{1}{2}} \exp\left\{\frac{-[r - nf(p)]^2}{2nf(p)[1 - f(p)]}\right\}$$

$$= \{2\pi n f(p)[1 - f(p)]\}^{-\frac{1}{2}} \exp\left\{\frac{-[S(p) - nf(p)]^2}{2nf(p)[1 - f(p)]}\right\}, \quad (8.1)$$

where the random sales r has been formally replaced by $S(p)$. In order to appreciate the significance of C:2, note that the left number of the inequality appearing there may be written as

$$\left| \left(\frac{df/f}{dp/p} \right) \frac{h}{p} \right| = \left| \eta \frac{h}{p} \right|,$$

η being the elasticity of the *expected* market share with respect to the firm's own asking price. On account of the second part of C: 1, then, one can assert that the means and variances of the two Gaussian variables, namely,

$$S(p) = nf(p) + \epsilon\sqrt{nf(p)[1 - f(p)]}, \qquad \epsilon \cap N(0, 1),$$
$$S(p + h) = nf(p + h) + \epsilon'\sqrt{nf(p + h)(1 - f(p + h))}, \qquad (8.2)$$
$$\epsilon' \cap N(0, 1)$$

differ only due to the change $\pm h$ in the price quoted. Now, observe that even though the firm may be "aware" of some loose "coordination," its sales may be substantially volatile in the face of a price change. This is the principal justification for employing two *distinct* random variables, ϵ and ϵ', in representing $S(p)$ and $S(p + h)$. At this stage, then, we may explicitly introduce a measure of "coordination" by supposing that ϵ and ϵ' are *correlated* and that the correlation is a *function* $R(h)$ of the price variation. Also, any material evidence that may lend support to the feeling of distrust—"others may not follow"—can be used to specify the shape of the function $R(h)$. This function is likely to decrease in $|h|$ and to attain a maximum value at $h = 0$. This implies, among other things, that $R(h) = 0$ for large values of $|h|$: The (random) sales before and after a change in the asking price are likely to become asymptotically independent [44, 45]. In general, then, $S(p)$ and $S(p + h)$ *will possess a bivariate Gaussian distribution with a correlation function* $R(h)$. The shape of $R(h)$ will obviously differ from firm to firm: Some firms may take a large change in price to have a value of their $R(h)$ as that attained by others with a smaller change in price. This suggests that $R(h)$ may be taken as an operational means of representing the *competitive strength* of a firm in oligopoly. In order to justify some of the operations which follow, these conditions on $R(h)$ will be introduced:

D: 1 $\quad R(h) = R(-h); \qquad \lim_{|h|\to 0} R(h) = 1.$

D: 2 $\quad \lim_{|h|\to 0} \frac{1}{|h|} [1 - R(h)] = \beta > 0.$

Some of the important consequences of these are the following, namely,

$$\lim_{h|\to 0} \frac{1}{|h|} [1 - R(h)]^2 = 0, \qquad \lim_{|h|\to 0} \frac{1}{|h|} [1 - R^2(h)] = 2\beta.$$

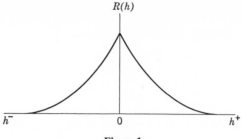

Figure 1

The assumptions D:1 and D:2 are satisfied by a function such as $R(h) = e^{-|h|\beta}$, as in Figure 1.

1.2 It is shown that under the assumptions D:1 and D:2 the limits of the conditional first and second moments of the *change* in sales, per unit of the variation, exist and help define a Guassian process $dS(p)$. Note, first, that $S(p + h) - S(p)$ is Gaussian because both $S(p)$ and $S(p + h)$ are so. Also, the conditional expectation is

$$E[S(p + h) - S(p) \mid S(p) = \xi]$$

$$= nf(p + h) + R(h)\left\{\frac{nf(p + h)[1 - f(p + h)]}{nf(p)[1 - f(p)]}\right\}^{\frac{1}{2}} [\xi - nf(p)] - \xi.$$

Expanding $f(p + h)$ and employing C:2, one obtains the following approximation:

$$E[S(p + h) - S(p) \mid S(p) = \xi] = nf(p)[1 - R(h)] + \xi[R(h) - 1]$$

$$+ \tfrac{1}{2}hR(h)\left[\frac{f'(p)}{f(p)} - \frac{f'(p)}{1 - f(p)}\right][\xi - nf(p)] + nf'(p)h + o(h^2).$$

Employing the condition D:1, and taking the limit as $h \downarrow 0$, the following is immediate:

$$\lim_{h \downarrow 0} E\left[\frac{S(p + h) - S(p)}{h} \,\middle|\, S(p) = \xi\right]$$

$$= nf'(p) + \frac{1}{2}\left[\frac{f'(p)}{(p)} - \frac{f'(p)}{1 - f(p)}\right][\xi - nf(p)] - \beta[\xi - nf(p)] \quad (8.3)$$

$$= m(p, \xi), \text{ say.}$$

Similarly, the conditional second moment may be calculated as follows:

$$E\{[S(p + h) - S(p)]^2 \mid S(p) = \xi\}$$

$$= \text{Var}\,[S(p + h) \mid S(p) = \xi] + (E[S(p + h) \mid S(p) = \xi])^2$$

$$- 2\xi E[S(p + h) \mid S(p) = \xi] + \xi^2$$

$$= nf(p + h)[1 - f(p + h)][1 - R^2(h)]$$

$$+ \left[nf(p + h) + R(h)\left\{\frac{nf(p + h)[1 - f(p + h)]}{nf(p)[1 - f(p)]}\right\}^{\frac{1}{2}} [\xi - nf(p)] \right]^2$$

$$- 2\xi\left[nf(p + h) + R(h)\left\{\frac{nf(p + h)[1 - f(p + h)]}{nf(p)[1 - f(p)]}\right\}^{\frac{1}{2}} \right.$$

$$\left. \times\, [\xi - nf(p)] \right] + \xi^2$$

Proceeding as before, the first term on the right member is approximated as

$$nf(p)[1 - f(p)]\left[1 + \frac{hf'(p)}{f(p)} - \frac{hf'(p)}{1 - f(p)}\right][1 - R^2(h)] + o(h^2);$$

the second term is approximated as

$$\left\{ nf(p)[1 - R(h)] + nf'(p)h + R(h)\xi \right.$$

$$\left. + \tfrac{1}{2}hR(h)\left[\frac{f'(p)}{f(p)} - \frac{f'(p)}{1 - f(p)}\right][\xi - nf(p)] \right\}^2 + o(h^2)$$

and the third term as

$$-2\xi\left\{ nf(p)(1 - R(h) + nf'(p)h + R(h)\xi \right.$$

$$\left. + \tfrac{1}{2}hR(h)\left[\frac{f'(p)}{f(p)} - \frac{f'(p)}{1 - f(p)}\right][\xi - nf(p)] \right\} + o(h^2)$$

Dividing through by h and taking D:2 into account, the following limit is obtained for the conditional second moment per unit of price variation:

$$\lim_{h\downarrow 0} E\left\{ \frac{[S(p + h) - S(p)]^2}{h} \,\middle|\, S(p) = \xi \right\} = 2nf(p)[1 - f(p)]\beta = s^2(p, \xi). \quad (8.4)$$

By the condition D:2, $\beta > 0$; hence $s^2(p, \xi)$ is nonnegative.

1.3 Doob [20] has shown that if the limits $m(p, \xi)$ and $s^2(p, \xi)$ exist *any* Markov Gaussian process—that is, a process in which the random variables are Gaussian and the transition probabilities are Markovian—satisfying (8.3) and (8.4) and possessing continuous sample functions with probability equal to one can be obtained as a solution to the stochastic equation

$$dS(p) = m[p, S(p)] \, dp + s[p, S(p)] \, dY(p), \qquad (8.5)$$

where $Y(p)$ is a real-valued stochastic process with (normalized) Gaussian independent increments, $\{Y(p') - Y(p)\}$, possessing the following properties:

$$E\{Y(p') - Y(p)\} = 0; \qquad E\{[Y(p') - Y(p)]^2\} = |p' - p|. \qquad (8.6)$$

Because the rest of what follows depends on (8.5), it is important to have an intuitive picture of the $\{S(p)\}$-process. Suppose that the price quotations lie in the interval $[a, b]$, and consider any two prices p' and p'' in this interval: $a \le p' \le p'' \le b$. Then the picture of the $\{S(p)\}$-process is roughly the following: $S(p')$ is the *sum* of $S(a)$ and appropriately scaled increments $dY(p')$ of the $\{Y(p)\}$-process. $S(a)$ is a random variable, independent of the differences $\{Y(p'') - Y(p')\}$; that is to say, the formula (8.5) has the following interpretation:

$$S(p) - S(a) = \int_a^p m[p', S(p')] \, dp' + \int_a^p s[p', S(p')] \, dY(p'). \qquad (8.7)$$

For any *given* sample function the first integral in the right member of this formula is a nonrandom quantity because $m[p', S(p')]$ is nonrandom. The second integral exists [20, p. 436] if, *for example*, for each p', $S(p')$ is a random variable independent of the totality of differences $\{Y(b) - Y(p'')$, $p'' > p'\}$. As readily seen, this condition matches the intuitive picture given. Also, any solution of (8.7) satisfies the following:

$$S(p) - S(p^*) = \int_{p^*}^p m[p', S(p')] \, dp' + \int_{p^*}^p s[p', S(p')] \, dY(p'), \qquad (8.8)$$

so that $S(p)$ depends only on $S(p^*)$ and the Y-differences for the price quotations between p^* and p. These latter differences or jumps are independent of $S(p^*)$, $S(a)$ and, if $p' < p^*$, are also independent of the differences between a and p^*. It follows, then, that the conditional distribution of $S(p)$ for a given $S(p')$, $p' < p^*$, is a function of $S(p^*)$ alone: The $\{S(p)\}$-process is *Markovian in price.*

1.4 A few observations on the representation (8.5) are in order. First, observe that (8.5) may be written

$$\frac{dS - m[p, S(p)] \, dp}{s[p, S(p)]} = dY(p).$$

The introduction of the interval-valued process $\{Y(p)\}$ has served the following purpose: The uncertainty in the level of sales of a firm at a given price is explicitly made to depend upon the magnitude of the departure of this price from its previous level. Second, one may consider $E[|dY(p)|^2]$ to be *proportional* to $|dp|$, the factor of proportionality being absorbed into the function $s[p, S(p)]$. This factor of proportionality or, more generally, the function $s[p, S(p)]$ is a natural indicator of the *rigidity* of competition, that is, of the existence of *effective price leadership*. For a strong price-leader, one would expect the magnitude of $m[p, S(p)]$ to be rather insensitive to $|\Delta p|$ and, similarly, the $s[p, S(p)]$ to be relatively small. As we will see in the development to follow, the transition probabilities of the Markov process are certainly to be influenced by the magnitude of $|\Delta p|$. It is now appropriate to consider the possibility that the stochastic process $\{dS(p)\}$ may be *unsymmetric* with respect to positive and negative variations of the price quoted. In other words, it is conceivable that the function $m(p, \xi)$ and $s^2(p, \xi)$ may differ according to whether one takes the limits $h \downarrow 0$ or $h \uparrow 0$—a *mathematical counterpart to the phenomenon* of *kinked demand curve*. Let it be observed, first, that the random variables $S(p)$ and $S(p + h)$ have a bivariate Gaussian distribution with the following unconditional moments:

$$E[S(p)] = nf(p); \quad \text{Var}\,[S(p)] = nf(p)[1 - f(p)];$$
$$E[S(p + h)] = nf(p + h); \quad \text{Var}\,[S(p + h)] = nf(p + h)[1 - f(p + h)],$$

and a correlation function $R(h)$, which decreases as $|h|$ increases. The *conditional* distribution of $[S(p + h) \mid S(p) = \xi]$ is also Gaussian, with

$$E[S(p + h) \mid S(p) = \xi]$$

$$= E[S(p + h)] + R(h)\frac{\sqrt{\text{Var}\,S(p + h)}}{\sqrt{\text{Var}\,S(p)}}\{\xi - E[S(p)]\}$$

$$= nf(p + h) + R(h)\frac{\sqrt{nf(p + h)[1 - f(p + h)]}}{\sqrt{nf(p)[1 - f(p)]}}\,[\xi - nf(p)], \quad (8.9)$$

for its mathematical expectation, and

$$\text{Var}\,[S(p + h) \mid S(p) = \xi] = \text{Var}\,[S(p + h)][1 - R^2(h)]$$
$$= nf(p + h)(1 - f[p + h])[1 - R^2(h)], \quad (8.10)$$

for its variance. Suppose, now, that the price asked in a batch of contacts in one period is the same as that asked in the previous period, that is, that $h = 0$. Then, since $\lim_{|h| \to 0} R(h) = 1$ (see D:1), the above expressions for conditional mean and variance give rise to the following:

$$E[S(p + h) \mid S(p) = \xi] \to nf(p) + \xi - nf(p) = \xi,$$
$$\text{Var}\,[S(p + h) \mid S(p) = \xi] \to 0. \quad (8.11)$$

In other words, the probability "mass" of the conditional distribution becomes concentrated at only one point, $S(p) = \xi$. Under this interpretation of a "zero variation" in the quotation, it is now possible to *interpret a kinked demand curve in terms of the nonsymmetric correlation function R(h)*. In view of the fact that in all the simulation experiments the stipulated functions $m(., .)$ and $s(., .)$ could at best be estimated as $\Phi(p)$ and $s(p)$, a simplified but asymmetric version of (8.5), namely,

$$dS(p) = \begin{cases} \Phi_1(p)\, dp + s_1(p)\, dY(p), & \text{if } dp > 0, \\ -\Phi_2(p)\, dp + s_2(p)\, dY(p), & \text{if } dp < 0. \end{cases} \tag{8.12}$$

will be employed in the rest of the discussion.

1.5   For the sake of definiteness, consider the case in which the firm raises its asking price from p to $p + z$. Define

$$J_1 = \int_p^{p+z} \Phi_1(x)\, dx, \qquad \Delta_1 = \int_p^{p+z} [s_1(x)]^2\, dx. \tag{8.13}$$

The transition probabilities can then be written as

$$\Pr\left[S(p+z) \leq \eta \mid S(p) = \xi\right] = P(p, \xi; p+z, \eta)$$

$$= \frac{1}{\sqrt{2\pi\Delta_1}} \int_{-\infty}^{\eta-\xi-J_1} \exp\left[\frac{-\lambda^2}{2\Delta_1}\right] d\lambda$$

$$= \int_{-\infty}^{\eta-\xi-J_1} \Psi_1(\lambda)\, d\lambda; \tag{8.14}$$

hence the transition probability density, $d_\eta P(p, \xi; p+z, \eta)$ is

$$d_\eta P(p, \xi; p+z, \eta) = \frac{1}{\sqrt{2\pi\Delta_1}} \exp\left[\frac{-(\eta - \xi - J_1)^2}{2\Delta_1}\right]. \tag{8.15}$$

Similarly, defining

$$J_2 = \int_{p-y}^{p} \Phi_2(x)\, dx, \qquad \Delta_2 = \int_{p-y}^{p} [s_2(x)]^2\, dx \tag{8.16}$$

for the situation in which the quotations are reduced from p to $p - y$, one obtains the following expression for the transition probability density:

$$d_\eta P(p, \xi; p-y, \eta) = (2\pi\Delta_2)^{-\frac{1}{2}} \exp\left[\frac{-(\eta - \xi - J_2)^2}{2\Delta_2}\right]. \tag{8.17}$$

The transition probability densities $d_\eta P(p, \xi; p+z, \eta)$ and $d_\eta P(p, \xi; p-y, \eta)$ will appear in Section 3 in the analysis of price rigidity.

2. SALES TRANSITION PROBABILITIES: DIFFERENTIATED OLIGOPOLY

The purpose of this section is to extend the preceding program of analysis to the case in which both price and selling expenses may be varied by the firm. Therefore, the Markov representation of the stochastic sales process (based upon a certain kind of limiting behavior of the conditional first and second moments) will play the key role. However, less emphasis will be placed on detailed derivation. The principal *assumption* underlying the derivations of this section is that the *sequence* in which price and selling expense are varied *has no effect* on the probabilistic properties of the sales process.

2.1   Recall from Chapter 4, Section 2 that the volume of sales of an individual firm was seen to be a Poisson variable, with the probability function

$$g(S; p, c) = e^{-A(p,c)} \frac{[A(p, c)]^S}{S!} .$$

When S is large, we noted the possibility of the approximation

$$G(S; p, c) = (2\pi A(p, c))^{-\frac{1}{2}} \exp \left[\frac{-[S - A(p, c)]^2}{2A(p, c)} \right] dS$$

which is Gaussian. This suggests that the random quantity $S(p, c)$ may be represented as a normalized variable, namely,

$$S(p, c) = A(p, c) + \epsilon_1 \sqrt{A(p, c)}, \qquad \epsilon_1 \cap N(0, 1). \tag{8.18}$$

Similar representations are also possible for the random sales at alternative levels of price and selling expenses per unit:

$$S(p + h, c) = A(p + h, c) + \epsilon_2 \sqrt{A(p + h, c)},$$
$$\epsilon_2 \cap N(0, 1), \quad (11.2)$$

$$S(p, c + k) = A(p, c + k) + \epsilon_3 \sqrt{A(p, c + k)},$$
$$\epsilon_3 \cap N(0, 1), \quad (11.3)$$

$$S(p + h, c + k) = A(p + h, c + k) + \epsilon_4 \sqrt{A(p + h, c + k)}$$
$$\epsilon_4 \cap N(0, 1). \quad (11.4)$$

Note that in each of these representations, p, c, h, and k are given magnitudes. Also, observe that in general there is some measure of correlation (hence statistical dependence because the random variables are Gaussian) between the sales before and after a price or selling expense variation.

It is plausible to assume[1] that the covariances between the ϵ's will be dependent on the magnitudes of the variations; in other words,

$$\text{Cov}(\epsilon_1, \epsilon_2) = R(h, 0), \qquad \text{Cov}(\epsilon_1, \epsilon_3) = R(0, k)$$
$$\text{Cov}(\epsilon_1, \epsilon_4) = R(h, k). \tag{8.19}$$

The following is explicitly assumed about the correlation functions:

E:1 The *size* of the correlation function is the same for upward and downward revisions of price and selling expenses, so that

$$R(h, .) = R(-h, .); \; R(., k) = R(., -k); \; R(h, k) = R(-h, -k).$$

E:2 Regardless of the amount of direction of previous changes, the correlations tend to be perfect (that is ± 1) as the variations $|h|$ or $|k|$ approach zero.

In other words, it is assumed that if the firm does not change its quotations and selling expenses between two successive planning periods the sales in the two periods are likely to be perfectly correlated. This, however, should *not* be taken to mean that the *actual* sales in the two periods will be *equal*. The precise formulation is the following:

$$\lim_{|h| \to 0} R(h, 0) = 1, \qquad \lim_{|k| \to 0} R(0, k) = 1, \qquad \lim_{|h|, |k| \to 0} R(h, k) = 1. \tag{8.20}$$

Finally, with a view toward ensuring the existence of the limits of conditional first and second moments, the following assumptions will be made:

E:3
$$
\begin{cases}
\lim_{|h| \to 0} \dfrac{R(h, 0) - 1}{|h|} = b_1, \qquad \lim_{|k| \to 0} \dfrac{R(0, k) - 1}{k} = b_2, \\[3mm]
\lim_{|h|, |k| \to 0} \dfrac{R(h, k) - 1}{|h| + |k|} = b_3.
\end{cases}
$$

---

[1] That the covariances between the sales before and after a change in price and/or selling expenses are an important tool of analysis should be obvious to the practical analysts. Their importance arises from the fact that in multivariate Gaussian distributions it is these covariances that account for the levels of the various conditional expectations or forecasts. Furthermore, from an heuristic viewpoint, such covariances are likely to *decrease* with increasing magnitude of the variations in price and/or selling expenses. This may come about because the individual firm *hopes* that its competitors will not retaliate for relatively small changes that *it* initiates, and the events in the market substantiate this hope. In other words, *the nature of the covariance functions has its origin in the prevalent tendency of the competitors to maintain the status quo in the market and to respond only to the large variations* in price/or selling expenses.

Consider the conditional expectation of change in sales, given that the sales experience at price p and selling expense c is known, for example, $S(p, c) = a$:

$$E[S(p + h, c + k) - S(p, c) \mid S(p, c) = a]$$

$$= A(p + h, c + k) - a + R(h, k) \frac{\sqrt{A(p + h, c + k)}}{\sqrt{A(p, c)}} [a - A(p, c)].$$

The associated second moment is seen to be

$$E[\{S(p + h, c + k) - S(p, c)\}^2 \mid S(p, c) = a]$$

$$= A(p + h, c + k)[1 - R(h, k)] + (\text{conditional expectation})^2.$$

Approximating $A(p, c)$ up to linear terms, one has

$$A(p + h, c + k) \cong A(p, c) + h \frac{\partial A}{\partial p} + k \frac{\partial A}{\partial c}. \tag{8.21}$$

Employing this approximation, and making use of the assumptions (E:3), it is seen that the following limits exist and are finite:

$$\lim_{(h,k) \to (0,0)} E\left[\frac{S(p + h, c + k) - S(p, c)}{|h| + |k|} \,\middle|\, S(p, c) = a \right] = m[p, c, S(p, c)], \tag{8.22}$$

$$\lim_{(h,k) \to (0,0)} E\left[\frac{\{S(p + h, c + k) - S(p, c)\}^2}{|h| + |k|} \,\middle|\, S(p, c) = a \right] = \sigma^2[p, c, S(p, c)].$$

When price alone is varied, these moments will be denoted by $m_1[p, S(p, c)]$ and $\sigma_1^2[p, S(p, c)]$; similarly, when selling expenses alone are varied, these will be indicated by $m_2[cS(p, c)]$ and $\sigma_2^2[c, S(p, c)]$, respectively. As in the preceding section, the existence of these moments makes it possible to represent the stochastic process of a change in sales as

$$dS(p, c) = m_1[pS(p, c)] \, dp + m_2[c, S(p, c)] \, dc$$

$$+ \sigma_1[p, S(p, c)] \, dY_1(p) + \sigma_2[c, S(p, c)] \, dY_2(c), \tag{8.23}$$

it being understood that by proper scaling one may express the variances as $|p' - p|$ and $|c' - c|$, respectively. The following version of (8.23) will be employed in the applications to follow:

$$dS(p, c) = m_1(p) \, dp + m_2(c) \, dc + \sigma_1(p) \, dY_1(p) + \sigma_2(c) \, dY_2(c). \tag{8.24}$$

The special feature of this version is that $S(p, c)$, the sales at the previous level of price and selling expenses, do not appear in the mean value functions $m_i(.)$ and the variance functions $\sigma_i(.)$. This seems to be more appropriate to the situation in which the sales of the firm in question are not too large a fraction of the industry sales, that is, a situation comparable to Chamberlin's "large group" case of monopolistic competition.

2.2 From the above development it is seen that due to a change in price p or selling expense c the *nonrandom component* of the change in sales is the expected value, namely,

$$M = \int_{(p)} m_1(x)\, dx + \int_{(c)} m_2(x)\, dx, \qquad (8.25)$$

and the variance of the change in sales is given by

$$\Delta = \int_{(p)} [\sigma_1(x)]^2\, dx + \int_{(c)} [\sigma_2(x)]^2\, dx. \qquad (8.26)$$

Analogous to the development in Section 1, it is now possible to write the transition probabilities

$$\Pr\,[S(p', c') \le \eta \,|\, S(p, c) = \xi] = H(p, c, \xi; p', c', \eta)$$
$$= (2\pi\Delta)^{-\frac{1}{2}} \int_{-\infty}^{\eta - \xi - M} e^{-W^2/2\Delta}\, dW$$

which are defined for p' and c' (distinct from p and c), respectively. Suppose, now, that the firm considers to raise its price quotations from p to $p + h$ and to raise the selling expenses from c to $c + k$. For this situation, it follows from (8.25) and (8.26) that

$$M = \int_{p}^{p+h} m_1(x)\, dx + \int_{c}^{c+k} m_2(x)\, dx;$$

$$\Delta = \int_{p}^{p+h} [\sigma_1(x)]^2\, dx + \int_{c}^{c+k} [\sigma_2(x)]^2\, dx.$$

Thus, the sales transition probability associated with the proposed course of action is given by

$$H(p, c, \xi; p + h, c + k, \eta) = (2\pi\Delta)^{-\frac{1}{2}} \int_{-\infty}^{\eta - \xi - M} e^{-W^2/2\Delta}\, dW$$

with the associated density function $d_\eta H(p, c, \xi; p + h, c + k, \eta)$:

$$d_\eta H(p, c, \xi; p + h, c + k, \eta) = (2\pi\Delta)^{-\frac{1}{2}} \exp\left[\frac{-(\eta - \xi - M)^2}{2\Delta}\right]. \qquad (8.27)$$

To sum up: *if* the conditions for the representation (8.23) are satisfied, and *if* the actual sales before the variation were ξ, then the transition probability density of sales for $p \to p^*$ and $c \to c^*$ is given by

$$\frac{1}{\sqrt{2\pi\Delta}} e^{-W^2/2\Delta},$$

where $W = \eta - \xi - M$, and M and Δ are defined in (8.25) and (8.26). Observe that a critical step in the derivation is the notion that the correlation $R(h, k)$ between the sales before and after a variation is dependent on the *size* of the variation. The special assumption *that the correlation would approach one as variations tend to be zero is simultaneously an indication of the degree of product differentiation and of the strength of competition.* A second critical observation is that the limiting conditional expectation and second moment of a *change* in sales per unit of the variation are the probabilistic analogues of what is known as "reaction function" in the language of the economists. Finally, it is not too difficult to see that the natural adjunct of this analysis is the concept of "conjectural variations" as discussed in Chapters 1 and 2.

2.3 It will be recalled that the Gaussian processes with increments $\{dY_1(p)\}$ and $\{dY_2(c)\}$ were assumed to be mutually independent. This assumption will now be relaxed and an attempt will now be made to generalize the model of sales transition probabilities. Thus consider the following covariance matrix $\sum_1$ for the joint distribution of $dY_1(p)$ and $dY_2(c)$:

$$\sum_1 = \begin{pmatrix} |dp|, & \sqrt{|dp| \cdot |dc|} \exp{(-|dp| - |dc|)} \\ \sqrt{|dp| \cdot |dc|} \exp{(-|dp| - |dc|)}, & |dc| \end{pmatrix}$$

(8.28)

This implies that the *squared* correlation coefficient is given by

$$r = e^{-|dp|-|dc|},$$

(8.29)

which is analogous to and carries substantially the same meaning as the correlation function $R(h, k)$, introduced earlier. Because of (8.28) and (8.29), the $\{dS(p, c)\}$ process representing the change in sales is seen to have the mean value $m_1(p)\, dp + m_2(c)\, dc$ and the covariance matrix $\sum_2$:

$$\sum_2 = \begin{pmatrix} \sigma_1^2(p) \cdot |dp|, & r\sigma_1(p)\sigma_2(c)\sqrt{|dp|\,|dc|} \\ r\sigma_1(p)\sigma_2(c)\sqrt{|dp|\,|dc|}, & \sigma_2^2(p)\,|dc| \end{pmatrix}$$

(8.30)

Consequently, the terms appearing in the Markov representation (8.23) will be modified as follows:

$$m[p, c, S(p, c)] = m_1[p, S(p, c)] + m_2[c, S(p, c)]$$
$$= b_3[a - A(p, c)] + \frac{1}{2}\left(\frac{\partial A}{\partial p} + \frac{\partial A}{\partial c}\right)\left[1 + \frac{a - A(p, c)}{2A(p, c)}\right],$$

(8.31)

$$\sigma^2[p, c, S(p, c)] = \sigma_1^2[p, S(p, c)] + \sigma_2^2[c, S(p, c)]$$
$$+ 2r\sigma_1[p, S(p, c)]\sigma_2[c, S(p, c)].$$

(8.32)

Therefore the expectation and variance of the Markov process have to be expressed as follows:

$$E[dS(p, c)] = m_1 |dp| + m_2 |dc|$$

$$\text{Var } [dS(p, c)] = \sigma_1^2 |dp| + \sigma_2^2 |dc| + 2r\sigma_1\sigma_2 |dp| \cdot |dc|.$$

Formula (8.25) will now be written with $m_1(.)$ and $m_2(.)$ computed as in (8.31); formula (8.26) will be modified on account of the mutual dependence between the $dY_1(p)$ and $dY_2(c)$. Thus, Δ will be replaced by Δ':

$$\Delta' = \int [\sigma_1(x)]^2 \, dx + \int [\sigma_2(y)]^2 \, dy + 2r \iint \sigma_1(x)\sigma_2(y) \, dx \, dy \quad (8.33)$$

and, hence, the transition probability function will be given by writing Δ' in place of Δ in formula (8.27):

$$\Pr [S(p', c') \leq \eta \mid S(p, c) = \xi] = \frac{1}{\sqrt{2\pi\Delta'}} \int_{-\infty}^{\eta - \xi - M'} e^{-w^2/2\Delta'} \, dw. \quad (8.34)$$

It should be observed that since the squared correlation is positive and so are $\sigma_1(p)$ and $\sigma_2(c)$, therefore, Δ' will be at least as large as the Δ obtained for the case in which the changes $\{dY_1(p)\}$ and $\{dY_2(c)\}$ are statistically independent.

3. SOME OBSERVATIONS ON THE MARKOV REPRESENTATION

Some of the more delicate issues associated with the Markov representation

$$dS(p) = m[p, S(p)] \, dp + s[p, S(p)] \, dY(p)$$

will be taken up in this section. Its chief purpose is to bring out the contacts of the theory with a certain class of stochastic equations. Some observations will also be made on functions of the sales process $S(p)$

$$S(p) = S(p') + \int_{p'}^{p} m[p'', S(p'')] \, dp'' \int_{p'}^{p} s[p'', S(p'')] \, dY(p'')$$

which have interesting and interpretable properties.

3.1   Suppose that (a) $m(p, \xi)$ and $s(p, \xi)$ are Baire functions[1] of p and ξ (for $\mathscr{P}: 0 \leq p < \infty$, $\mathscr{X}: 0 < \xi < \infty$) and that on each compact

---

[1] That is, functions measurable with respect to some given class of (two-dimensional, in the present case) Borel-measurable sets $\mathscr{F}$:

$$\mathscr{F}: \{(p, \xi): m(p, \xi) \leq a, s(p, \xi) \leq b\}.$$

subset of $\mathscr{P}$ there is a constant k such that

$$|m(p, \xi)| \leq k\sqrt{1 + \xi^2}, \qquad 0 \leq s(p, \xi) \leq k\sqrt{1 + \xi^2} \qquad (8.35)$$

$$|m(p, \xi') - m(p, \xi)| \leq k|\xi' - \xi|, \qquad |s(p, \xi') - s(p, \xi)| \leq k|\xi' - \xi|$$

and (b) $\{Y(p), 0 \leq p < \infty\}$ is a real-valued Gaussian process with independent increments, such that $Y(0) = 0$ and

$$E[\{Y(p)\}] = 0, \qquad E[\{|Y(p) - Y(p')|^2\}] = |p' - p|,$$

and having almost all of its sample functions continuous. With these assumptions Ito [68] has shown that there exists a Markov process $\{S(p), p \in \mathscr{P}\}$ which possesses a transition probability function[2] whose sample functions are almost all continuous and which satisfies the symbolic equation

$$S(p') = S(p) + \int_p^{p'} m[p'', S(p'')] \, dp'' + \int_p^{p'} s[p'', S(p'')] \, dY(p''), \qquad (8.36)$$

where $S(p)$ is defined on the same measure-space Ω as the $Y(.)$ and independent of the $\{Y(p)\}$-process. The solution of (8.36) is unique, that is, if the (diffusion) coefficients m and s^2, on the one hand, and $S(p)$ and $Y(p')$, on the other hand, are specified, then any two $\{S(p')\}$-processes obtained from (8.36) are equivalent:

$$\Pr[S_1(p', \omega) = S_2(p', \omega), p' \in \mathscr{P}] = 1.$$

The transition probability function[2] is uniquely determinable from $m(., .)$ and $s(., .)$; indeed, one may take

$$P(p, \xi; p', \mathscr{A}) = \Pr[S(p') \in \mathscr{A} \mid S(p) = \xi]$$

with a corresponding evaluation of $P(p'', \xi; p, \mathscr{A})$ by means of a solution of (8.36) in the interval $\mathscr{P} \cap [p'', \infty]$.

---

[2] Given a Markov process $\{S(p), p \in \mathscr{P}\}$ with state space the closed set $\mathscr{C}$, there is a function P, with arguments $p' \in \mathscr{P}, p \in \mathscr{P}$,

$$\Pr[S_\omega(p') \in \mathscr{A} \mid S_\omega(p) = \xi] = P(p, p', \xi, \mathscr{A}) \text{ a. e.}$$

The following hypotheses are made about the $P(.)$ function:

1. For each given p, p', ξ the function $P(p, p', \xi, .)$ is a probability measure, and for each given p, p' and $\mathscr{A}$, the function $P(p, p', ., \mathscr{A})$ is a Baire function.

2. $P(p, p', \xi,) = \begin{cases} 1, & \text{if } \xi \in \mathscr{A}, \\ 0, & \text{otherwise.} \end{cases}$

3. $P(p, p'', \xi, \mathscr{A}) = \int_\delta P(p, p', \xi, d\eta) P(p', p'', \eta, \mathscr{A}), p \leq p' \leq p''.$

3.2 It should be observed that the conditions (8.35) imply the following bounds on the conditional probabilities and moments of the $\{S(p)\}$-process:

$$\Pr\left[\max_{p \le u \le p+h} |S_\omega(u) - \xi| \,|\, S(p) = \xi\right] \le (1 + \xi^2)^{3/2}\, 0(h\sqrt{h})^3$$

$$E[S_\omega(p + h) - \xi \,|\, S(p) = \xi] = \int_p^{p+h} m(p', \xi)\, dp' + \sqrt{1 + \xi^2}\, 0(h\sqrt{h})$$

$$E[(S_\omega(p + h) - \xi)^2 \,|\, S(p) = \xi] = \int_p^{p+h} s^2(p', \xi)\, dp' + (1 + \xi^2)\, 0(h\sqrt{h}$$

$$(8.37)$$

where each $0(.)$ is uniform in ξ and p (p in a compact subset of $\mathscr{P}$). The evaluations (8.37) bring out the significance of the coefficients m and s^2 as the *differential increments of the mean and variance*. In the derivations of Sections 1 and 2, however, the argument was reversed and attention was focused on

$$\lim_{h \to 0}\left[E\, \frac{[S(p + h) - \xi]^2}{h}\,\bigg|\, S(p) = \xi\right] ;$$

it was maintained that if these limits did exist as $m[p, S(p)]$ and $s^2[p, S(p)]$ then one could construct a Markov process with the aid of (8.12).

3.3 The net profits $\Pi[S(p)]$ of the firm constitute an important class of functions of the stochastic sales process. Thus, it is of considerable practical importance to search for conditions that may ensure some interesting probabilistic properties of $\Pi[S(p)]$. From the economists' viewpont, the following question is of some interest under oligopolistic conditions: Under what circumstances can the firm expect its predicted profits for the next period to be almost always equal to the current periods' profits? *When are anticipations perfectly realized?* Let $\{\prod_p, p \in \mathscr{P}\}$ be the stochastic process representing profits due to a price set at p; let $E[|\prod_p|] < \infty$, and let $p_1 < p_2 < \cdots < p_{n+1}$. Then the question may be formulated as follows: For what class of functions $\Pi(.)$ is it true that

$$E[\prod_{p_{n+1}} |\, \prod_{p_1}, \prod_{p_2}, \ldots, \prod_{p_n}] = \prod_{p_n}$$

with probability one? This, again, is equivalent to asking for conditions on the function $\Pi[S(p)]$ that will make Π a *martingale*. For the special case in which the $\{S(p), p \in \mathscr{P}\}$ process is generated as a solution of (8.35) and (8.36) Doob [20, Th. 8.2] has shown that if (a) $\Pi'(.)$ and

---

[3] The notation $g(x) = 0[f(x)]$ means that $|g(x)| < kf(x)$ whenever x is sufficiently close to a given limit.

$\Pi''(.)$ are continuous, if (b) $\Pi(.)$ satisfies the differential equation

$$\frac{s^2}{2} \frac{d^2\Pi}{d\xi^2} + m \frac{d\Pi}{d\xi} = 0, \tag{8.38}$$

and if (c) $\Pi(.)$ is continuous on the state space of the $\{S(p)\}$-process, then $\{\Pi[S(p)]\}$ is a martingale. Unfortunately, Eq. (8.38), which implies that

$$\frac{s^2}{2} \frac{d\Pi}{d\xi} + m\Pi = \text{constant},$$

does not appear to have a simple realistic intepretation in terms of the revenue and cost function.

4. AN APPLICATION: ANALYSIS OF PRICE RIGIDITY

The purpose of this section is to apply the model of sales transition probabilities to the pricing decision in a firm in undifferentiated oligopoly. For any period of customer inquiries the decision problem is one of raising, reducing, or holding constant, whatever price was quoted in the previous period. As may well be anticipated, the analysis must rest upon specific assumptions about the behavior of the total cost function. For the sake of definiteness, it will be assumed that the total cost function $C(x)$ has the following property:

$$\frac{dC}{dx} > 0, \qquad 0 < x < \infty, \qquad (x = \text{output}).$$

It will be seen that under this assumption the model can explain the phenomenon of price rigidity in an oligopoly in which the firms optimize expected long-run net profits.

4.1 Consider, first, the situation in which there is a proposal to raise the price from p to $p + z$ $(z > 0)$. Then, the appropriate probability density of transition, $d_\eta P(p, \xi; p + z, \eta)$ is given by (8.15). Also, the net profits associated with the sale of $S(p + z) \equiv \eta$ units is $(p + z)\eta - C(\eta)$. On the other hand, starting with η and following an optimal policy in all the subsequent periods of contact, the *maximum total discounted future profits* is given by a procedure due to Bellman [6]. This is computed as $A(\lambda, z)$, or $A(z)$:

$$A(z) \equiv (p + z)[\xi + \lambda + J_1] - C(\xi + \lambda + J_1) + kf(\xi + \lambda + J_1), \tag{8.39}$$

where k $(0 < k < 1)$ is a discount factor and $\lambda = \eta - \xi - J_1$. Since $A(z)$ is a random variable, we consider its mathematical expectation,

$$E[A(z)] = \int_{-\infty}^{\infty} e^{-\lambda^2/2\Delta_1} A(z) \frac{d\lambda}{\sqrt{2\pi \Delta_1}} \tag{8.40}$$

For the case in which the price is proposed to be reduced from p to $p - y$, one may similarly define $B(\lambda, y)$ or $B(y)$:

$$B(y) \equiv (p - y)[\xi + \lambda + J_2] - C(\xi + \lambda + J_2) + kf(\xi + \lambda + J_2), \quad (8.41)$$

and consider its mathematical expectation,

$$E[B(y)] = \int_{-\infty}^{\infty} e^{-\lambda^2/2\Delta_2}\, B(y)\, \frac{d\lambda}{\sqrt{2\pi\,\Delta_2}}. \quad (8.42)$$

The solution to the problem of price decision is therefore the solution of the following functional equation of dynamic programming:

$$F(\xi) = \sup \begin{cases} \text{policy } A: \ \max_{z \geq 0} E[A(z)], \\[2mm] \text{policy } B; \ \max_{y \geq 0} E[B(y)], \end{cases} \quad (8.43)$$

$F(\xi)$ being the maximum total expected discounted future profits, due to an optimal policy, given that $\xi\ [= S(p)]$ is the sale due to the price quoted in the previous period. But from (8.11) it may be recalled that in the event of a "zero change," the probability mass is concentrated at ξ. Thus, $F(\xi)$ is *not less than* the total expected discounted future profits due to a policy of (a) not changing the price asked in the current period and (b) following an optimal policy in the future periods. That is,

$$F(\xi) \geq \xi p - C(\xi) + kF(\xi) \to F(\xi) \geq \frac{1}{1 - k}\,[\xi p - C(\xi)]. \quad (8.44)$$

Now, introduce the following notation:

$$\begin{aligned} \Psi_1(\lambda) &= (\sqrt{2\pi\,\Delta_1})^{-1} e^{-\lambda^2/2\Delta_1}, & \Psi_2(\lambda) &= (\sqrt{2\pi\,\Delta_2})^{-1} e^{-\lambda^2/2\Delta_2} \\ U(\lambda, z) &= \xi + \lambda + J_1, & V(\lambda, y) &= \xi + \lambda + J_2. \end{aligned} \quad (8.45)$$

In this notation the inequality (8.44) leads to the following bounds for the optimal returns $F_A(\xi)$ and $F_B(\xi)$ from the policies A and B, respectively:

$$F_A(\xi) = \max_{z \geq 0} \int_{-\infty}^{\infty} \Psi_1(\lambda)\{U(\lambda, z)(p + z) - C[U(\lambda, z)] + kf[U(\lambda, z)]\}\, d\lambda \quad (8.46)$$

$$\geq \frac{1}{1 - k} \max_{z \geq 0} \int_{-\infty}^{\infty} \Psi_1(\lambda)\{(p + z)U(\lambda, z) - C[U(\lambda, z)]\}\, d\lambda$$

and, similarly, for the policy of price reduction,

$$F_B(\xi) \geq \frac{1}{1 - k} \max_{y \geq 0} \int_{-\infty}^{\infty} \Psi_2(\lambda)\{(p - y)V(\lambda, y) - C[V(\lambda, y)]\}\, d\lambda. \quad (8.47)$$

Note that z^*, the optimum increase in price, can be positive only for ξ exceeding *some critical level;* otherwise, $z^* = 0$. A similar remark also applies to y^*, the optimal reduction in price. We may interpret this formal result to mean that *the firm will not have any inducement to change the price unless the sales due to the existing policy are in some sense "adequate."* Precise definition of adequacy is taken up in Chapter 9.

4.2 But the fact that there are such critical levels has certain implications in regard to price rigidity. To facilitate the discussion, suppose that the cost function is linear and that the mean values and variances of the $dS(p)$ process are constant:

$$C(x) = \alpha + \beta x, \qquad \Phi_1(p) = -a_1, \qquad \Phi_2(p) = a_2,$$
$$s_1(p) = b_1, \qquad s_2(p) = b_2.$$

Consequently, one has the following determinations of Δ_i, $U(.)$, and $V(.)$

$$\Delta_1 = \int_p^{p+z} b_1{}^2 \, du = b_1{}^2 z, \qquad\qquad \Delta_2 = \int_{p-y}^p b_2{}^2 \, du = b_2{}^2 y,$$

$$U(\lambda, z) = \xi + \lambda - a_1 z, \qquad V(\lambda, y) = \xi + \lambda + a_2 y,$$

which lead to the following special form of the inequalities (8.46) and (8.47):

$$F_A(\xi) \geq \max_{z \geq 0} \frac{1}{1-k} [(\xi - a_1 z)(p+z) - \alpha - \beta(\xi - a_1 z)], \qquad (8.48)$$

$$F_B(\xi) \geq \max_{y \geq 0} \frac{1}{1-k} [(\xi + a_2 y)(p-y) - \alpha - \beta(\xi + a_2 y)]. \qquad (8.49)$$

The right members of these expressions give the optimal *unconstrained* z and y

$$z^* = \frac{1}{2a_1} [\xi - a_1(p - \beta)], \qquad y^* = \frac{1}{2a_2} [a_2(p - \beta) - \xi],$$

and the nonnegativity constraints on z^* and y^* imply that

$$\xi \geq a_1(p - \beta); \qquad \xi \leq a_2(p - \beta). \qquad (8.50)$$

Suppose, now, that $a_1 > a_2$, and consider the case in which $p - \beta > 0$; that is, price is greater than marginal cost of production. The optimal policy is *not* to change the current level of quotation if it is found that $a_2(p - \beta) \leq \xi \leq a_1(p - \beta)$. In light of the lower bounds, then, the complete decision rule may be expressed as follows:

$$y^* > 0, \quad \text{if} \quad 0 \leq \xi < a_2(p - \beta),$$
$$z^* = 0, \quad y^* = 0, \quad \text{if} \quad a_2(p - \beta) \leq \xi < a_1(p - \beta), \qquad (8.51)$$
$$z^* > 0, \quad \text{if} \quad \xi \geq a_1(p - \beta).$$

Next, consider the case in which $p - \beta < 0$, so that $a_1(p - \beta) < 0$ and $\xi > a_1(p - \beta)$. This indicates that the optimal policy is to raise the price quotations per unit until $p - \beta$ becomes positive and, from then on, to apply the decision rules (8.51). Such decision rules indicate the maximization of the long-run expected net profits. Observe that the "kink" in the demand curve is sharper if a_1 is considerably larger than a_2, that is, if the expected loss of sales far exceeds the expected gain in sales. The sharper the kink, the larger the interval: $a_2(p - \beta) \leq \xi < a_1(p - \beta)$. This suggests that *keeping the price unchanged is optimal in a large number of cases*. The greater "resistance to price changes" is thus *derived* as a consequence of the business practice of optimizing expected long-run net profits. These conclusions are not specific to the case of $C(x) = \alpha + \beta x$; they are, in general, true of even quadratic total cost functions.

Chapter 9

PRICES, PRODUCTION, AND INVENTORIES

The purpose of this chapter is to analyze the interdependence of price and production-inventory decisions of a firm in oligopoly. Such interdependence is seen to influence the decision-making of a firm. The principal result indicates the kind of stability that was found in Chapter 8, Section 4.

1. MAXIMIZING SHORT-RUN PROFITS

It was seen in Chapter 8, Section 4, that there might be a tendency toward price rigidity in an undifferentiated oligopoly. While part of this was due to the shape of the cost function, an equally important role was played by the *goal* pursued by the firms, namely, the maximization of expected discounted *long-run* net profits. The task of this section is to examine the consequences of maximizing the expected *short-run*, or single-period, net profits.

1.1 Consider the problem of maximizing the net profits of the current period only. The appropriate expression is obtained by dropping out the term $kf(\xi + \lambda + J_1)$ from $A(z)$ in (8.39); let it be denoted by $A^*(z)$. Then, (8.45) leads to

$$E[A^*(z)] = \int_{-\infty}^{\infty} \{(p + z)U(\lambda, z) - C[U(\lambda, z)]\}\Psi_1(\lambda)\, d\lambda$$

for the expected single-period net profits if the price were to be raised in the current period from p to $p + z$. Similarly, if the price were to be reduced to $p - y$, the expected net profits would be

$$E[B^*(y)] = \int_{-\infty}^{\infty} \{(p - y)\, V(\lambda, y) - C[V(\lambda, y)]\}\, \Psi_2(\lambda)\, d\lambda.$$

99

Therefore the optimization of single-period or immediate expected net profits would call for a price that would secure

$$\sup \left[\max_{z \geq 0} E[A^*(z)]; \quad \max_{y \geq 0} E[B^*(y)] \right].$$

From the development of Chapter 8, Section 4, it may be seen that except for a multiplicative constant of $1/(1 - k)]$, the lower bounds of $E[A(z)]$ and $E[B(y)]$ are equal to $E[A^*(z)]$ and $E[B^*(y)]$, respectively. That is to say, the *price policies that attempt to optimize the short-run expected net profits have the same structure as those that attempt to optimize the long-term expected net profits.* If the lower bounds in (8.44) could be sharpened, stronger statements could be made about the pricing policy that would maximize the long-run performance. On the other hand, it should be noted that the *pricing strategies that follow from a short-run optimization are optimal in any event*; they cannot be improved further. Thus a firm that follows such strategies will do best in the short run and will not be worse off in the long run.

2. THE STRUCTURE OF DECISION PROBLEM

The applications of the "static" models in Chapter 7 were primarily concerned with situations in which the unit of the product was produced on order. When the product is mass-produced on standard specifications and especially when the unit is relatively inexpensive, it is a common experience that delivery must be instantaneous, otherwise a unit of demand is very likely to be diverted to one of the rival firms. Thus, in addition to managing the price, there is need to manage production and inventories. The principal result of this section may be summed up as follows: the optimal amount and direction of price adjustment depend on (a) the sales S_0 of the immediately past period, (b) the inventory $I \geq 0$ on hand at the beginning of the "current" period, and (c) the price p quoted in the previous period. This is derived from a policy of optimizing the single-period or immediate net profits. The development rests upon two assumptions: first, that the effects of the current decision to set the inventory at some level will materialize in the current period; second, that production does not take a long time.

2.1 Let $q(\geq 0)$ denote the production quantity and I the initial inventory. Then, under the assumptions introduced above, $I \geq 0$, and the current availability is $z = q + I \geq 0$. The total demand η during the current period[1] may exceed or fall short of z. If $\eta < z$, the system incurs a holding cost, $h(z - \eta)$, which is a function of the amount that could not be sold; similarly, when $\eta > z$, the system incurs an aggregate shortage cost, $g(\eta - z)$. In general, $h(.)$ and $g(.)$ are monotone nondiminishing in their arguments, and $h(0) = 0 = g(0)$. Let $c(z - I)$ denote the production cost of the output q; this also will be monotone increasing in its argument: $dc/dq > 0$, $0 < q < \infty$. It will be recalled from Chapter 8, Section 1, that the transition probabilities of sales are given by

$$\Pr\left[S(p') \le \eta \mid S(p) = S_0\right] = \frac{1}{\sqrt{2\pi}} \int_{-\infty}^{\zeta} e^{-\lambda^2/2} \, d\lambda, \quad \text{if } p' > p,$$

$$\Pr\left[S(p'') \le \eta \mid S(p) = S_0\right] = \frac{1}{\sqrt{2\pi}} \int_{-\infty}^{\zeta'} e^{-\lambda^2/2} \, d\lambda, \quad \text{if } p'' < p, \tag{9.1}$$

where ζ and ζ' are normalized quantities defined as follows:

$$\zeta \equiv \frac{1}{\sqrt{\Delta}}\left[\eta - S_0 - \int_{p}^{p'} \Phi_1(\theta) \, d\theta\right], \qquad \zeta' \equiv \frac{1}{\sqrt{\Delta'}}\left[\eta - S_0 - \int_{p''}^{p} \Phi_2(\theta) \, d\theta\right],$$

$$\Delta \equiv \int_{p}^{p'} \sigma_1^2(\theta) \, d\theta, \qquad\qquad \Delta' \equiv \int_{p''}^{p} \sigma_2^2(\theta) \, d\theta. \tag{9.2}$$

Suppose, now, that the price were to be *raised* from p to $p + y$, $y > 0$. Two possible situations are to be taken into account: (a) $\eta \le z$, so that the net profits for the current period are $(p + y)\eta - h(z - \eta) - c(z - I)$; (b) $\eta \ge z$ and, therefore, the net profits for the current period are $(p + y)z - g(\eta - z) - c(z - I)$. Therefore, the expected single-period net profits are $N_1(y, z)$:

$$N_1(y, z) = \frac{1}{\sqrt{2\pi}} \int_{-\infty}^{z} [(p + y)\eta - h(z - \eta) - c(z - I)]e^{-\zeta^2/2} \, d\zeta$$

$$+ \frac{1}{\sqrt{2\pi}} \int_{z}^{\infty} [(p + y)z - g(\eta - z) - c(z - I)]e^{-\xi^2/2} \, d\eta,$$

where ζ is defined as in (9.2). Let

$$\xi = \frac{1}{\sqrt{\Delta}}\left[z - S_0 - \int_{p}^{p+y} \Phi_1(\theta) \, d\theta\right], \qquad u(\lambda, y) =$$

$$S_0 + \lambda\sqrt{\Delta} + \int_{p}^{p+y} \Phi_1(\theta) \, d\theta;$$

---

[1] On account of the assumption that a demand is lost for good if it is not satisfied out of the inventory on hand, a distinction has to be drawn between "sale" and "demand" during a period. In other words, "demand" during a period is the larger of (a) the actual sales *plus* the sales that could be made if there were sufficient inventory on hand and (b) the actual sales.

then, the expression for expected single-period net profits may be written as

$$N_1(y, z) = \frac{1}{\sqrt{2\pi}} \int_{-\infty}^{\xi} [(p + y)u(\lambda, y) - h(z - u(\lambda, y))]e^{-\lambda^2/2} \, d\lambda$$

$$+ \frac{1}{\sqrt{2\pi}} \int_{\xi}^{\infty} \{(p + y)z - g[u(\lambda, y) - z]\}e^{-\lambda^2/2} \, d\lambda \qquad (9.3)$$

$$- c(z - I),$$

Suppose, next, that the price were to be *lowered* from p to $p - x$, $x > 0$. It may be verified that the expected single-period net profits would be $N_2(x, z)$:

$$N_2(x, z) = \frac{1}{\sqrt{2\pi}} \int_{-\infty}^{\xi'} \{(p - x)v(\lambda, x) - h[z - v(\lambda, x)]\}e^{-\lambda^2/2} \, d\lambda$$

$$(9.4)$$

$$+ \frac{1}{\sqrt{2\pi}} \int_{\xi'}^{\infty} \{(p - x)z - g[v(\lambda, x) - z]\}e^{-\lambda^2/2} \, d\lambda - c(z - I),$$

with ξ' and $v(\lambda, x)$ defined as

$$\xi' = \frac{1}{\sqrt{\Delta'}}\left[z - S_0 - \int_{p-x}^{p} \Phi_2(\theta) \, d\theta\right], \qquad v(\lambda, x) = S_0 + \lambda\sqrt{\Delta'}$$

$$+ \int_{p-x}^{p} \Phi_2(\theta) \, d\theta.$$

Note that the holding costs $h[z - u(\lambda, y)]$ and $h[z - v(\lambda, x)]$ associated with a change in price and the shortage costs $g[u(\lambda, y) - z]$ and $g[v(\lambda, x) - z]$ due to a change in price explicitly depend on two decision variables; the current availability z and the variation $+y$ or $-x$ in price. The dependence on the price variations is traceable to the fact that the probability of transition of sales from S_0 has been represented to be dependent upon the amount and direction of the change in price. Finally, suppose that the price were to remain *unchanged*. Then the expected single-period net profits would be

$$F_1(z) = pS_0 - h(z - S_0) - c(z - I) \quad \text{if} \quad z > S_0,$$

$$(9.5)$$

$$F_2(z) = pz - g(S_0 - z) - c(z - I) \quad \text{if} \quad z < S_0.$$

To sum up: the price and production strategy is to be chosen so as to secure

$$H(S_0, I) = \sup \begin{cases} \text{policy } A: \max_{z \geq I, y \geq 0} N_1(y, z) \\ \text{policy } B: \max_{z \geq I, x \geq 0} N_2(x, z) \\ \text{policy } C: \sup_{z \geq I} \{F_1(z), F_2(z)\} \end{cases} \tag{9.6}$$

Note that as $x \to 0$ or $y \to 0$, the policy B or A tends to the policy C.

3. THE STRUCTURE OF OPTIMAL DECISION RULE: UNDIFFERENTIATED OLIGOPOLY

In light of the foregoing derivations, it would appear that the problem of determining optimal strategies is essentially one of empirical determination of the functions (9-3) to (9-5), followed by an appropriate optimization procedure. In a *given* empirical setting this is undoubtedly the only course open to the analyst. However, in the present section, an attempt will be made to explore some *qualitative properties* of the optimal decision rule. Since a great deal depends upon the cost functions $c(.)$, $h(.)$ and $g(.)$, the discussion will be restricted to the following: (a) the marginal costs of holding and shortage are constant, (b) there are fixed costs of production, and the marginal cost of production is a constant, and (c) the parameters defining the transition probabilities are constant:

$$\Phi_1(\theta) = -a_1, \qquad \Phi_2(\theta) = a_2, \qquad \sigma_1(\theta) = b_1, \qquad \sigma_2(\theta) = b_2,$$
$$(a_i > 0, b_i > 0).$$

3.1 Consider, first, the strategy "A," namely, the decision to raise the price. On account of the assumptions introduced above, it is seen that

$$h[z - u(\lambda, y)] = hz - hu(\lambda, y), \qquad g[u(\lambda, y) - z] = gu(\lambda, y) - gz, \tag{9.7}$$

$$u(\lambda, y) = S_0 + \lambda b_1\sqrt{y} - a_1 y, \qquad \xi = \frac{z - S_0 + a_1 y}{b_1\sqrt{y}}$$

where h, g, α and β are all positive. Substituting these in (9-3), $N_1(y, z)$ is determined as

$$N_1(y, z) = \int_{-\infty}^{\xi} [(p + y)u(\lambda, y) - hz + hu(\lambda, y)]e^{-\lambda^2/2}\frac{d\lambda}{\sqrt{2\pi}}$$

$$+ \int_{\xi}^{\infty} [(p + y)z - gu(\lambda, y) + gz]e^{-\lambda^2/2}\frac{d\lambda}{\sqrt{2\pi}} - \alpha - (z - I)\beta.$$

Defining

$$F(\xi) \equiv \int_{-\infty}^{\xi} e^{-\lambda^2/2} \frac{d\lambda}{\sqrt{2\pi}}$$

and partially differentiating $N_1(y, z)$ with respect to its arguments,

$$\frac{\partial N_1}{\partial y} = [S_0 - a_1(2y + p + h + g)_{-z}]F(\xi) + (z + a_1 g)$$

$$- \frac{b_1}{2\sqrt{2\pi y}}(p + h + g + 3y)e^{-\xi^2/2}, \quad (9.8)$$

$$\frac{\partial N_1}{\partial z} = -(h + p + y + g)F(\xi) + (p + y + g) - \beta.$$

From here on, the analysis will rest upon a thorough examination of the signs of these derivatives at the corner points, that is, of the quantities,

$$\left(\frac{\partial N_1}{\partial y}\right)_{y=0, z=I} \quad \text{and} \quad \left(\frac{\partial N_1}{\partial z}\right)_{y=0, z=I}.$$

To simplify the notation $(\xi)_{z=I}$ is denoted by ξ^* and $[F(\xi)]_{z=I}$ is denoted by $F(\xi^*)$.

3.2 Suppose that $S_0 > I$. Because

$$\lim_{y \to 0} F(\xi^*) = 0 \quad \text{and} \quad \lim_{y \to 0} \frac{1}{\sqrt{y}} \exp\left[-\frac{(\xi^*)^2}{2}\right] = 0,$$

it may be seen that

$$\left(\frac{\partial N_1}{\partial y}\right)_{y=0, z=I} = I + a_1 g; \quad \left(\frac{\partial N_1}{\partial z}\right)_{y=0, z=I} = p + g - \beta. \quad (9.9)$$

The first of these partial derivatives is *always positive* because $I \geq 0$, $a_1 > 0$, and $g > 0$. In regard to the second expression in (9.9), one must recognize two distinct situations:(a) $p + g > \beta$. In this case $(\partial N_1/\partial z)_{y=0, z=I}$ is strictly positive. Hence the solutions y^* and z^* of the first order conditions of optimum (that is, of the equations $\partial N_1/\partial y = 0$, $\partial N_1/\partial z = 0$) will have the following property:

$$y^* > 0, \quad z^* > I.$$

(b) $p + g \leq \beta$: In this case, $(\partial N_1/\partial z)_{y=0, z=I} \leq 0$. Suppose, now, that y^* and z^* are the solutions of the first order conditions of optimum, without regard to the constraints; also, let $N_1(y^*, z^*) = N_1^*$. If $z^* < I$, then such a solution is to be discarded; otherwise, if $z^* \geq I$, the solution is accepted. Next suppose that $dN_1(y, I)\, dy = 0$ is solved for y, and let the local optimum of $N_1(y, I)$ be denoted by $N_1{}^{**}$. Then the constrained optimal solution is given by the (y, z)-pair that secures the sup $[N_1{}^*, N_1{}^{**}]$.

Next, consider the situation in which $S_0 < I$. It may be seen that

$$\lim_{y \to 0} F(\xi^*) = \lim_{y \to 0} \int_{-\infty}^{\xi^*} e^{-\lambda^2/2}\, \frac{d\lambda}{\sqrt{2\pi}} = 1,$$

and that

$$\lim_{y \to 0} \frac{1}{\sqrt{y}} \exp\left[-\frac{(\xi^*)^2}{2}\right] = 0.$$

Hence, the partial derivatives have the following values at the corner points:

$$\left(\frac{\partial N_1}{\partial y}\right)_{y=0,\,z=I} = S_0 - a_1(p + h); \qquad \left(\frac{\partial N_1}{\partial z}\right)_{y=0,\,z=I} = -(h + \beta). \quad (9.10)$$

Since both h and β are positive, the second one of these derivatives is always negative. With regard to the sign of $(\partial N_1/\partial y)_{y=0,\,z=I}$, however, one should consider two possible situations: (c) $I > S_0 > a_1(p + h)$, so that the derivative in question is positive; the technique of analysis is the same as in the case a above. (d) $a_1(p + h) > I$, in which the event (that is, with $S_0 < I$ also) raising price under *no* circumstance can be an optimal policy.

Finally, consider the case in which $S_0 = I$. Here, by setting $z = I + \delta$, $\delta > 0$, it may be seen that one obtains a solution similar to the one obtained for $S_0 < I$.

3.3   With the strategy B (reducing the price for the current period), the criterion of performance is the expression $N_2(x, z)$ of (9-4). Employing the simplified forms for $\Phi_2(.)$ and $\sigma_2(.)$, it is found that

$$N_2(x, z) = \int_{-\infty}^{\xi'} \{(p - x)\, v(x, \lambda) - h[z - v(\lambda, x)]\} e^{-\lambda^2/2}\, \frac{d\lambda}{\sqrt{2\pi}}$$

$$+ \int_{\xi'}^{\infty} \{(p - x)z - g[v(\lambda, x) - z]\} e^{-\lambda^2/2}\, \frac{d\lambda}{\sqrt{2\pi}} - \alpha - (z - I)\beta,$$

with ξ' and $v(\lambda, x)$ defined as

$$\xi' = \frac{1}{b_2\sqrt{x}} [z - S_0 - a_2 x], \qquad v(\lambda, x) = S_0 + \lambda b_2 \sqrt{x} + a_2 x.$$

$$F(\xi') \equiv \int_{-\infty}^{\xi'} e^{-\lambda^2/2}\, \frac{d\lambda}{\sqrt{2\pi}} ;$$

then the partial derivatives of $N_2(x, z)$ may be written as follows:

$$\frac{\partial N_2}{\partial x} = [z - S_0 + a_2(h + g + p - 2x)]F(\xi')$$

$$-(z + a_2 g) - \frac{b_2}{2\sqrt{2\pi x}}(h + g + p - 3x)\exp\left[\frac{-(\xi')^2}{2}\right], \quad (9.11)$$

$$\frac{\partial N_2}{\partial z} = -(h + g + p - x)F(\xi') + (g + p - x) - \beta.$$

Again, as in the preceding paragraph, the analysis will be carried out on the basis of the signs of these partial derivatives at the corner points $(x = 0, z = I)$. For the sake of shorter notation, let $[\xi']_{z=I} = \bar{\xi}$, and $[F(\xi')]_{z=I} = F(\bar{\xi})$.

3.4.1 First suppose that $S_0 > I$. For this case, it is easily verified that

$$\lim_{x \to 0} F(\bar{\xi}) = 0 \quad \text{and} \quad \lim_{x \to 0} \frac{1}{\sqrt{x}}\exp\left[\frac{-(\bar{\xi})^2}{2}\right] = 0$$

and, therefore, at $y = 0$ and $z = I$ the partial derivatives (9.11) have the following values:

$$\left(\frac{\partial N_2}{\partial x}\right)_{x=0, z=I} = -I - a_2 g; \qquad \left(\frac{\partial N_2}{\partial z}\right)_{x=0, z=I} = p + g - \beta.$$

The first of these quantities is always negative because $I \geq 0$ and a_2 and g are positive (by assumption). In regard to the sign of $\partial N_2/\partial z$, two possible situations should be distinguished: (a) $p + g < \beta$. Here $(\partial N_2/\partial z)_{x=0\ z=I}$ is negative, which means that the reduction of price is *not* an optimal or even a desirable course of action when $S_0 > I$ and $p + g < \beta$. (b) $p + g > \beta$. In this case, $(\partial N_2/\partial z)_{x=0\ z=I}$ is positive. The situation in which $S_0 > I$ *and* $p + g > \beta$ is the same as the one considered in the previous paragraph under (a); that is to say, the optimal strategy is to raise the price.

Next, suppose that $S_0 < I$. Here, it may be seen that

$$\lim_{x \to 0} F(\bar{\xi}) = I, \quad \text{and} \quad \lim_{x \to 0} \frac{1}{\sqrt{x}}\exp\left[\frac{-(\bar{\xi})^2}{2}\right] = 0.$$

Consequently, the value of the partial derivatives at the corner points are

$$\left(\frac{\partial N_2}{\partial z}\right)_{x=0, z=I} = -(h + \beta); \qquad \left(\frac{\partial N_2}{\partial x}\right)_{x=0, z=I} = -S_0 + a_2(p + h). \quad (9.12)$$

On account of the assumptions introduced earlier, the first of these two quantities is negative. In order to examine the sign of the second, we distinguish the following cases: (c) $a_2(p + h) > I$. Here $S_0 < I$ implies that $S_0 < a_2(p + h)$. The method of analysis is to compare the values of $N_2(x, z)$ in a manner indicated in (b) of the preceding discussion of the strategy A. (d) $a_2(p + h) < I$. In this case, the previous results hold, provided that the sales of the previous period are such that $S_0 < (p + h)a_2$. (e) $a_2 > a_1$, $a_2(p + h)$ and $a_1(p + h)$ are each less than I, and $a_2(p + h) > S_0 > a_1(p + h)$. In this case, a further comparison with case (c) of strategy A is required to determine the optimal policy.

3.4.2 The analysis of this section may be conveniently summed up in the following diagram indicating the optimality of various policies in the regions in the space of values of (a) the sales S_0 of the immediately preceding period and (b) the inventory I on hand at the beginning of the current of decision period—in which one or the other policy would be optimal. The precise *level* of the price to set is, of course, to be numerically computed from the equations developed in this section.

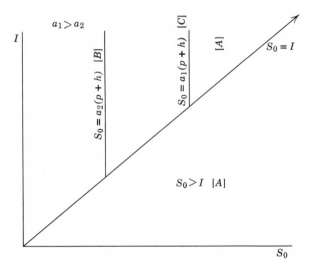

It will be fruitful, once more, to recall from Chapter 8, Section 3.2 the issue of "price rigidity." Economists have maintained that "resistance to price alteration" derives from oligopolistic market position and is reflected in the phenomenon of "rigid prices." They also maintain that such rigidity would not exist if the sellers were not oligopolistics. This is explained by the "kinked demand" theory of oligopoly:

"The difference in the response which an oligopolist may expect on the part of his rivals to his price cuts, on the one hand, and his price boosts, on the other, will be reflected in the demand curve depicting the expected sales at various prices. If the seller's price reductions are limited by his rivals, but his price increases are not, his price increases would lose him much more business than his price reductions would gain him . . . . In other words . . . the demand curve has a kink at the current price. The sharper the kink . . . the greater will be the resistence to a price change, even in the face of important changes in the conditions confronting the seller" (Machlup [40]).

Indeed, *probabilistic* counterparts of kinked demand curves have already been presented in Chapter 8, Section 1, where we characterized the probability distribution of changes of a firm's sale under the impact of a price variation. The *expected rate of change* in sales due to an increase of price was allowed to be different from that due to a reduction of price; consequently, the *expected change in* the level of sales was allowed to be different under the policies of raising and lowering the price.

4. STRUCTURE OF OPTIMAL DECISIONS: DIFFERENTIATED OLIGOPOLY

The analysis resembles that of an undifferentiated oligopoly. There is, however, a special feature: In addition to having a "kink" with respect to the price charged by it, the firm may experience a kink—perhaps of a different kind and amount—with respect to selling expenses. The analysis attempts to characterize the situations in which the latter kink may tend to disappear. Contrary to the classical treatment, it will be assumed that there is no entry into the group or, which amounts to the same thing, there is a high risk associated with entry.

The purpose of this section is twofold. It attempts to show how the various strategies (and there are nine of them) become eligible at various levels of the sales scored in the previous period. Also, two specific issues are considered. (a) Supposing that *one* of the two decision variables— price and selling expenses—were to be set at some arbitrary level; what happens to the probability of holding sales in a specified interval or band? (b) Under what conditions can one expect a "rigidity" in price or selling expenses? The fact that a large number of strategies is available for consideration imposes limitations on the depth in which the analysis can be carried out. Two assumptions therefore are introduced with a view toward simplifying the illustrative computations:

A:1 The total cost function is of the form $K(S) = A + BS$, in which A and B are positive constants.

A:2 The limiting first and second conditional moment functions are independent of the levels of price and selling expenses of the firm.

It is important to observe, however, that the assumption A:2 makes the underlying situation take on *some* of the broad features of what Chamberlin has called the "large group" case.

A full list of strategies and the associated parameters are presented in Table 9.1.

TABLE 9.1
STRATEGIES AND PARAMETERS

Strategy $\sum_i$	Δp	Δc	$m_{1i}[p]$	$m_{2i}[c]$	$\sigma_{1i}[p]$	$\sigma_{2i}[c]$
$\sum_1$	$-h$	$-k$	m_{11}	$-m_{21}$	s_{11}	s_{21}
$\sum_2$	0	$-k$	0	$-m_{22}$	0	s_{22}
$\sum_3$	$+h$	$-k$	$-m_{13}$	$-m_{23}$	s_{13}	s_{23}
$\sum_4$	$-h$	0	m_{14}	0	s_{14}	0
$\sum_5$	0	0	0	0	0	0
$\sum_6$	$+h$	0	$-m_{16}$	0	s_{16}	0
$\sum_7$	$-h$	$+k$	m_{17}	m_{27}	s_{17}	s_{27}
$\sum_8$	0	$+k$	0	m_{28}	0	s_{28}
$\sum_9$	$+h$	$+k$	$-m_{19}$	m_{29}	s_{19}	s_{29}

4.1 Assuming that production is made strictly on order, the (random) net profits from the sales of the current period are

$$\pi(\eta) = (p - c)\eta - K(\eta).$$

The probability of achieving sales η is conditional upon the sales S_0 of the immediately past period and is a function of the variations h and/or k. As in Chapter 8, Section 4, the principal interest lies in the discounted future net profits, commencing with η and following an optimal policy from then on. Thus, let

$$F_i(S_0, h, k) = \text{total discounted net profits due to the}$$
$$i\text{th strategy } \sum_i, i = 1, \ldots, 9;$$

its mathematical expectation is

$$E[F_i(S_0, h, k)] = \int_{-\infty}^{\infty} [(p + h - c - k)\eta - K(\eta)]e^{-w^2/2\Delta_i} \frac{dw}{\sqrt{2\pi \Delta_i}}$$
$$+ \alpha \int_{-\infty}^{\infty} J(\eta)e^{-w^2/2\Delta_i} \frac{dw}{\sqrt{2\pi \Delta_i}},$$

(9.13)

where $J(\eta)$ is the *maximum* expected total discounted future profits due to an initial sales position η and α is a discount factor ($0 < \alpha < 1$). Following the dynamic programming formulation of Section 2 above, we write

$$J(S_0) = \sup_i \left[(i): \max_{h \geq 0, k \geq 0} E[F_i(S_0, h, k)] \right]$$
$$\equiv \sup_i [E_i^*(S_0)]. \tag{9.14}$$

It was seen, however, that in the "no change" situation ($h = 0$, $k = 0$) the probability mass of the conditional distribution of η becomes concentrated at S_0. This means that $E_i^*(S_0) \geq (p - c)S_0 - K(S_0) + \alpha E_i^*(S_0)$, that is,

$$E_i^*(S_0) \geq \frac{1}{1 - \alpha} \pi(S_0).$$

Thus, for instance, we would have for the strategy Σ_9:

$$E_9^*(S_0) = \max_{h \geq 0 \; k \geq 0} \int_{-\infty}^{\infty} [(p + h - c - k)\Phi_9 - K(\Phi_9) + \alpha J(\Phi_9)]$$
$$\times e^{-w^2/2\Delta_9} \frac{dw}{\sqrt{2\pi \Delta}}$$

and it has the lower bound given by

$$E_9^*(S_0) \geq \frac{1}{1 - \alpha} \max_{h \geq 0, k \geq 0} \int_{-\infty}^{\infty} [(p + h - c - k)\Phi_9 - K(\Phi_9)]$$
$$\times e^{-w^2/2\Delta_9} \frac{dw}{\sqrt{2\pi \Delta_9}}. \tag{9.15}$$

Solving for the maximum return, one would obtain the optimal variations h_9^* and k_9^*, optimizing the right member of (9.15). That these magnitudes will be *functions* of S_0 may be seen as follows: Employing the condition that $h_9^* \geq 0$ and $k_9^* \geq 0$, constraints on S_0 would be found such that if S_0 satisfied these constraints, then the use of h_9^* and k_9^* indeed would be indicated. (The unconstrained optimal variations in each of the nine cases are shown in Table 9.2.) The dependence of the *constrained* variations on the S_0 is also not too difficult to demonstrate. Thus, in the case of the strategy Σ_9, for example, we have

$$\bar{h}_9 = (m_{29} - m_{19})^{-1}[S_0 - (p - c - B)m_{29}] \geq 0$$
$$\bar{k}_9 = (m_{29} - m_{19})^{-1}[-S_0 - (p - c - B)m_{19}] \geq 0.$$

The first of these inequalities implies that

$$\frac{S_0}{m_{29} - m_{19}} \leq \frac{(p - c - B)m_{29}}{m_{19} - m_{29}},$$

TABLE 9.2

UNCONSTRAINED OPTICAL p, c VALUES

Strategy Σ_i	Δp	Δc	h_i	k_i
Σ_1	$-h$	$-k$	$\dfrac{S_0}{m_{21}-m_{11}}+(p-c-B)\dfrac{m_{21}}{m_{21}-m_{11}}$	$\dfrac{S_0}{m_{21}-m_{11}}+(p-c-B)\dfrac{m_{11}}{m_{21}-m_{11}}$
Σ_2	0	$-k$	——	$\dfrac{S_0}{2m_{22}}-\tfrac{1}{2}(p-c-B)$
Σ_3	$+h$	$-k$	$\dfrac{S_0}{m_{23}-m_{13}}+(p-c-B)\dfrac{m_{23}}{m_{23}-m_{13}}$	$\dfrac{S_0}{m_{23}-m_{13}}+(p-c-B)\dfrac{m_{13}}{m_{23}-m_{13}}$
Σ_4	$-h$	0	$\dfrac{-S_0}{2 \cdot m_{14}}+\tfrac{1}{2}(p-c-B)$	——
Σ_5	0	0	——	——
Σ_6	$+h$	0	$\dfrac{S_0}{2 \cdot m_{16}}-\tfrac{1}{2}(p-c-B)$	——
Σ_7	$-h$	k	$\dfrac{S_0}{m_{27}-m_{17}}+(p-c-B)\dfrac{m_{27}}{m_{27}-m_{17}}$	$\dfrac{-S_0}{m_{27}-m_{17}}-(p-c-B)\dfrac{m_{17}}{m_{27}-m_{17}}$
Σ_8	0	k	——	$\dfrac{-S_0}{m_{28}}+\tfrac{1}{2}(p-c-B)$
Σ_9	$+h$	k	$\dfrac{-S_0}{m_{29}-m_{19}}-(p-c-B)\dfrac{m_{29}}{m_{29}-m_{19}}$	$\dfrac{-S_0}{m_{29}-m_{19}}-(p-c-B)\dfrac{m_{19}}{m_{29}-m_{19}}$

while the second inequality implies that

$$\frac{S_0}{m_{29} - m_{19}} \le \frac{(p - c - B)m_{19}}{m_{19} - m_{29}}.$$

(See Table 9.3 for analogous conditions appropriate to the nine strategies.) Note that in any strategy in which there are concurrent nonzero changes in price and selling expenses, the S_0 must *simultaneously* satisfy the constraint imposed by h and k.

4.2 Suppose that the firm chooses to fix the selling expense at some *arbitrary* level $c = c_0$, so that the only variations to be considered are with respect to the price p. Three strategies (see Table 9.1), $\sum_4$, $\sum_5$, and $\sum_6$, correspond to this situation. It is also clear that if $m_{16} > m_{14}$, the solution to the price decision problem rests upon the sign of $p - c_0 - B$.

1. $p - c_0 - B > 0$. In this case, $\sum_4$ becomes admissible if S_0 satisfies the inequality $S_0 \le m_{14}(p - c_0 - B)$; $\sum_5$ becomes admissible if S_0 is in the interval $m_{14}(p - c_0 - B) < S_0 < m_{16}(p - c_0 - B)$, and $\sum_6$ becomes admissible when $S_0 \ge m_{16}(p - c_0 - B)$. In other words, the firm has the following decisions to take according as S_0 belongs to one or the other of the intervals:

$$m_{14}(p - c_0 - B) < \begin{cases} S_0 \le m_{14}(p - c_0 - B)\colon\ p \to p - h_4{}^* \\ S_0 < m_{16}(p - c_0 - B)\colon\ p \to p \\ S_0 \ge m_{16}(p - c_0 - B)\colon\ p \to p + h_6{}^*. \end{cases}$$

The *amounts* of the optimal variations will, of course, have to be found by the optimization procedure indicated above.

2. $p - c_0 - B \le 0$. Here, the implication is that $m_{16}(p - c_0 - B) \le 0$, because $m_{16} > 0$ and $p - c_0 B \le 0$. However, since $S_0 \ge 0$, it is seen that $S_0 \ge m_{16}(p - c_0 B)$. Thus the strategy $\sum_6$ is applicable: p must be raised by $h_6{}^*$ until sales are found to satisfy the inequality $S_0 \le m_{16}(p - c_0 B)$. It may also be observed that if $m_{16} < m_{14}$, it is possible for S_0 to satisfy the inequalities appropriate to $\sum_4$ and $\sum_6$ simultaneously; the selection of strategy in such an event must rest on a comparison of the relevant $E_i{}^*(S_0)$. It is now easy to see how one may determine the *probability of holding the sales in a preassigned interval*, say $\eta_1 \le S(p, c) \le \eta_2$. Suppose, for the sake of an illustration, that the sales S_0 of the previous period satisfy the inequality $S_0 \le m_{14}(p - c_0 - B)$, so that the strategy $\sum_4$ becomes available. Let the optimal reduction in price by $h_4{}^*$ (>0), and define

$$M_4 \equiv \int_{p-h_4{}^*}^{p} m_{14}\, dp' = m_{14}h_4{}^*, \qquad \Delta_4 \equiv \int_{p-h_4{}^*}^{p} (s_{14})^2\, dp' = (s_{14})^2 h_4{}^*.$$

TABLE 9.3
IMPLIED CONSTRAINTS ON INITIAL SALES

Strategy $\sum_i$	Δp	Δc_1	Constraint on S_0 Imposed by $h \geq 0$	Constraint on S_0 Imposed by $k \geq 0$
$\sum_1$	$-h$	$-k$	$\dfrac{S_0}{m_{21}-m_{11}} \geq (p-c-B)\dfrac{-m_{21}}{m_{21}-m_{11}}$	$\dfrac{S_0}{m_{21}-m_{11}} \geq (p-c-B)\dfrac{-m_{11}}{m_{21}-m_{11}}$
$\sum_2$	0	$-k$	———	$S_0 \geq m_{22}(p-c-B)$
$\sum_3$	$+h$	$-k$	$\dfrac{S_0}{m_{23}-m_{13}} \leq (p-c-B)\dfrac{-m_{23}}{m_{23}-m_{13}}$	$\dfrac{S_0}{m_{23}-m_{13}} \geq (p-c-B)\dfrac{-m_{13}}{m_{23}-m_{13}}$
$\sum_4$	$-h$	0	$S_0 \leq m_{14}(p-c-B)$	———
$\sum_5$	0	0		———
$\sum_6$	$+h$	0	$S_0 \geq m_{16}(p-c-B)$	———
$\sum_7$	$+h$	$+k$	$\dfrac{S_0}{m_{27}-m_{17}} \geq (p-c-B)\dfrac{-m_{27}}{m_{27}-m_{17}}$	$\dfrac{S_0}{m_{27}-m_{17}} \leq (p-c-B)\dfrac{-m_{17}}{m_{27}-m_{17}}$
$\sum_8$	0	$+k$	———	$S_0 \leq m_{28}(p-c-B)$
$\sum_9$	$+h$	$+k$	$\dfrac{S_0}{m_{29}-m_{19}} \leq (p-c-B)\dfrac{-m_{29}}{m_{29}-m_{19}}$	$\dfrac{S_0}{m_{29}-m_{19}} \leq (p-c-B)\dfrac{-m_{19}}{m_{29}-m_{19}}$

The conditional probability that sales may be in the desired interval is given by

$$\Pr\left[\eta_1 \le S(p - h_4^*, c_0) \le \eta_2 \,\middle|\, S(p, c_0) = S_0\right]$$

$$= \frac{1}{\sqrt{2\pi \Delta_4}} \int_{\eta_1}^{\eta_2} \exp\left[-(\eta - S_0 - M_4)^2/2\Delta_4\right] d\eta. \qquad (9.16)$$

On the other hand, if S_0 were to satisfy the inequality, $S_0 \ge m_{14}(p - c_0 - B)$, then the strategy Σ_6 would be applicable and the calculation of the required probability would proceed with the determination of M_6 and Δ_6. Finally, observe that if S_0 were to be in the interval, $m_{14}(p - c_0 - B) < S_0 < m_{16}(p - c_0 - B)$, then according to the results of Chapter 8, the *expected* sales during the current period would be S_0 with probability one.

4.3 It will be appropriate at this stage to raise the following question: *When can a strategy of "no change" be expected to be optimal for the firm?* Under what circumstances will the firm have sufficient incentive *not* to

TABLE 9.4

Strategy Σ_i	Parameters		Strategy Σ_i	Parameters	
	m_{1i}	m_{2i}		m_{1i}	m_{2i}
1	1,100	1,000	6	1,000	—
2	—	1,000	7	1,100	1,000
3	900	1,000	8	—	200
4	200	—	9	1,000	1,100
5	—	—			

introduce a change in price and/or selling expenses? The practical interest in this question is obvious, for an explanation of "rigidity" may be furnished if one can establish that the *rationale for a "no change" is likely to materialize with a high frequency.* As in the case of *undifferentiated* oligopoly, such rigidity—stability of business habits and practices—will be seen to have a deep structural base. In other words, even if there is no overt collusion, it may appear to an external observer *as though* the firms were in collusion.

Let it be recalled from Table 9.1 that the "no change" strategy Σ_5 applies when S_0 belongs to some appropriate interval. For the sake of an illustration, suppose that the parameters of the nine strategies are as shown in Table 9.4 and that $p - c - B = 10$. Substituting into the inequalities of Table 9.3, it may be seen that for $2{,}000 \le S(p, c) \le 10{,}000$, the firm will not have an incentive to change its unit price or selling expense if the sales lie in the same interval. The probabilities of getting into a state (if not already there) of "no incentive to change" or equilibrium state are simple to calculate; they are

$$\frac{1}{\sqrt{2\pi \Delta_i}} \int_{2,000}^{4,000} \exp\left[-\frac{(\eta - S_0 - M_i)^2}{2 \Delta_i}\right] d\eta, \qquad i \neq 5, \qquad (9.17)$$

where Δ_i and M_i are computed according to formulas discussed in the preceding chapter. Next consider the situation in which the parameters of the strategies are

$$m_{1i} = m_1 > 0, \qquad m_{2i} = m_2 > 0, \qquad m_2 > m_1,$$
$$(i = 1, 2, \ldots, 9), \qquad p - c_0 - B > 0. \qquad (9.18)$$

Then, with these data, it may be seen from Table 9.3 that *every* positive value of S_0 belongs to at least one of the S_0-intervals defined for the strategies $\sum_1$ to $\sum_4$ or $\sum_6$ to $\sum_9$. In other words, the firm will adopt $\sum_5$ only if it secures the greatest of the lower bounds on the expected discounted profits. These examples illustrate how we may determine the likelihood for a firm to be in a state in which it has no incentive to change its price and/or selling expense. The method of analysis consists of examining if the sales would fall more frequently in the inverval that ensures the optimality of $\sum_5$. The *likelihood of a frequent occurrence of this event is precisely the likelihood of "rigidity"*. It is possible to develop this explicity, although such expressions will not convey anything more than what has been indicated above. However, the following may be said: If an interval $S_0' < S_0 < S_0''$ does exist for $\sum_5$ and if some empirical S_0 does not belong there, then the transition probabilities of entering the "equilibrium" state are

$$\frac{1}{\sqrt{2\pi \Delta_i}} \int_{S_0'}^{S_0''} \exp\left[-\frac{(\eta - S_0 - M_i)^2}{2 \Delta_i}\right] d\eta, \qquad i \neq 5. \qquad (9.19)$$

If the firm is in "equilibrium" (with its sales in $S_0' < S_0 < S_0''$) and if the "no change" strategy maximizes the expected discounted total profits, then, as was seen before, the probability of remaining in this state is one. This even suggests that we may define a degree of price-flexibility—and *mutatis mutandis*, selling expenses flexibility—in the following manner:

degree of price flexibility, = Pr $[S_0$ is not in the interval appropriate for $\sum_2$, $\sum_5$, or $\sum_8]$ + Pr $[S_0$ is in the interval appropriate for $\sum_2$, $\sum_5$, or $\sum_8$, *and* $E_2^*(S_0)$, $E_5^*(S_0)$ or $E_8^*(S_0)$ does not furnish the absolute maximum of profits]. (9.20)

4.4 It remains to examine more carefully the special concept of "equilibrium" state introduced in the preceding paragraphs. Evidently, this is *not* the "equilibrium" in the classical sense, that is, the equilibrium of *output* of an individual firm in monopolistic competition [12, 13]. In the standard treatment of monopolistic competition, the firm is supposed to vary its output; however, in the models presented the price and selling expense are those that are susceptible to variations.[2] Furthermore, the analytical framework of this book does not extend to the equilibrium of the *group* of firms. Thus of the *two* conditions of classical equilibrium (marginal revenue equals marginal cost and price or average revenue equals average cost), the second one has no counterpart in the present scheme of analysis. However, the analyses of *optimal* policies discussed above do rest on a principle somewhat similar to the first condition. But here, again, direct comparison is not possible because the relevant variations are not in respect of output. There is a second reason why we cannot directly compare the results of the two analyses: sales (and therefore costs and revenues) are seen as *random* magnitudes in the present scheme of analysis. One *possible* mode of comparison is to interpret the "revenue" and "cost" as *mathematical expectations* of the corresponding random variables. Thus the first condition of equilibrium would read

$$\frac{\partial E[K(S)]}{\partial p} = \frac{\partial E[R(S)]}{\partial p} \quad \text{or} \quad \frac{\partial E[K(S)]}{\partial c} = \frac{\partial E[R(S)]}{\partial c}, \qquad (9.21)$$

according to whether one emphasizes price or selling expense variations. Similarly, the second condition of equilibrium would read

$$\frac{E[K(S)]}{S} = \frac{E[R(S)]}{S}. \qquad (9.22)$$

A common framework in which the two analyses may be compared can be set up by treating the quantity offered for sale as the parameter. It is but one step from here to probabilize the classical model: imagine that the firm receives a *random price* $\tilde{p}$ after offering a determinate quantity S to the market. The basic means of analysis is a stochastic *price*-process, $\tilde{p} = \tilde{p}(S)$; for a given value of S, p is a random variable. The probability density $f(\tilde{p})$ of $\tilde{p}$ is parametrized by S and we write $f(\tilde{p}) = f(\tilde{p}; S)$.

---

[2] This is the principal justification for "differentiated oligopoly" instead of "monopolistic competition." When the group of firms in a differentiated oligopoly tends to grow in number, it is conceivable that one may encounter certain characteristics that may also occur in the "large group" case of monopolistic competition. But such resemblance is purely fortuitous and, furthermore, it should be noted that the number of firms, by itself, does not play a role in the present analysis.

The *expected revenue* in a single period is seen to be

$$E[R(S)] = SE[\tilde{p}(S)] = S \int_0^\infty \tilde{p}(S) f(\tilde{p}; S) \, d\tilde{p}.$$

Let $C(S)$ denote the unit selling expense function and let the aggregate cost of S, the quantity offered, be denoted by $C(S)S + K(S)$, where $K(S)$ is the aggregate production cost. The expected total cost, evidently, is $C(S)S + K(S)$, because S is not random. Thus, the interpretation (9.21) is equivalent to

$$S \frac{d}{dS} \{E[\tilde{p}(S)]\} + E[\tilde{p}(S)] = SC'(S) + C(S) + K'(S), \qquad (9.23)$$

where primes indicate differentiation. But this is as far as one can go. Chamberlin's analysis does not furnish any clue to the distribution of $\tilde{p}(S)$ and one needs the (S, M, Y)-specifications to *derive* such a distribution. It appears, then, that one cannot directly compare a quantity-variation model with a model of price-variation or selling expense variation. There is, however, a very *restricted* sense in which such a comparison *can* be made. Consider the model of price-variation with the associated condition of optimality,

$$p \frac{\partial}{\partial p} E[S(p, c)] + E[S(p, c)] = \frac{\partial}{\partial p} E[C(S)S] + \frac{\partial}{\partial p} E[K(S)], \quad (9.24)$$

which says that the marginal revenue and marginal cost—both reckoned with respect to the variations of price—are to be equal. Now, the random variable S of the stochastic process $S(p, c)$ was shown to possess a Poisson distribution with mean-value $A = A(p, c) = E[S(p, c)]$. Let $C(S) = c$, a constant. Then (9.24) is simplified as follows:

$$p \frac{\partial A}{\partial p} + A(p, c) = c \frac{\partial A}{\partial p} + L \frac{\partial A}{\partial p}, \qquad (9.25)$$

where L is defined as in (7.16). Rearranging terms and observing that $A(p, c) = \mu(p)\lambda(C)$, it is seen from (9.25) that

$$(p - c - L)\mu'(p) + \mu(p) = 0. \qquad (9.26)$$

With appropriate restrictions, this may be regarded as an analogue of equation (9.23). Next, consider the second condition of equilibrium (unit revenue = unit cost) in which the decision variable is the output. Because the entities on the two sides of the equation are *random* variables, the equation has to be interpreted in some appropriate fashion. A simple although not unique interpretation is to equate the mathematical expectations. This leads to

$$E \frac{R(S)}{S} = \frac{C(S)}{S} \qquad (9.27)$$

which, again, is seen to imply that

$$E[\tilde{p}(S)] = C(S) + \frac{K(S)}{S}. \qquad (9.28)$$

Again, the left member of this equation cannot be explicitly evaluated unless the probability distribution of the random function $\tilde{p}(S)$ is either stipulated in advance or derived from the structural characteristics of the market. Because the present models consider the *sales* as random outcomes of price and selling expense, (9.27) reads

$$E \frac{R(S)}{S} = E \frac{C(S)}{S}, \qquad (9.29)$$

where the mathematical expectation is computed with respect to the probability distribution of the *sales*. Equation (9.29) implies that

$$p = c + \sum_{S=1}^{\infty} K(S)S^{-1}e^{-A(p,\,c)}[A(p,\,c)]^S(S!)^{-1}. \qquad (9.30)$$

Equations (9.28) and (9.30) are the nearest analogues of each other for the two models of competition with product differentiation. In general, however, there is no reason to expect that in a differentiated oligopoly the two conditions of equilibrium (marginal revenue = marginal cost and price = unit cost) will be simultaneously satisfied. That is to say, *there is no reason for* (9.26) *and* (9.30) *to be jointly satisfied;* (9.26) *will hold in any event and, typically,* (9.30) *will not.* Thus, there may not exist a level of price p that satisfies the following equation:

$$\frac{\mu(p)}{d\mu/dp} = \sum_{S=1}^{\infty} [K(S) - K(S-1) - A(p,\,c)\, K(S)S^{-2}]e^{-A(p,\,c)}\frac{[A(p,\,c)]^{S-1}}{(S-1)!} \qquad (9.31)$$

The gap between the optimal price and the expected unit cost (corresponding to the optimal price) will, perhaps, tend to vanish as the competition comes close enough to the kind for which Chamberlin formulated the tangency condition. Again, such "convergence" does not take place along a *single dimension* (such as the number of firms) and the issue cannot be resolved in the context of a micro theory.

Chapter 10

A VERIFICATION

Models of probabilistic dependence of a firm's sales upon its own price have been developed in Chapters 4 to 9. It has been seen that these could be derived from specifications about the market environment and business practices. The common feature of all of these models is that they are computable from observables, that is, data pertaining to the firm's own activities. We might still ask if this kind of model-building could be called a "theory" in the sense that it can *explain* the outcomes of oligopolistic competition in a given situation. The bulk of Chapters 7 to 9 was indeed, devoted to this issue. There it was shown that the general program or method outlined in Chapter 3 could explain some of the typical phenomena of oligopolistic competition. What is more important, the explanation did not rest on the psychological disposition and personality of the entrepreneurs. The general question of the explanatory power of the theory is closely associated with the question of *verifiability* of the theory. It is to this question that this chapter is devoted.

The core of this chapter is concerned with the analysis of data generated by a program which simulated the (S, M, Y)-complex assumed in the models of Chapter 4. It has been ascertained that in spite of interfirm variations (of cost-structure and of the mode of decision-making) the probability distributions of sales of individual firms did conform to the result predicted by deductive methods. An equally interesting outcome of the analysis is the confirmation of the hypothesis that the Markovian transition probabilities of sales are parametrized by the firm's own price; it is presented in Chapter 14, Section 3.

1. THE NATURE OF VERIFICATION

A precise formulation is made of what is *to be meant* by verification and, then, the general framework for verification is indicated.

1.1 It may be recalled from the derivation of the models that their applicability to a particular firm would depend on how closely its environment agrees with the (*S*, *M*, *Y*)-configurations and other working assumptions introduced in the model.[1] In practice, then, any test of hypothesis must be done with data from a firm that does operate under the appropriate configurations. Consider, for example, the celebrated hypothesis that consumers maximize utility. When several simplifications are made and the appropriate framework of observation is set up, the *statistical* relationship between market demand, price, and income conforms to the logical implications of the hypothesis. The degree of such conformity depends upon how well the simplifications represent the essential realities of a given situation. Thus we say that the "utility maximization" theory of consumer behavior is applicable in the sense that it explains observations of consumer behavior in the market. This is *not* the sense in which the theory presented here is applicable; as has been made clear, the approach is not designed to *explain* the macroscopic behavior of price-output-profits in an oligopolistic industry *of real life*. Because it has been developed in terms of variables pertinent to an individual firm, it is to be verified also in terms of these variables. It is not relevant to discuss verification in terms of the aggregate or macroscopic outcomes that are of interest to the "industry" or similar artificial units. This is not merely because it is difficult to define and identify an "industry" under conditions of oligopoly. Indeed, as has been forcefully argued by the economists (Fellner [22], Machlup [40], Shubik [48, 49]), it is even meaningless in oligopolistic situations to look for a well-knit scheme of reasoning and analysis or a fixed body of conclusions. But this does not mean that the search for a theory should be *replaced* by massive empirical investigations or case studies. To sum up, therefore, the proper question to pose is the following: *How much* of the preceding analysis is *verifiable*, and *how can* it be verified? On the positive side, the approach of this monograph has consistently emphasized the need for and possibility of deriving the probability distribution of sales as seen by the firm. Under suitable specifications it has been shown how these probabilities will be parametrized by the firm's own decision variables. Thus, it is asserted that the present "theory" will be *adequately tested if the postulated probability distributions* (for example, the binomial and Poisson models of Chapter 4) *are empirically validated*.[2]

---

[1] Furthermore, as shown in Chapters 7 and 9, the choice of an optimal strategy for a firm rests upon whether the firm in question has *experienced* a dependence of it sales on the level of or change in its price and/or selling expense.

[2] Another conceivable test would be to compare the observed net profits with those due to the decision rules computed according to the theory, assuming that the competitors did not use similar optimal rules. But this has not been attempted because a proper comparison would call for a computation of the expected net profits in some other fashion which, clearly, is not unique.

1.2 It is appropriate, therefore, to raise the question of availability and quality of data one needs to test these hypotheses. The prospects in this regard appear to be almost forbidding. Although there are industries[3] that roughly satisfy the (S, M, Y)-specifications of Chapter 4, it is not ordinarily possible to obtain reasonably homogeneous time-series data on the sales and price offerings of a firm. The reasons are largely institutional in nature. Even if the right kind of data were available, it is clear that real-life data would exhibit the effects of several factors that might have been ignored in the development of the model. Thus we need *idealized* data; that is, data in which "extraneous" effects are minimized in the direction of controlled experimentation. In other words, *the only means of testing the theory is to generate artificial data[4] by some mechanism that reproduces the structural characteristics of the market*, that is, the (S, M, Y) configurations appropriate to the model. It should be emphasized, for the sake of completeness, that there is no presupposition that the sales outcomes would have a preassigned distribution.

2. SIMULATION: REPRODUCING THE (S, M, Y)-COMPLEX OF AN UNDIFFERENTIATED OLIGOPOLY

This section describes essential components of a device that was employed for approximately reproducing the (S, M, Y)-specifications of an undifferentiated oligopoly. This device should not be confused with what is more commonly known as "simulation." Simulation typically consists of artificially reproducing—by means of mathematical models—given observations on a system's output. Since real-life data are not available, one cannot meaningfully speak of simulation.

2.1 Let it be recalled from Chapter 4, Section 1, that an undifferentiated oligopoly was considered in which the sellers were not supposed to communicate among themselves. This key feature was incorporated in the computer program in the following manner: *Neither the past sales and prices nor the currently planned prices of other firms are to be taken as inputs into the computation of price and output decisions of an individual firm.* Next, recall the specification that sellers do not know the buyer's

---

[3] See, for example, Fellner [22, pp. 169–171].

[4] There are at least three good reasons for this practice. First, there are some outstanding precedents for generating data for inquires of this kind. (Cyert and March [18], is a good example.) Second, there is a substantial body of literature which describes in detail some of the more important characteristics and activities of competing firms. (For example, Kaplan [34], Fouraker and Siegel [23], and Haynes [26].) Finally, the availability of large and fast digital computers makes it possible to compute the outcome of the interaction of decisions of several firms in a given market.

"maximum demand price," and that the buyers do not communicate among themselves either in respect of their maximum demand prices or in regard to the prices at which they close the transaction. The computer program would treat this specification in the following manner: First, the *size of demand* is chosen from some arbitrary distribution which is held fixed for the entire epoch or run.[5] Second, an arbitrary but fixed table of probabilities is employed to determine the *chance that demand will be exercised* if the lowest quotation is less than x. This is also in accord with the other specification, namely, that buyers choose the seller that quotes the lowest price, provided that the lowest price is less than the maximum price they are prepared to pay rather than go without the product. By introducing these two probabilities *provision is made for the contingency that a firm may be confronted with a demand greater than the amount it can sell most profitably*. The appearance of such a contingency calls for *adjustments* in two directions. Clearly, there is a considerable freedom in the choice of rules for such adjustments. Without violating the (S, M, Y)-specifications, it was assumed that any demand not satisfied in a given market period would be regarded as lost to the entire group of firms in the next period. Second, a *decision-making procedure* was incorporated in the program. Since procedures would depend upon the objective(s) pursued by the firm, a distinction was drawn between two types of firms: Those that aim at maximizing single-period net profits and those that aim at maximizing the current period's sales. The *profit-maximizing* firms accept orders up to an optimum level determined by the price contemplated, provided that orders at that price exceed the optimum output; otherwise, they accept all orders. On the other hand, the *sales-optimizing* firms aim at making as much sales as possible, subject only to some minimum level of profits; this minimum level, of course, varies from firm to firm. The program employed for data generation considered eight firms of which six were sales-optimizers and the rest profit-maximizers. The minimum levels of profits assigned to the sales-optimizers were held constant over the "epoch," even when these goals were not realized. In this respect, there has been no goal-adaptation in the program.

2.2   Decisions regarding the expansion of production facilities were not admitted. Consistent with this limitation, the firms were *initially endowed with considerable "excess" capacity*, so that the firm's unit variable production costs would not increase sharply as the firm attempts

---

[5] An epoch or run consists of 100 to 125 market periods. Market periods should be distinguished from price-planning periods, which are internal to the firms; their lengths are not the same.

to secure a larger share of the market. The unit variable cost function $(K(S)/S$ in the notation of Chapter 7) was assumed to be of the following form:

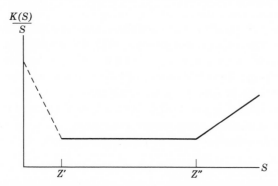

The points Z' and Z'' were chosen to vary from firm to firm and so were the slopes to the right and left of the horizontal segment of the curve; the height of the curve, however, was chosen to be the same for all the firms. Thus all firms were made comparable in respect to technology.

2.3 An important component of the computer program was the routine that would lead to revision of price quotations from one planning period to another. Precisely *how* this is done and what formulas are employed is irrelevant to the analysis. Thus, the manner in which a firm would employ its own sales and profits experience in shaping its price policy during the planning period was regarded as a *behavioral characteristic* of the firm. It should be emphasized, however, that the optimality considerations developed in Chapter 7 and 9 were not[6] applied to this end. Such a procedure would not lend sufficient variety to the outcomes to provide an honest test of the power of the theory. The first step in the design of behavioral rules is to define the *sales performance.* For the nth period, it is defined as the ratio

$$R_{n, n-1} = \frac{S_n - \hat{S}_n}{\hat{S}_n},$$ (10.1)

where $\hat{S}_n$ is the single-valued estimate of sales (of the nth period) derived from the data up to the $(n-1)$st period. The formula of estimation is a behavioral characteristic of the firm and so is the length of the time-series used as input in the forecasting formula. The *reaction patterns* of the

[6] Under very special assumptions it is possible to place a correspondence between these "rules of thumb" and the "optimal" rules derived in the preceding chapters. However, any correspondence that may be discovered in the operation of the program is purely accidental.

firms were defined by the following family of functions:

$$\Delta p_{n-1} \equiv p_n - p_{n-1} = u(\pi_{n-1}) + v(R_{n,n-1}), \qquad (10.2)$$

with π_{n-1} representing the net profits during the immediately past period. The functions $u(.)$ and $v(.)$ are nonlinear and their derivatives are discontinuous. They are exhibited below, with S^* denoting the volume of sales that would (a) maximize expected net profits, if the firm is a profits maximizer, (b) maximize the volume of sales that also secures a minimum level of profits, if the firm is a sales maximizer.

The slopes of $u(.)$ and $v(.)$, when not zero, were assumed to vary from firm to firm, depending upon the initial capacity and upon the range of the horizontal segment of the unit variable cost curves.

2.4 The program was run according to an experimental design: Two levels each were chosen for the dispersion (among firms) of the initial

TABLE 10.1

PATTERNS OF REACTION

		$\pi > 0$	$\pi < 0$
$R > 0$		$u(\pi) = 0$ $\Delta p_n = 0$ $v(R) = 0$	$u(\pi) \neq 0$ $\Delta p_n > 0$ $v(R) \neq 0$
$R < 0$	$S < S^*$	$u(\pi) = 0$ $\Delta p_n < 0$ $v(R) \neq 0$	$u(\pi) \neq 0$ $\Delta p_n < 0$ $v(R) \neq 0$
	$S > S^*$	$u(\pi) = 0$ $\Delta p_n = 0$ $v(R) = 0$	$u(\pi) \neq 0$ $\Delta p_n > 0$ $v(R) = 0$

endowment of capacity and one of the parameters of the reaction pattern described in Table 10.1. In the experiments corresponding to each of the four cells of the design, the random aggregate demand (the n of Chapter 6, Section 1) was taken to be serially uncorrelated, with a constant mean and a relatively small coefficient of variation. Ten time-series of prices, profits, and sales were generated for each of the eight firms; each series of a length up to 150 corresponding to a sequence of 150 random values of the aggregate demand. For each firm, therefore, the ensemble of realizations of the random sales and profits consists of ten time-series or "sample records."

3. TESTING THE BINOMIAL MODEL AND σ(*p*)

This section summarizes the tests made on the sample records with a view toward examining the validity of the hypothesis that the sales probabilities of an individual firm under the given specifications are given by a binomial distribution.

3.1   For each firm the data relevant to the test procedure consist of ten time-series of price offered and the market share realized by the firm.[7] On account of very sharp fluctuations in the first 30 to 50 periods the full length of the sample records could not be utilized. Only 60 observations from each sample record were made use of. A profit-maximizing firm was chosen arbitrarily, and four of its sample records were arbitrarily selected, each having the same initial and terminal periods. The records were then pooled to obtain Table 10.2.

TABLE 10.2
PRICE AND MARKET SHARE

Price	Average Market Share
5.7	0.297
5.8	0.296
5.9	0.287
6.0	0.159
6.1	0.001

It is interesting to observe that as the price quotations increase, the market share falls off rapidly, vanishing abruptly beyond a certain level. Relationships of this kind may be approximated by smooth functions

$$\hat{\sigma} = \frac{k}{1 + \exp{[F(p)]}} , \qquad (10.3)$$

where $F(p)$ is such that as p decreases, the $\hat{\sigma}$ tends to reach a fixed level, while as p increases the $\hat{\sigma}$ tends to zero. Let x denote the price and y

---

[7] The market share of a firm was computed as the ratio of its sales during a market period to the aggregate sales by the group during that period. Market share was not used by any of the firms as an input into its price reaction rules, the reason being the assumption that firms do not communicate among themselves.

the market share; then making the transformation

$$F(x) = \ln\left(\frac{k}{y} - 1\right),$$
(10.4)

on the original data, it is found that the unknown function in (10.3) is a *parabola*. Because k in (10.3) is not known in advance, the following procedure was adopted: a value of $k(k = k')$ was selected by inspection, a new variable $w = \ln(k'/y - 1)$ was defined, and a polynomial regression of w on x was computed. Both the choice of k and of the degree of the polynomial being arbitrary, several trials were made before a "good fit" was obtained. For the data given $k = 0.298$ and $w = -70.27 + 1.93x^2$ appear to give the best fit.[8] Thus, in terms of the original variables, the market-share function is estimated[9] as

$$\hat{\sigma} = \hat{\sigma}(p) = \frac{0.298}{1 + \exp(-70.27 + 1.93p^2)}.$$
(10.5)

3.2   The empirical market shares for the firm in question were obtained for price quotations in the range, $5.8 \le p \le 5.9$ from each of the six (remaining) sample records, excluding the ones that were employed for determining $\hat{\sigma}(p)$. In order to reduce the sampling fluctuations, these were pooled and for the full range of variation of the aggregate demand n the empirical distribution of market share shown in Tables 10.3 and 10.4 was obtained.

The average level of price quotations was 5.86, and the estimate of the firm's market share at this average price is $\hat{\sigma}(5.86) = 0.288$. The estimate of the variance of the predicted market share is $0.288(1 - 0.288)/n$, n being the aggregate industry demand. Because the average level of n was approximately 4300 units per period, the estimate of the variance is 0.5×10^{-4}. On the other hand, the variance of the *empirical* market share was seen to be 0.259×10^{-3}. Allowing for this discrepancy,[10] one may

---

[8] This may be seen from the analysis of variance given below.

[9] The regression thus obtained is only a statistical *estimate* of the assumed regression function $f(p)$; it is subject to sampling errors. Thus, the market share predicted by the formula (10.5) may fail, in *some* sample records, to substantiate the probability law derived in Chapter 6. This question could be pursued in depth if more sample records were available.

[10] One reason for the empirical variance to be larger than the theoretical variance of 0.00005 may be seen in the facts that (a) in the data-generating process, the aggregate demand n was chosen to be random and (b) the range of variations of n underlying Table 10.4 is much larger than is required for the ideal case. For better results, however it would be more appropriate to generate additional data and classify them by the price-intervals *and* n-intervals; only then the theoretical model could be given a fair trial with greater confidence.

TABLE 10.3
RELATIVE EFFICIENCY OF ALTERNATIVE POLYNOMIAL FORMS FOR $F(x)$

	Least Squares Estimates			
k^*	$w = a + bx + cx^2$		$w = a^* + c^*x^2$	
0.298	$a = -67.52$ $b = -0.93$ $c = 2.01$	$F_{2,2} = 24.61$	$a^* = -70.27$ $c^* = 1.93$	$F_{1,3} = 73.7$
0.300	$a = -59.00$ $b = -0.04$ $c = -59.18$	$F_{2,2} = 8.37$	$a^* = -59.31$ $c^* = -1.63$	$F_{1,3} = 25.11$
0.310	$a = -43.02$ $b = -0.02$ $c = 1.18$	$F_{2,2} = 3.50$	$a^* = -43.22$ $c^* = 1.18$	$F_{1,3} = 10.41$

consider the regression estimate of 0.288 as the *mean value* and the empirical variance of 0.259×10^{-3} as the variance of the random market share. In Chapter 8 it was argued that for a large and effectively constant n, the distribution of sales and, hence, of the market share could be approximated by an appropriate Gaussian distribution. Thus, the *hypothesis to be tested is that the market share is* $N(0.288; 0.259 \times 10^{-3})$. The statistical procedure of curve-fitting was applied and the Pearsonian χ^2 was seen to have a value of 3.31. From Table 10.4 it may be noted that the number of class-intervals or the total number of degrees of freedom is 5; two of these are lost in computing the sum and the variance and the appropriate degree of freedom is 3. Since $\chi_3^2(0.95)$ is 7.81, the observed χ^2 is not significant at the 95% level and, therefore, there is *no evidence for rejection* of the hypothesis.

TABLE 10.4
EMPIRICAL DISTRIBUTION OF MARKET SHARE
IN THE TEST SAMPLE RECORDS

Market Share	Frequency
≤ 0.265	25
$0.265^+ - 0.285$	118
$0.285^+ - 0.305$	137
$0.305^+ - 0.315$	42
> 0.315	13

3.3 A few comments on the variance of $\hat{\sigma}$ follow. The fact that $\hat{\sigma}$ is seen to have a variance larger than that predicted by the binomial model has its origin in the assumption that the *n units of demand* confronting the firm in a given market period are all statistically *independent*. This may be seen as follows. Let N = total number of *buyers* in a period; ν_i = number of units of demand from the ith buyer, $i = 1, \ldots, N$. Let ρ denote the intraclass correlation (Kendall [36]). Then, the variance of $\hat{\sigma}$ is approximately given by

$$V(\hat{\sigma}, p) \cong \frac{f(p)(1 - f(p))}{N}\left[\frac{1}{\bar{\nu}} + \rho\left(c^2 + \frac{\nu - 1}{\nu}\right)\right], \tag{10.6}$$

where c is the coefficient of variation of the ν_i and $\bar{\nu} = \dfrac{1}{N}\sum_{i=1}^{N}\nu_i$. Now suppose that a buyer has more than one unit of demand and suppose that if he decides to purchase he makes *all* his purchases from a single firm. In this case, the intraclass correlation coefficient is one, hence (10.6) is reduced to

$$V(\hat{\sigma}; p) \cong N^{-1}f(p)[1 - f(p)](1 + c^2). \tag{10.7}$$

But since $n = \sum_{i=1}^{N}\nu_i$, it is readily verified that if $\nu_i \geq 1$, then

$$V(\sigma;\ p) \geq n^{-1}f(p)[1 - f(p)]. \tag{10.8}$$

Thus, in the limiting case, when $\nu_i = 1$, hence, $c = 0$ and $N = n$, the variance predicted by the binomial model will be equal to the sample variance. To sum up: For the case in question the departure of the *observed* variance of $\hat{\sigma}$ from the *theoretical* one *may* be due to the fact that the buyers possibly came with different amounts of demand. Since the mechanism employed to generaie the artificial data did not consider the *number* of buyers in a given per^nd, this latter result could not be verified.

4. REPRODUCING THE (S, M, Y)-COMPLEX OF A DIFFERENTIATED OLIGOPOLY

The organization of this section is similar to that of Section 2: A summary description is given of the device employed for approximately reproducing the specifications of a differentiated oligopoly situation (see Chapter 4, Section 2). Since the firms have *two* weapons of competition, the data-generating mechanism is a little more complicated than in the case of an undifferentiated oligopoly. It may be conceptually divided into three segments, each segment reflecting the results of a major decision by seller or buyer. The three segments or parts are repeated each price-planning period for an arbitrary number of periods, the usual number being somewhere between 75 and 125.

4.1 Each seller has a planned price p and a planned selling expense c for each planning period. Corresponding to these, there is an anticipation of sales $\hat{S}$. These anticipations are single-valued estimates of the conditional expectation of sales, given the past observations on the firm's *own* price offerings and selling expenses.[11] Between one planning period and the next neither the sales anticipation nor the policy decisions are allowed to vary.

4.2 Unknown to the firms, the "community of buyers," endowed with certain behavioral characteristics, allocates a random budget to the products of the firms. This generates the potential sales of "inquiry units" of the model of Chapter 4, Section 2. At the same time, depending upon whether it aims at maximizing net profits or maximizing sales and stabilizing net profits, the firms accept orders according to the rule:

Orders accepted = min [potential sales; optimal sales].

Production costs are incurred accordingly. The detailed mechanism that secures these may be described as follows. A random total budget B is drawn from an arbitrary distribution. This budget is allocated to each firm so that the unit price of the firm times its sales—that is, pS—equals its share of the budget. The allocation is made on the principle that the community of buyers tends to maximize its utility for a product, subject only to a budget constraint. This is achieved in the program in the following manner: It is supposed that V_i is the "average community utility" for the product of the ith seller, while p_i is his price and X_i denotes his potential sales; the community of buyers then maximizes utility[12]

$$U = \sum_{i=1}^{N} U_i(X_i, V_i)$$

[11] Typically, this is done by means of linear regression. Initially, each firm is endowed with a regression equation; after a period of time—which, again, varies from firm to firm—the regression equation is updated in light of more recent experience. Thus, there is an element of adaptiveness in the formation of anticipations.

[12] It is not maintained that real-life buyers actually do so. It is included in the program partly as a convenient method for the allocation of demand and partly as an experimental device to study the outcomes arising from such a pattern of behavior. The essential point is that *some* notion of buyer's utility is implicit in the very fact of product differentiation. The effect of price and selling expense policy is to induce a "loyalty" and, hence, a "utility," That the degree of product differentiation is more or less directly affected by the *levels* of selling expenses is seen to be built in. The function $U_i(X_i, V_i)$ is directly influenced by the spending c_i in the following manner: If the c_i allocated for a period is larger than the average c_i over several periods in the past, then V_i is increased slightly, while if c_i is smaller than this average, then V_i is decreased. Seen from the viewpoint of the firm, the outcome of this mechanism is not known because all the firms may simultaneously change their selling expenses c_i, and hence their V_i.

subject to the constraint, that is, $B = \sum_{i=1}^{N} p_i X_i$. This determines the potential sales of the ith firm:

$$X_i = \frac{Bh_i(p_i, V_i)}{\sum_{i=1}^{N} h_i(p_i, V_i)}. \tag{10.9}$$

As a consequence of this allocation of sales, the ith firm may discover that it receives more inquiries than it can profitably produce and sell. The consequences of this kind of situation depend on the kind of attitude taken by the firms. Two kinds of attitudes are distinguished. The *profit-maximizing* firm takes into account its selling expenses, price quotations, and the total production cost function and calculates the sales S_i^* that will maximize its net profits for the next period. A *profit-stabilizing* firm on the other hand, calculates S_{0i}, the maximum sales that will leave a profit not less than some desired level π_{0i}.[13] In any event, if a firm is approached for purchases larger than S^* or S_0, it will *accept* the smaller of the two; otherwise, it will accept whatever is forthcoming. In other words, after the sellers have been made aware of the potential sales (X_i), each seller makes a decision for S_i, the actual sales. If the firm is a profit-maximizer, $S_i = \min [S_i^*, X_i]$; if the firm is a profit-stabiliser, S_i is chosen as $S_i = \min [X_i, S_{0i}]$. Under the assumption that buyers *would not* be lost to the *system*,[14] all rejected sales are added to the total consumer budget for the next market period. The unit variable cost of production is assigned to be of the same kind as in Section 1.

As in the previous section, the location of the points R_1 and R_2 and the slopes to the left and right of these points differ among the firms. The height of the horizontal section of the curve is approximately the same for all the firms. These stipulations effectively represent the common situation in which firms have excess capacities in the sense that even if they were to acquire a large volume of sales they would still be operating most often to the left of R_2. But since each firm has a different capacity (represented by R_2), the profits π_0 a large firm would like to make is different from the π_0 for a small firm. Therefore, a concept of "investment" I is introduced; I is taken to be proportional to R_2.

[13] This is equivalent to assuming that a seller will accept inquiries until he has enough orders to reach his objective of maximum profits or some minimum "floor level" of profit. If he does not reach this sales level, he holds on to the orders he has acquired. If, on the other hand, this sales level is surpassed, then he rejects all subsequent customers. It is these customers who come back to the market in the next period.

[14] The minimum profits π_{0i} differ from firm to firm, although for a given firm the π_{0i} is held fixed. Thus the firms do not change their "goals," even when the actual profits exceed or fall short of the target profits over a long period of time.

4.3 The most important segment of the data-generation scheme is the one which computes the "responses," that is, the decisions to change the quotations and/or selling expenses for the planning period. Two assumptions are made in regard to the behavioral rule that generates these responses. The first is that each firm can specify, on appropriate scales, the extent to which it has attained its objectives. The second is that, on account of inertia, conservatism, and so on, there are *intervals* on these scales on which the firm is content to do nothing. At the end of the nth planning period, the firm has the observations on the sales X_n, it could have, and on the sales $\hat{S}_n$, anticipated for the period. It can also compare X_n with $\tilde{S}_n$, the common symbol for both the profit-maximizing sales and the profit-stabilizing sales. Let the actual *return* and the anticipated return on investment be denoted by $r_n = \pi_n/I$ and $\hat{r}_n = \hat{\pi}_n/I$ respectively. The *sales performance* was measured by $\sigma_n = [X_n - S_n]/S_n$ and *profit performance* by $\delta_n = \hat{r}_n - r_n$. Let $u_1(\delta_n)$ denote the change in planned price triggered by an observation δ_n and let $v_1(\delta_n)$ denote the change in planned price due to an observation σ_n. Let $u_2(\delta_n)$ and $v_2(\delta_n)$ similarly denote the proposed change in selling expenses triggered by the observations δ_n and σ_n. Then the price-reaction rule is

$$\Delta p_n \equiv p_{n+1} - p_n = u_1(\delta_n) + v_1(\sigma_n) \tag{10.10}$$

and the selling expense reaction is

$$\Delta c_n \equiv c_{n+1} - c_n = u_2(\delta_n) + v_2(\sigma_n). \tag{10.11}$$

These rules are further enriched by the following considerations: a firm that is not earning its desired rate of return may be expected to increase its prices and possibly its selling expenses to compensate for the possible loss of sales due to the price increase. If its actual rate of return is adequate but the sales are less than it needs, then the firm may be expected to reduce the price and increase the selling expenses. A firm which is not attaining at least its optimal sales would tend to increase its selling expense and vary its price quotations according to the state of its rate of return. The *reaction rules* or the firm's disposition to market events may now be summed up as in Tables 10.5 and 10.6. The functions $u_1(.)$, $u_2(.)$, $v_1(.)$, and $v_2(.)$ were made to vary among firms in proportion to the capacity (Z'') of the firm. In addition, another device was employed to reflect the *inertia and conservatism* of the firms: if σ and δ were in some arbitrary interval around zero ($|\delta| < \epsilon_1$ and $|\sigma| < \epsilon_2$), the firm would do nothing, regardless of its sales and profit outcomes.

TABLE 10.5
Price Reaction

		$\delta \geq 0$	$\delta < 0$
$\sigma \geq 0$		$u_1(\delta) \neq 0$ $\Delta p > 0$ $v_1(\sigma) \neq 0$	$u_1(\delta) \neq 0$ $\Delta p > 0$ $v_1(\sigma) = 0$
$\sigma < 0$	$X \geq S$	$u_1(\delta) = 0$ $\Delta p = 0$ $v_1(\sigma) = 0$	$u_1(\delta) \neq 0$ $\Delta p > 0$ $v_1(\sigma) = 0$
	$X < S$	$u_1(\delta) = 0$ $\Delta p < 0$ $v_1(\sigma) \neq 0$	$u_1(\delta) \neq 0$ $\Delta p > 0$ $v_1(\sigma) \neq 0$

TABLE 10.6
Selling Cost Reaction

		$\delta \geq 0$	$\delta < 0$
$\sigma \geq 0$		$u_2(\delta) \neq 0$ $\Delta c > 0$ $v_2(\sigma) \neq 0$	$u_2(\delta) = 0$ $\Delta c = 0$ $v_2(\sigma) = 0$
$\sigma < 0$	$X \geq S$	$u_2(\delta) = 0$ $\Delta c = 0$ $v_2(\sigma) = 0$	$u_2(\delta) \neq 0$ $\Delta c > 0$ $v_2(\sigma) = 0$
	$X < S$	$u_2(\delta) = 0$ $\Delta c > 0$ $v_2(\sigma) \neq 0$	$u_2(\delta) \neq 0$ $\Delta c > 0$ $v_2(\sigma) \neq 0$

5. TESTING THE POISSON HYPOTHESIS

This section is concerned with the statistical tests of the hypothesis that the sales of individual firms are distributed Poisson, with a mean value function $A(p, c) = \mu(p) \, \lambda(c)$, with properties postulated in Chapter 4, Section 2.

5.1 Each sequence of 75 to 125 price-planning periods showing the market activities of eight firms is considered as a sample record or "run."

Six runs were employed in testing the hypotheses made in Chapter 4, Section 2. The first hypothesis was that over some appropriately chosen intervals of price and selling expenses, a firm's sales would be a Poisson variable, with mean-value $A(p, c) = \mu(p) \lambda(c)$. In order to test this, the total range of variation of price was chosen to be 1.0 and that for the selling cost was chosen to be 0.5. Tests were made for 11 combinations of price quoted and selling expenses incurred for a profit-maximizing firm; five of the six sample records were made use of. A Kolmogorov-Smirnov test (Siegel [50] pp. 48–51) was employed in place of the usual χ^2-test.[15]

TABLE 10.7

Test of Poisson Model

Run	Price Interval	Selling Cost Interval	Number of Observations	Average Sales	Standard Deviation	D	Probability of Deviation D
1	29–30	7.0– 7.5	5	2,126	46.1	0.3936	0.20
1	23–24	9.5–10.0	6	3,395	58.3	0.2040	0.20
2	25–26	8.5– 9.0	6	2,667	51.6	0.3393	0.20
2	22–23	9.0– 9.5	9	3,388	58.2	0.1697	0.20
2	19–20	11.5–12.0	7	4,924	70.2	0.2981	0.20
3	28–29	7.0– 7.5	8	2,415	49.1	0.1731	0.20
3	27–28	7.5– 8.0	7	2,568	50.7	0.1778	0.20
3	26–27	8.5– 9.0	19	3,015	54.9	0.2829	0.10
4	28–29	6.5– 7.0	9	2,580	50.8	0.1801	0.20
4	25–26	7.5– 8.0	8	2,910	54.0	0.1711	0.20
5	27–28	8.0– 8.5	16	2,462	49.6	0.2660	0.15

The last column of Table 10.7 may be interpreted to provide adequate evidence that sales have a Poisson distribution with a parameter θ estimated by average sales.

5.2   The second hypothesis was that θ is a function of p and c. It was argued in Chapter 4, Section 2, that θ should be of the form $\mu(p)\lambda(c)$. A simple model that satisfies the stipulations was chosen as $\mu(p)\lambda(c) = ap^{-b}c^r$, with a, b, and c being positive. For two firms (one a profit maximizer and the other a profit stabilizer), estimates of a, b, and r were obtained through multiple regression analysis with the form

$$\log \theta = \log a - b \log p + r \log c. \qquad (10.12)$$

---

[15] Siegel makes the following plea for the superiority of the *KS*-test: The Kolmogorov-Smirnov one-sample test treats individual observations separately and thus, unlike the χ^2 test for one sample, need not lose information through combining categories. When samples are small, and therefore adjacent categories must be combined before χ^2 may properly be computed, the χ^2 test is definitely less powerful than the Kolmogorov-Smirnov test. Moreover, for very small samples the χ^2 test is not applicable at all, but the Kolmogorov-Smirnov test is. These facts suggest that the Kolmogorov-Smirnov test may in all cases be more powerful than its alternative, the χ^2 test (Siegel, *loc. cit.*).

Final estimates of a, b, and r were obtained as averages of estimates obtained from each of six runs. The equation for the profit-maximizer was

$$\hat{\theta} = 24{,}100p^{-1.21}c^{0.34}$$

and for the profit stabilizer

$$\hat{\theta} = 136{,}000p^{-1.72}c^{0.27}.$$

The multiple correlation coefficients R of the run estimates varied between 0.985 and 0.999 for the profit maximizer and between 0.839 and 0.976 for the profit stabilizer.

PART THREE

Chapter **11**

PURE COMPETITION: RANDOM PRICES

In its content and organization this chapter is a digression from the main stream of the preceding analysis. It is concerned with a kind of competition in which the firms have no material reason for or evidence of a conflict of interests. In this competition there is no "struggle" among the firms to grab a larger share of the market; also, there is no feeling of "being watched" and no need for a firm to watch others. It will be seen that from the viewpoint of an individual firm the essential *uncertainty* is about the *price* received for the product. This leaves only one decision variable at the disposal of the firm: the amount of output to offer on the market. Also, it leaves open the possibility of speculating about the future of prices. The implications are investigated in considerable depth in Chapter 13.

The present chapter is organized as follows: a model of the probability distribution of price is derived from the (S, M, Y)-specifications (Section 1), some empirical evidence is presented (Section 2), and an attempt is made to link this reasoning and procedure with that of the simultaneous equations approach of econometry (Section 3). In Section 4 an alternative analysis is presented, primarily with a view toward bringing out the relationship of the present work with the classical analysis. A brief discussion of a dynamic model is presented in Section 5.

1. CHARACTERISTICS OF MARKET PRICES

The situation to be examined here is characterized by the fact that no firm has the "feeling of being watched," hence does not feel the need to watch the "others." The usual explanation of this phenomenon is sought in (a) the largeness of the *number* of buyers and sellers and (b) the homogeneity of the product. In light of the observations in Chapters 4 to 6,

135

this explanation does not appear to be complete. The minimum basis of competition is to be sought in the fact that there is *bargaining* between buyers and sellers and that this is based upon an almost costless *communication and information* concerning the current state of the market. It is these facts, combined with the *homogeneity* of the product that produce the outstanding feature of competition: a *uniform price* is to prevail at the end of the bargaining process. But no individual buyer or seller *sets* the price. Seen from the viewpoint of an individual transactor, this appears as and reinforces the *parametric* nature of the market price.

But precisely because it is a parameter, there is prior *uncertainty* about the level of the price at which the market will be closed. Thus, alike from the viewpoint of the "external observer" and of an individual transactor, the *market price* takes on the features of a *random* variable. The purpose of this section is to characterize the randomness of market price.

1.1   What is commonly known among economists as a "purely competitive" market situation can be characterized in terms of the following (S, M, Y)-specifications. In regard to the *organization* of the market it is postulated that

M:1   The product is homogeneous: no buyer can stand to gain or lose in deciding not to buy from a particular seller.

M:2   There is a large number of buyers and sellers, and the maximum amount each can buy or sell is a negligibly small fraction of the aggregate demand or the aggregate potential supply.

M:3   There is free bargaining between buyers and sellers.

The bargaining process may take on a variety of forms. For the present purposes it is appropriate to consider two extreme types. In the one there is a possibility of *recontracting*, such that no transaction takes place until the end of the period during which the buyers and sellers will have made all the bargaining and rebargaining and inquiries they would care for. In the other the *mobility within the market need not be "perfect,"* that is, the buyers and/or sellers are relatively less "energetic" or communication and information are not costless. It is very likely, then, that transactions will be *bunched* at several distinct prices, each price being established during different segments of the same market period. In these instances, one may speak of an average of such prices. The dispersion of the *individual* prices (each established for one "bunch" of transactions) about the average will depend on a number of factors. The most important of these is the nature of the product itself.[1]

1.2 In regard to the characteristics of *communication and information*, the following postulates are made:

Y:1 There is communication among the sellers in respect to the current price inquiries from the buyers; similarly, there is communication among the buyers in respect to the current price offers from the sellers.

Y:2 The information that is communicated is available from specialized institutions and facilities, but at a cost.[2]

In view of the fact that most markets are not ideally located at a single point in space but are spread over a cluster of points, communication may not be complete.[3] The *principle* that furnishes a basis for the establishment of prices is already contained in the postulates M:1 to M:3: The market is to be *cleared at the market price*. As in classical theory, this means that a pair of numbers—the market price and the quantity transacted—is simultaneously established. This observation is the key to the construction of a probability distribution of price. But the need for a probability distribution should again be emphasized: *quantities* are the decision variables of both buyers and sellers; it is the price that is formed in the market by forces on which no individual has a control.

2. DERIVATION OF PRICE PROBABILITIES

The purpose of this section is to demonstrate how the form of the probability distribution of market prices has its root in the specifications introduced in the preceding section. Throughout the discussion, it will be tacitly assumed that the buyers do not become sellers, and vice versa.

2.1 In conformity with the postulates of M:2 suppose that q, the quantity offered (for purchase or sale) by an *individual*, is bounded in some

---

[1] There are commodities in respect to which the distinction between buying and selling positions is not well defined. Such, for instance, is the case with the titles to wealth (stocks and bonds). That is to say, a buyer may become a seller and vice versa. This is particularly true whenever there is uncertainty about the distant future of prices and whenever, in addition, immediate delivery is not required for the consummation of a transaction.

[2] A good deal seems to depend not only on the level of these costs, but also on peoples' relative disposition to them.

[3] In the framework of classical theory, this situation would be characterized as one of pure but imperfect competition. In some sense, there seems to be a connection between the "largeness of numbers" of both buyers and sellers, on the one hand, and the "perfectness" of competition on the other hand.

interval $Q: a \leq q \leq b$. Let $w(q)$ denote the event that in an arbitrarily selected contact the offer does not exceed some quantity y; then,

$$w(q) = \begin{cases} 1, & \text{if } a \leq q \leq y, \\ 0, & \text{otherwise.} \end{cases} \tag{11.1}$$

A "likelihood" of this event may be defined in the following manner:[4]

$$L(a \leq q \leq y) = \frac{y - a}{b - a} = \alpha; \qquad L(y < q \leq b) = \frac{b - y}{b - a} = 1 - \alpha. \tag{11.2}$$

Next, observe that in pure competition the buyers and sellers make their *decisions independently*. Thus the choices $w(q)$ are to be independent in the statistical sense. The phenomenon of independence may be represented in a manner similar to the one presented in Chapter 5. Define $T_\alpha(q)$ as

$$T_\alpha(q) = \begin{cases} \dfrac{q}{y - a}, & \text{if } a \leq q \leq y, \\ \dfrac{q - (y - a)}{b - y}, & \text{if } y < q \leq b \end{cases} \tag{11.3}$$

and then recursively define the sequence $\{w_k(p)\}$ as

$$w_1(p) = w(q); \qquad w_k(p) = w_{k-1}[T_\alpha(q)], \qquad k = 2, 3, \ldots. \tag{11.4}$$

Next consider the postulates M:3 and M:1 in combination with Y:2. As was observed in Section 1, transactions are bunched at several prices which, in general, are not too widely scattered. In addition, the bunches themselves are statistically independent. Thus the outcome of a period's market operations will have the representation shown in Figure 1 in which $p = p(q)$ can be approximated as

$$p(N, q) = \sum_{j=1}^{N} c_j I_{[p^{-1}(c_j)]}(q), \tag{11.5}$$

where the summation is over the number of bunches. The randomness lies in the *lengths of the projections* on the q-interval over which the values c_j are taken on. Over a succession of market periods, these lengths vary in a random fashion.

[4] Note that in this construction, $L(.)$ is not made to depend upon y. In practice, it will depend not only on y, but also on other parameters, such as disposable income, on the buyers' side, and expected unit profit or cost, on the sellers' side. These considerations will be taken up in Section 4.

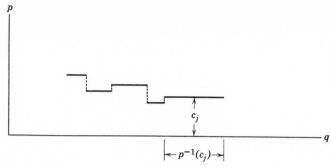

Figure 11.1

2.2 First suppose that N in expression (11.5) is a constant or nearly so. (This is relaxed in Section 4.) Also define the normalized function $\delta_k(q)$:

$$\delta_k(q) = \frac{w_k(q) - \alpha}{\sqrt{m_j \alpha(1 - \alpha)}}, \qquad k = 1, 2, \ldots, m_j,$$

where m_j indicates the number of δ's in the jth bunch. Then, in terms of the $\delta_k(q)$, we have the following representation for the price formed in the market in some arbitrarily chosen market period:

$$p(N, q) = \sum_{j=1}^{N} c_j \sum_{k=1}^{m} \delta_k(q). \tag{11.6}$$

As we have seen in Chapter 5, the probability $\Pr[p(q) \le x]$ can be evaluated as a limiting measure:

$$\Pr[p(q) \le x] = \mu^* = \lim_{m_1, m_2, \cdots, m_N \to \infty} \mu(N)$$

$$= \lim_{m_1, m_2, \cdots, m_N \to \infty} \mu\left[q : \sum_{j=1}^{N} c_j \sum_{k=1}^{m_j} \delta_k(q) \le x\right]. \tag{11.7}$$

In order to determine the $\mu(N)$, define $u = p(N, q)$ and let

$$g(u) = \begin{cases} 1, & \text{if } u \le x, \\ 0, & \text{otherwise.} \end{cases}$$

for which there is a Fourier representation;

$$g(x) = \frac{1}{2\pi} \iint_{-\infty}^{\infty} \exp\left[i\xi(u - x)\right] g(u) \, du \, d\xi.$$

Now $\mu(N)$ is the mathematical expectation of the set function $g(.)$, so that

$$\mu(N) = \int_a^b g\left[\sum_{j=1}^{N} c_j \sum_{k=1}^{m_j} \delta_j(q)\right] dq, \tag{11.8}$$

which (on a change in the order of integration and an integration with respect to q) gives

$$\mu(N) = \frac{1}{2\pi} \int_{-\infty}^{\infty} \int_{-\infty}^{\infty} \exp(i\xi u) g(u) \, du \, d\xi H(\xi), \qquad (11.9)$$

with $H(\xi)$ defined as follows:

$$H(\xi) = \prod_{j=1}^{N} H_{m_j}(\xi),$$

$$H_{m_j}(\xi) = \left[(1-\alpha) \exp\left(i\xi c_j \sqrt{\frac{\alpha}{(1-\alpha)m_j}} \right) + \alpha \exp\left\{ -i\xi c_j \sqrt{\frac{1-\alpha}{\alpha m_j}} \right\} \right]^{m_j}.$$
$$(11.10)$$

Note that $H_{m_j}(\xi)$ may be expanded as follows:

$$H_{m_j}(\xi) = \left\{ (1-\alpha)\left[1 + (i\xi c_j)\sqrt{\frac{\alpha}{(1-\alpha)m_j}} + \frac{\frac{1}{2}(i\xi c_j)^2\alpha}{(1-\alpha)m_j} + \cdots \right] \right.$$

$$\left. + \alpha \left[1 + (-i\xi cf)\sqrt{\frac{1-\alpha}{\alpha m_j}} + \frac{1}{2}(-i\xi c_j)^2\frac{1-\alpha}{\alpha m_j} + \cdots \right] \right\}^{m_j}$$

$$= \left[1 - \frac{1}{2}c_j^2\xi^2 + 0\left(\frac{1}{m_j}\right) \right]^{m_j}. \qquad (11.11)$$

Let the m_j ($j = 1, \ldots, N$) be ordered in some sequence and suppose that the largest tends to infinity[5] first, then the next largest, and so on. Then,

$$\lim_{m_1 \to \infty} H_{m_1}(\xi) = \exp\left(\frac{-\xi^2 c_1^2}{2} \right), \ldots, \qquad \lim_{m_N \to \infty} H_{m_N}(\xi) = \exp\left(\frac{-\xi^2 c_N^2}{2} \right).$$

Thus, formula (11.7) can be evaluated[6] as follows:

$$\mu^* = \lim_{m_1 \to \infty, \cdots, m_N \to \infty} \frac{1}{2\pi} \int_{-\infty}^{\infty} \int_{-\infty}^{\infty} e^{i\xi u} g(u) \left[\prod_{j=1}^{N} H_{m_j}(\xi) \right] du \, d\xi$$

$$= \frac{1}{2\pi} \int_{-\infty}^{\infty} \int_{-\infty}^{\infty} \exp\left(i\xi u - \frac{1}{2}\xi^2 \sum_{j=1}^{N} c_j^2 \right) g(u) \, du$$

$$= \frac{1}{c\sqrt{2\pi}} \int_{-\infty}^{\infty} g(u) e^{(-u^2/2c^2)} \, du, \qquad \left(c^2 \equiv \sum_{j=1}^{N} c_j^2 \right),$$

$$= \frac{1}{c\sqrt{2\pi}} \int_{-\infty}^{x} e^{(-u^2/2c^2)} \, du, \qquad (11.12)$$

[5] Here, as elsewhere, "tending to infinity" essentially means that m_j becomes sufficiently large. This is precisely the reflection of the postulate that there are sufficiently many buyers and sellers.

[6] The method consists in performing the limit operation under the sign of integration. This, unfortunately, is not valid in the present case because $g(u) \exp[i\xi u]$ is not absolutely integrable. However, *Kac*[32] has given a derivation which shows that the end result, that is, expression (11.12) is formally correct.

which establishes that the probability distribution of prices in a purely (but not necessarily perfectly) competitive market is Gaussian. The analysis shows that any parameter that influences the elementary probability α will also affect the mean-value of the distribution; similarly, any factor that affects the numbers c will also serve to modify the variance of the distribution.

3. JOINT DISTRIBUTION OF PRICE AND AGGREGATE QUANTITY

The model of prices under pure competition was seen to predict the probabilities of *market* prices, regardless of the volume traded. It did not attempt to explain *how* a level of price and an associated level of quantity traded are established simultaneously in a competitive market. Econometry is concerned precisely with this explanation and, hence, it is appropriate to examine how the present technique of analysis is related to that of econometry. More specifically, an attempt will be made to develop the joint probability distribution of price and quantity in a competitive market, and a few observations will be made on the significance of statistical specifications in the estimation of econometric simultaneous equations models.

3.1 Two essential steps can be distinguished in the classical analysis of the formation of price and aggregate quantity traded in a competitive market. First, the aggregate buyers' and sellers' behavior equations[7] are postulated as

$$X = f(p, \alpha), \qquad Y = g(p, \beta),$$

X and Y denoting the "planned" quantities, and α and β representing the parameters influencing these plans. Second, since the market is to be cleared at a uniform price, the equilibrium condition $X = Y$ is adjoined to the above equation. Thus the complete system is

$$X = f(p; \alpha), \qquad Y = g(p; \beta), \qquad X = Y, \qquad (11.13)$$

which may also be written in an equivalent form

$$H_1(p, q; \alpha) = 0, \qquad H_2(p, q; \beta) = 0, \qquad (11.14)$$

q being the aggregate volume traded. When linearly independent over

---

[7] These equations seek to describe the buying and selling *plans* or intentions of the buyers and sellers, each in the aggregate. In the classical scheme of analysis, these are developed as deterministic relationships and conceived of as aggregates of decisions of individual buyers and sellers.

some appropriate domain of the (p, q)-space, the equations in (11.14) serve to "determine" the market price, $p^0 = F(\alpha, \beta)$, and the aggregate quantity traded, $q^0 = G(\alpha, \beta)$. In econometry p and q are regarded as *endogenous* or mutually determined, and α and β are treated as *exogenous* or determining variables. As applied to the phenomena of market equilibria, the conceptual framework of econometry ordinarily consists of viewing p and q as random or chance-determined variables. The randomness is ascribed to the fact that the parameters α and β are only surrogates for a large number of other excluded variables. Thus, a random variable is introduced in the right member of each of the equations in (11.14) which, after an approximate linearization, takes the form

$$By + \Gamma z = u, \qquad |B| \neq 0. \tag{11.15}$$

(Here y is a vector $\{p, q\}$ and z is a vector $\{\alpha, \beta\}$; u is a vector of Gaussian variables, with $E[u] = 0$, and $E[u\,u'] = \Sigma$.) The *assumption* is made that z and u are statistically independent, that is,

$$\Pr[u \leq u^* \mid z = z^*] = \Pr[u \leq u^*].$$

This assumption is essential to the procedure by which the behavior equations are estimated from empirical data (Koopsman-Hood [37], 124–126). The model (11.5) leads to the so-called "reduced form":

$$y = \_B^{-1}\Gamma z + B^{-1}u = \Pi z + v.$$

This system has the following interpretation:

$$\begin{aligned} E[y \mid z = z^*] &= E[\textstyle\prod z + v \mid z = z^*] \\ &= \textstyle\prod z^* + E[v \mid z^*]. \end{aligned}$$

But since u is statistically independent of z, so is v (because v is obtained from u by a nonsingular linear transformation) and, hence, $E[v \mid z = z^*] = 0$. Consequently,

$$y \equiv E[y \mid z = z^*] = \textstyle\prod z^*. \tag{11.16}$$

Consider, for instance, the first of these equations, that is, $y_1 = \sum_j \prod_{1} z_j{}^*$, which says that given $\alpha = z_1{}^*$ and $\beta = z_2{}^*$, the conditional expectation of the demand is determined. The construction seems to be somewhat artificial: Why should the parameter β of the supply equation affect the buyers' plan? But, of course, the artificiality can be removed if it is recognized that (11.16) is *not* a system of *behavior* equations. What, then, is the true implication of (11.16)? Observe that $v \equiv B^{-1}u$ has a mean-value $E[v] = 0$ and covariance $E[v \cdot v'] = B^{-1}\Sigma(B^{-1}) = S$. But since v is

Gaussian, one may write the following *conditional joint density* function of the price and quantity traded

$$K \frac{1}{\sqrt{|S|}} \exp\left[-\tfrac{1}{2}(y - \prod z)'S^{-1}(y - \prod z)\right], \qquad (11.17)$$

K being a suitable constant. A construction will be presented in which there will be no reference to conditional probabilities; also, there will be no need to assume linearity of the behavior equations.

3.2 Consider a group of buyers, more or less homogeneous with respect to disposable income. Thus, one may conceive of two numbers a and b serving, respectively, as the uniform lower and upper bounds for the incomes θ_i of every individual i ($i = 1, 2, \ldots, N$) in the group. Define the normalized numbers $(\theta_i - a)/(b - a)$ which all lie between 0 and 1. Let Ω denote the unit interval, $\Omega = [\omega : 0 \le \omega \le 1]$. Next, in conformity with the ground rules of Section 2, suppose that the buyers in question are *final* buyers and consider the following model of an individual consumer's choice process. The process is regarded as being composed of two sub processes. In the first place, the consumer decides *whether* he will buy a unit. This is a binary decision and may be conveniently represented[8] by a two-valued function:

$$\Phi(\omega) = \begin{cases} 0, & \text{if } 0 \le \omega \le \alpha, \\ 1, & \text{if } \alpha \le \omega \le 1. \end{cases} \qquad (11.18)$$

This binary decision does *not* lead to a *demand, unless it is accompanied by a decision to pay the price.* Put another way, there are two situations: The demand-price[9] may be (a) at least equal to the going price or (b) less than the going price. This, again, can be represented by a two-valued function. Thus, suppose that the demand prices W_i ($i = 1, 2, \ldots, N$) of all the members of the group have a uniform lower bound a^* and a uniform upper bound b^*. Observe that the mapping $\lambda = (W - a^*)/(b^* - a^*)$ maps all the demand prices on the unit interval: $\Lambda = [\lambda : 0 \le \lambda \le 1]$. But since the demand price can always be expressed as a function of the income, such as $W = k\theta$ ($0 < k < \infty$), it follows that λ and ω are related as follows:

$$\lambda = \frac{k\theta - a^*}{b^* - a^*} = c\omega + d, \quad \text{say.}$$

[8] Note that here is a provision for treating the so-called "inferior" goods case: If the income is *above* some level, the consumer may decide *not* to buy the product. In order to represent such pathological cases, it will be sufficient to consider the complement of the $\Phi(\omega)$ given in (11.18).

[9] This is the maximum price the consumer is prepared to pay rather than go without the unit of the product.

Thus, we define the following two-valued function on Λ:

$$\Psi(\lambda) = \begin{cases} 0, & \text{if } d \leq \lambda \leq \beta, \\ 1, & \text{if } \beta < \lambda \leq c + d. \end{cases} \tag{11.19}$$

$\Psi(\lambda) = 1$ indicates the occasion when the demand price is at least as great as the going price. The number of *joint occurrences* of $\Phi(\omega) = 1$ and $\Psi(\lambda) = 1$ is precisely the indicator of the formation of an individual buyer's demand. For the sake of definiteness, the following measures or probabilities[10] will be postulated for the function $\Phi(\omega)$ and $\Psi(\lambda)$:

$$\mu[\omega: \Phi(\omega) = 0] = \alpha, \qquad\qquad \mu[\omega: \Phi(\omega) = 1] = 1 - \alpha,$$

$$\mu[\lambda: \Psi(\lambda) = 0] = \frac{\beta - d}{c} = \nu, \qquad \mu[\lambda: \Psi(\lambda) = 1] = 1 - \nu. \tag{11.20}$$

Because there are four possible pairs of values of $\Phi(.)$ and $\Psi(.)$, the following conditional probabilities need to be specified:

$$\mu_{ij} = \mu[(\omega, \lambda): \Psi(\lambda) = j \mid \Phi(\omega) = i], \qquad i, j = 0, 1. \tag{11.21}$$

The μ_{ij} play the role of summary descriptors of individual behavior. Furthermore, they define an implicit relationship between α and ν by means of the following system of equations:

$$(\nu, \quad 1 - \nu) = (\alpha, \quad 1 - \alpha)\begin{pmatrix} \mu_{00}, & \mu_{01} \\ \mu_{10}, & \mu_{11} \end{pmatrix}. \tag{11.22}$$

3.3 The functions $\Phi(\omega)$ and $\Psi(\lambda)$ and the elementary probabilities μ_{ij} serve only to characterize *an* arbitrary individual. Therefore, some scheme is needed for describing the *mutually independent decisions* of several individuals. The one to be used here is a simple adaptation of a similar scheme introduced in Chapter 5. It consists, first, of defining two transformations

$$T_\alpha(\omega) = \begin{cases} \dfrac{\omega}{\alpha}, & 0 \leq \omega \leq \alpha, \\[2mm] \dfrac{\omega - \alpha}{1 - \alpha}, & \alpha < \omega \leq 1, \end{cases} \qquad T_\nu(\lambda) = \begin{cases} \dfrac{\lambda}{\nu}, & 0 \leq \lambda \leq \nu, \\[2mm] \dfrac{\lambda - \nu}{1 - \nu}, & \nu < \lambda \leq 1. \end{cases}$$

$$\tag{11.23}$$

and then recursively constructing two sequences, $\{\Phi_j(\omega), j = 1, \ldots, N\}$ and $\{\Psi_j(\lambda), j = 1, 2, \ldots, N\}$ in the following manner:

$$\begin{aligned} \Phi_1 &= \Phi(\omega), & \Phi_j(\omega) &= \Phi_{j-1}[T_\alpha(\omega)], & j &= 1, 2, \ldots, N; \\ \Psi_1 &= \Psi(\lambda), & \Psi_j(\lambda) &= \Psi_{j-1}[T_\nu(\lambda)], & j &= 1, 2, \ldots, N. \end{aligned} \tag{11.24}$$

---

[10] All measures are to be linear measures throughout the present discussion.

By construction, the $\{\Phi_j(\omega)\}$ and $\{\Psi_j(\lambda)\}$ are each a sequence of mutually independent choice functions for the N individuals. Thus, the aggregate or *market* demand function may be represented as the pair

$$Q_N(\omega) = \sum_{j=1}^{N} \Phi_j(\omega); \qquad P_N(\lambda) = \sum_{j=1}^{N} \Psi_j(\lambda). \tag{11.25}$$

A meaningful version of a demand function is the system of probabilities

$$\Pr\,[Q(\omega) \le q,\, P(\lambda) \le p],$$
$$= \lim_{N \to \infty} \Pr\,[Q_N(\omega) \le q,\, P_N(\lambda) \le p]. \tag{11.26}$$

These will be shown to exist in an appropriate sense as the number N of consumers tends to increase indefinitely. The essential step is to normalize the quantities $\Phi_j(\omega)$ and $\Psi_j(\lambda)$. Recall from the definitions that

$$\begin{aligned}
E[\Phi_j(\omega)] &= 1 - \alpha, & E[\Psi_j(\lambda)] &= 1 - \nu, \\
\text{Var}\,[\Phi_j(\omega)] &= N\alpha(1 - \alpha), & \text{Var}\,[\Psi_j(\lambda)] &= N\nu(1 - \nu).
\end{aligned} \tag{11.27}$$

With the aid of (11.27), define the functions $\epsilon_j(\omega)$ and $\delta_j(\lambda)$,

$$\epsilon_j(\omega) = \frac{\Phi_j(\omega) - (1 - \alpha)}{\sqrt{N\alpha(1 - \alpha)}} = \begin{cases} A \equiv \dfrac{\sqrt{1 - \alpha}}{\sqrt{N\alpha}}, & 0 \le \omega \le \alpha, \\[2ex] B \equiv +\dfrac{\sqrt{\alpha}}{\sqrt{N(1 - \alpha)}}, & \alpha < \omega \le 1, \end{cases}$$

$$\delta_j(\lambda) = \frac{\Psi_j(\lambda) - (1 - \nu)}{\sqrt{N\nu(1 - \nu)}} = \begin{cases} C \equiv -\dfrac{\sqrt{1 - \nu}}{\sqrt{N\nu}}, & 0 \le \lambda \le \nu, \\[2ex] D \equiv +\dfrac{\sqrt{\nu}}{\sqrt{N(1 - \nu)}}, & \nu < \lambda \le 1, \end{cases}$$

and consider the normalized version of (11.25);

$$U(N,\,\omega) = \sum_{j=1}^{N} \epsilon_j(\omega), \qquad V(N,\,\lambda) = \sum_{j=1}^{N} \delta_j(\lambda). \tag{11.28}$$

The next step is to determine the limiting form of joint probability distribution of $U(N,\,\omega)$ and $V(N,\,\lambda)$. Define the set function

$$g[U(N,\,\omega),\, V(N,\,\lambda)] = \begin{cases} 1, & \text{if } U(N,\,\omega) \le q,\, V(N,\,\lambda) \le p, \\ 0, & \text{otherwise.} \end{cases}$$

Then, the required probability is given by

$$\mu(N) = \Pr [U(N, \omega) \le q, V(N, L) \le p]$$

$$= \int_{\Omega \times \Lambda} g[U(N, \omega), V(N, \lambda)] \, d\mu(\omega, \lambda), \qquad (11.29)$$

which is the mathematical expectation of $g[U(N, \omega), V(N, \lambda)]$. But since $g(., .)$ has an integral representation

$$g(U, V) = (2\pi)^{-2} \iint\limits_{-\infty}^{\infty} \iint\limits_{-\infty}^{\infty} g(u, v)$$

$$\times \exp \{i\xi[u - U(N, \omega)] + i\eta[v - V(N, \lambda)]\} \, du \, dv \, d\xi \, d\eta,$$

therefore, the computation of the required probability $\mu(N)$ rests upon the evaluation of the following integral:

$$\mu(N) = (2\pi)^{-2} \int_0^1 \int_0^1 \left\{ \iiiint\limits_{-\infty}^{\infty} g(u, v) \exp (i\xi u + i\eta v) \, du \, dv \, d\xi \, d\eta \right.$$

$$\left. \times \exp [-i\xi U(N, \omega) - i\eta V(N, \lambda)] \right\} d\omega \, d\lambda$$

$$= (2\pi)^{-2} \iiiint\limits_{-\infty}^{\infty} g(u, v) \exp (i\xi u + i\eta v) \cdot J(N, \xi, \eta) \, d\xi \, d\eta, \qquad (11.30)$$

where the function $J(N, \xi, \eta)$ is defined as

$$J(N, \xi, \eta) = \int_{\Omega \times \Lambda} \exp [-i\xi U(N, \omega) - i\eta V(N, \lambda)] \, d\mu(\omega, \lambda)$$

$$= \int_{\Omega \times \Lambda} \exp \left[-i\xi \sum_1^N \epsilon_j(\omega) - i\eta \sum_1^N \delta_j(\lambda) \right] d\mu(\omega, \lambda).$$

From the definition of the functions $\epsilon_j(\omega)$ and $\delta_j(\lambda)$ and from the Eqs. (11.20) to (11.22) the integral $J(N, \xi, \eta)$ is seen to be

$$J(N, \xi, \eta) = [\alpha e^{i\xi A}(\mu_{00} e^{i\mu B} + \mu_{01} e^{-i\eta C}) + (1 - \alpha)e^{-i\xi D}(\mu_{00} e^{i\eta B} + \mu_{11} e^{-i\eta C})]^N, \qquad (11.31)$$

the N-fold product being due to the independence of one (ϵ, δ) pair from another. Expanding (11.31) in power-series around $\xi = 0$ and $\eta = 0$ and retaining terms of the order up to ξ^2, η^2, and $\xi\eta$, we have

$$J(N, \xi, \eta) = \left[1 - \frac{1}{2N} (\xi^2 + \eta^2 + 2\xi\eta\rho) \right]^N \qquad (11.32)$$

where the constant ρ is defined as

$$\rho = (r_1 r_2)^{-1}[-\alpha\mu_{00}(r_1 r_2)^2 + \alpha\mu_{10}r_1^2 + (1-\alpha)\mu_{10}r_2^2 - (1-\alpha)\mu_{11}],$$

$$r_1 \equiv \frac{\sqrt{1-\alpha}}{\sqrt{\alpha}}, \qquad r_2 \equiv \frac{\sqrt{1-\nu}}{\sqrt{\nu}}. \tag{11.33}$$

Substituting (11.32) into (11.30) we have

$$\mu(N) = (2\pi)^{-2} \iiiint\limits_{-\infty}^{\infty} g(u, v)$$

$$\times \exp\left(i\xi u + i\eta v\right)\left[1 - \frac{1}{2N}(\xi^2 + \eta^2 + 2\xi\eta\rho)\right]^N du\,dv\,d\xi\,d\eta.$$

Following the procedure described in Chapter 5, it is seen that

$$\Pr\left[Q(\omega) \leq p,\, P(\lambda) \leq p\right] = \lim_{N \to \infty} \mu(N)$$

$$= \frac{1}{2\pi}\int_{-\infty}^{q}\int_{-\infty}^{p} \exp\left[-\frac{1}{2(1-\rho^2)}(u^2 + v^2 - uv\rho)\right]\frac{du\,dv}{\sqrt{1-\rho^2}}. \tag{11.34}$$

Equation (11.34) gives the joint distribution of demand quantity and demand price. It is a (bivariate) Gaussian distribution with the correlation coefficient ρ being a function of two sets of parameters: (1) the threshold disposable income associated with α and (2) a measure of the buyer's inertia or readiness as indicated by the μ_{ij}. From a strictly mathematical viewpoint, the procedure shown above is an application of the well-known central limit theorem. Equation (11.34) may be put to two uses: First, one may derive the conditional expectation of demand quantity given a price. The functional dependence of this expectation on the threshold income is clearly brought out, as it should be in any representation—deterministic or probabilistic—of market demand function. Second, one may also obtain the conditional expectation of demand price, given a demand quantity; this, also, will be parametrized by the threshold income. It should be observed that *no random variable has been "introduced" in ad hoc manner.* Indeed, the randomness and its specific measure (the bivariate Gaussian probability) were developed exclusively from the postulates underlying the classical demand function. Furthermore, in the derivation presented here, there has been no occasion to make use of the hypothesis (11.15); it has been shown that such a hypothesis is completely extraneous.

3.4 Now that the technique has been demonstrated in the case of the market *demand* function, the market supply function may be constructed in an analogous manner. The essential step is to set up appropriate choice functions; but here, as in the case of the demand function, it appears that the selection of such functions is not unique. However, a considerable insight is furnished by the nature of the business environment and the motivation of individual firms. A scheme which is not too artificial and which is also directly suggested by the conditions of pure competition is the following: Consider R the *revenue need*, and let R_j denote the revenue need of the jth firm in a suitably defined category of firms. Introducing uniform upper and lower bounds for the R_j, let the individual revenue needs be mapped into the unit interval $X = [x: 0 \leq x \leq 1]$. This is one of the required sample spaces. Next, define on X the two-valued function $L(x)$:

$$L(x) = \begin{cases} 0, & \text{if } 0 \leq x \leq a, \\ 1, & \text{if } a < x \leq 1. \end{cases} \tag{11.35}$$

The occurrence of $L(x) = 1$ does not imply that a supply decision is made. In order that an intention to supply may generate a *supply function*, something is required in addition: The going price must at least cover the unit cost. Thus, introduce a new variable C, the unit cost. After mapping the individual firm's unit costs C_j on the unit interval $Y = [y: 0 \leq y \leq 1]$ (and, thus, setting up another sample-space) define another two-valued function $M(y)$:

$$M(y) = \begin{cases} 1, & \text{if } 0 \leq y \leq b, \\ 0, & \text{if } b < y \leq 1. \end{cases} \tag{11.36}$$

An individual firm's supply function comes into effect only when the event $\{L(x) = 1, M(y) = 1\}$ occurs. From this stage on, the procedure is the same as was employed for the demand function.

4. AN INDUCED RANDOMNESS

An alternative representation of the randomness in market price is sought in a simple modification of the "classical" model of market equilibrium: The demand and supply decisions are retained as non-probabilistic functions of the undetermined price, but the *numbers* of buyers and sellers are regarded as *random*. Thus, the requirement that the market is to be cleared at a single price makes the price appear as a "draw" from a distribution.

4.1 Suppose that there are distinct homogeneous groups of buyers and sellers and that the demand functions and supply functions of these groups are distinguished by appropriate values of certain parameters.

Thus, there are group supply functions

$$q_i^{(s)} = q_i^{(s)}(p; \sigma_i), \qquad i = 1, 2, \ldots, n,$$

in which p is the undetermined market price and σ_i is the parameter distinguishing the ith class. Similarly, there are group demand functions

$$q_j^{(d)} = q_j^{(d)}(p; \beta_j), \qquad j = 1, 2, \ldots, m,$$

each group being distinguished by the value of its parameter β. (Since the groups are homogeneous, members of a given group all have the identical demand or supply function.) Now suppose that *random numbers* of sellers and buyers of different groups participate in the market operations of a given period. Let S_i be the random number of sellers coming from the ith group and let B_j be the random numbers of buyers from the jth group of buyers. Then the condition that the market would clear at a uniform price would read as follows:

$$\sum_{i=1}^{n} S_i q_i^{(s)}(p) = \sum_{j=1}^{m} B_j q_j^{(d)}(p), \qquad (11.37)$$

where the parameters σ_i and β_j have been suppressed. Equation (11.37) is to be interpreted to mean that

$$\Pr\left[\sum_{i=1}^{n} S_i q_i^{(s)}(p) \le x\right] = \Pr\left[\sum_{j=1}^{m} B_j q_j^{(d)}(p) \le x\right] \qquad (11.38)$$

at all continuity points of the two distributions. The solution of (11.37) gives the probability distribution of market price. This principle is illustrated in the following paragraph.

4.2 Suppose for the sake of definiteness that there is only one class of buyers with a demand function

$$q^{(d)}(p) \equiv \beta p^{-m}, \qquad (m > 0, \beta > 0) \qquad (11.39)$$

and only one class of sellers with a supply function

$$q^{(s)}(p) \equiv \sigma p^n, \qquad (n > 0, \sigma > 0). \qquad (11.40)$$

(These functions are assumed to exist on some appropriate domain of values of p.) Then the condition of market equilibrium takes on the simple form:

$$S\sigma p^n = B\beta p^{-m}. \qquad (11.41)$$

Next, suppose that the random variables S and B are independently *exponentially* distributed with parameters λ_s and λ_b, respectively. Letting $U = S/B$ and $A = \beta/\sigma$, equation (11.41) may be written as

$$U = Ap^{-(m+n)}. \qquad (11.42)$$

The probability density of U is seen to be

$$\Phi(u) = \lambda_b \lambda_s \int_0^\infty \exp\left[-(\lambda_s u + \lambda_b)b\right]b \, db$$

$$= \lambda_s \lambda_b (\lambda_s u + \lambda_b)^{-2};$$

but because $|du/dp| = (m + n)Ap^{-(m+n+1)}$, the usual rule for transformation of probabilities leads to the following probability function for prices:

$$\Psi'(p) \, dp = (m + n)\lambda_s \lambda_b Ap^{m+n-1}(A\lambda_s + \lambda_b p^{m+n})^{-2} \, dp. \quad (11.43)$$

(That $\Psi'(p)$ is an "honest" probability density may be checked by a straightforward integration.) It may be verified that the mathematical expectation of price is

$$E[p] = \frac{\pi/a}{a \sin(\pi/a)}\left(\frac{B\lambda_s}{\sigma\lambda_b}\right)^{1/a}, \qquad a \equiv m + n. \quad (11.44)$$

One may observe that as $1/\lambda_b$ (the mean number of buyers) increases and/or as $1/\lambda_s$ (the mean number of sellers) decreases, there is an increase in the *mean-value* of market price. This is an "operational" counterpart of the classical explanation of variations in the market price.

5. A FAMILY OF DYNAMIC MODELS

The principal aim of this section is to consider the dynamics of prices. Consistent with the outlook presented earlier, an attempt is made to characterize the dynamics of the *probability*-distribution of prices in a competitive market. Broadly speaking, two techniques are available for the purpose. One consists in postulating the probabilities of changes in the price level and, thus, constructing a difference or difference-differential *equation in the probability function*. This is not emphasized in the work to follow. The other consists in postulating a differential *equation for sample functions* of the stochastic price process. According to this procedure, a differential equation is developed (from the postulates about the market) for the dynamics of prices; then, random disturbances (also following from the postulates about the market) are introduced either as a forcing term or as one of the coefficients of the differential equation. The probability structure of these elements, thus, are seen to induce a probability structure in the (random) solution.

5.1 Economists often emphasize that the movements of prices are interrelated primarily because products stand in the relationship of substitutiveness or complementarity among themselves. In other words, the natural setting for the analysis of price movements is the multi-commodity market. For such markets, Arrow [1] and Samuelson [46] have indicated the following technique of analysis. Let $D_i(p_1, \ldots, p_n)$ and $S_i(p_1, \ldots, p_n), i = 1, 2, \ldots, n$, be the n demand and supply functions, the arguments $p_1, \ldots, p_n$ denoting the prices. If the excess demands, positive or negative, are denoted by $E_i = D_i(p_1, \ldots, p_n) - S_i(p_1, \ldots, p_n)$ then the movement of price is described by the system of differential equations

$$\frac{dp_i}{dt} = f_i(E_1, E_2, \ldots, E_{n-1}), \qquad i = 1, 2, \ldots, n - 1,$$
$$p_i(0) = p_{i0}$$
(11.45)

These are $n - 1$ equations because one of the commodities is what the economists call the "numéraire." Equation (11.45) emphasizes that the movement of the price of an individual commodity depends upon the levels of the excess demands of *all* the other commodities. In practice, these "other" excess demand functions cannot be established without a knowledge of how buyers and sellers make their plans and how they react to the discrepancies between actual and anticipated prices. This lack of knowledge may be made good by introducing a random function. Thus, the price of a given product is supposed to move in time according to

$$\frac{dp}{dt} = f[D(p) - S(p)].$$
(11.46)

If the function is linear and $D(p)$ and $S(p)$ possess appropriate differentiability (in some interval of variation of price), then the right member of (11.46) can be expanded in Taylor series around the equilibrium level. Retaining terms up to the first order, one obtains

$$\frac{dp}{dt} = -\alpha(t)\, p(t) + u(t), \qquad p(t_0) = p_0$$
(11.47)

where $u(t)$ is a *random* function (or stochastic process) playing the role of a surrogate for all the influences that have been ignored. Equation (11.47) portrays the fact that in the absence of interaction with other prices the price of the given commodity would evolve according to

$$\frac{dp}{dt} + \alpha(t)\, p(t) = 0, \qquad p(0) = p_0;$$

but the influence of $u(t)$ keeps the system in motion and imparts randomness to it. An alternative representation of the same phenomenon may be given by the scheme

$$\frac{dp}{dt} = -\beta(t)\, p(t), \qquad p(t_0) = p_0, \tag{11.48}$$

in which $\beta(t)$ is a stochastic process representing the random magnitudes of $|(dD/dp) - (dS/dp)|$ at various instants of time.   In order to avoid the question of differentiability of the $p(t)$-process, the equations (11.47) and (11.48) would be written as

$$\int_{t_0}^{t} dp(\tau) = -\int_{t_0}^{t} \alpha(\tau)\, p(\tau)\, d\tau + \int_{t_0}^{t} u(\tau)\, d\tau, \tag{11.49}$$

$$\int_{t_0}^{t} dp(\tau) = -\int_{t_0}^{t} p(\tau)\, \beta(\tau)\, d\tau. \tag{11.50}$$

For the discussion to follow, it is essential to set up a rigorous framework in which the solutions of (11.49) and (11.50) may be said to exist and may be interpreted.   First, consider the problem of *existence* of the integrals in (11.49) and (11.50) and, hence, of making precise the sense in which one may interpret these equations.   The integrals will be understood in the Riemann sense.   Thus,

$$\int_{t_0}^{t} u(\tau)\, d\tau \equiv \int_{t_0}^{t} u(\tau, \omega)\, d\tau = J(\omega),$$

a random variable defined on the space Ω, on which the stochastic process $u(t) \equiv u(t, \omega)$ is defined.   But, as is well known in the theory of integration,

$$J(\omega) = \lim_{\delta \to 0} \sum_{k=0}^{n-1} u(t_k, \omega)[t_{k+1} - t_k], \tag{11.51}$$

where $\delta = \max(t_{k+1} - t_k)$ and $\{t_k\}$ is a system of points of subdivision of $[t_0, t]$.   Since the right member of (11.51) is a random variable, one must precisely characterize the *convergence*.   For this purpose, it will be quite adequate to assume that the convergence is *in the mean-square*, that is,

$$\lim_{\delta \to 0} E\left[\left\{ J(\omega) - \sum_{k=0}^{n-1} u(t_k, \omega)(t_{k+1} - t_k) \right\}^2 \right] = 0; \tag{11.52}$$

it is this interpretation that will be adhered to in the developments to follow.   Consistent with the above, the *differentiability* of the solution $p(t)$ will be understood to mean

$$\lim_{\delta t \to 0} E\left[\left| \frac{dp}{dt} - \frac{p(t + \delta t) - p(t)}{\delta t} \right|^2 \right] = 0. \tag{11.53}$$

It should be observed that if $p(t)$ is *assumed* to be continuous in the mean (over some interval of time), that is, if

$$\lim_{\delta t \to 0} E[|p(t + \delta t) - p(t)|^2] = 0,$$

then certainly it is integrable in the mean-square, and thus, one would have

$$E\left[\left|\frac{d}{dt}\int_{t_0}^{t} p(\tau)\,d\tau - p(t)\right|^2\right] = 0.$$

There will be no occasion later on to make use of this assumption for $p(t)$, although it will be explicitly assumed that $u(t)$ is continuous in the mean-square. It only remains to point out the well-known limitation [10] on the interpretation of the solution. As mentioned earlier in this section, the "solution" is *not* (11.49) or (11.50), but the *probability distribution* of the changes

$$p(t) - p(t_0) \equiv \int_{t_0}^{t} dp(\tau).$$

In other words, only the socalled "temporal law,"

$$F_n(p_1, t_1; \ldots, p_n, t_n) = \Pr\,[p(t_1) \leq p_1, \ldots, p(t_n) \leq p_n],$$

is derived for the stochastic $p(t)$-process and, therefore, one cannot answer questions that cannot be answered with a knowledge of the temporal law only.

5.2 Consider (11.47) with $\alpha(t)$ a nonrandom constant

$$\alpha(t) = \alpha > 0, \tag{11.54}$$

and introduce the following assumptions about the $u(t)$-process: $u(t)$ is a stationary Gaussian random function with the following parameters:

$$[A_1] \qquad E[u(t)] = \mu; \qquad \text{Cov}\,[u(t'), u(t'')] = k\delta(t' - t'') - \mu^2,$$

where $\delta(t' - t'')$ is the Dirac δ-function. Let $u_\omega(t)$ be a *sample* function of the $u(t)$-process and let Δt be a small interval of time. Then, the behavior of $p(t)$ can be described by the following version of (11.49):

$$\Delta p_\omega = -\alpha \int_{t_0}^{t_0 + \Delta t} p_\omega(\tau)\,d\tau + \int_{t_0}^{t_0 + \Delta t} u_\omega(\tau)\,d\tau$$

$$= -\alpha p_\omega\,\Delta t + \int_{t_0}^{t_0 + \Delta t} u_\omega(\tau)\,d\tau,$$

and on averaging over the ensemble Ω we have

$$E[\Delta p] = -\alpha E[p]\,\Delta t + \mu\,\Delta t,$$
$$\text{Var}\,[\Delta p] = k\,\Delta t - \mu^2(\Delta t)^2. \tag{11.55}$$

It is seen that

$$\lim_{\Delta t \to 0} \frac{E[\Delta p]}{\Delta t} = -\alpha E[p] + \mu = -\alpha\bar{p} + \mu,$$

$$\lim_{\Delta t \to 0} \frac{\text{Var}\,[\Delta p]}{\Delta t} = k, \tag{11.56}$$

which implies that the instantaneous changes in price would have a mean-value $= \mu - \alpha\bar{p}$ and a variance $= k$. Since the Δp has been obtained by linear transformations on the Gaussian random variables u_t, therefore, Δp is also Gaussian; thus

$$\text{Pr [instantaneous change} \le x] = \int_{-\infty}^{x} \exp\left[-\frac{(\xi - \mu + \alpha\bar{p})^2}{2k^2}\right]\frac{d\xi}{\sqrt{k2\pi}}. \tag{11.57}$$

It is now possible to generalize (11.57) with a view toward obtaining the *joint distribution* of $p_1 \equiv p(t_1)$ and $\dot{p}_2 \equiv (dp/dt)_{t=t_2}$ for $t_2 > t_1$. Thus, define

$$x_i \equiv x(t_i) = \frac{p(t_i) - E[p(t_i)]}{\text{Var}\,[p(t_i)]}, \qquad i = 1, 2, \tag{11.58}$$

and the appropriate covariance matrix $\sum_x$:

$$\sum_x = \begin{pmatrix} E(x_1^2), & E(x_1, \dot{x}_2) \\ E(x_2, \dot{x}_1), & E(\dot{x}_2^2) \end{pmatrix} = \begin{pmatrix} K_x(t_1, t_1), & K_{x\dot{x}}(t_1, t_2) \\ K_{x\dot{x}}(t_1, t_2), & K_{\dot{x}}(t_2, t_2) \end{pmatrix}. \tag{11.59}$$

Now observe that the sample functions $\{p(t, \omega)\}$ of the process

$$\frac{dp}{dt} + \alpha p(t) = u(t), \qquad \alpha > 0$$

will, with probability one, asymptotically take on the form

$$p(t) = \int_0^t e^{-\alpha(t-\tau)} u(\tau)\,d\tau$$

and recall the assumption $[A_1]$ that $u(t)$ is *stationary*. Therefore the $p(t)$ process is also stationary; hence the correlation matrix $\sum_x$ takes on the following form:

$$
\Sigma_x = \begin{pmatrix} K_x(0), & \dfrac{d}{dt}K_x(t) \\[2mm] \dfrac{d}{dt}K_{\dot x}(t), & K_{\dot x}(0) \end{pmatrix} \equiv \begin{pmatrix} b, & b\theta(t) \\[2mm] b\theta(t), & b' \end{pmatrix}. \tag{11.60}
$$

(Use has been made of the result [45] that $K_x = \partial K_x/(\partial t_1, \partial t_2)$ and that $K_{xx} = \partial K_x/\partial t_2$.) It may be verified that

$$
\Sigma_x^{-1} = \frac{1}{b[b' - b\theta(t)^2]} \begin{pmatrix} b', & -b\theta(t) \\ -b\theta(t), & b \end{pmatrix};
$$

hence the joint distribution may be written as

$$
f_2(x_1, \dot x_2; t) = \frac{1}{2\pi\sqrt{\lambda^2 - \theta(t)^2}} \exp\left[\frac{\lambda^2 x^2 + \dot x_2{}^2 - 2\theta(t)x_1\dot x_2}{-2b(\lambda^2 - \theta(t)^2)} \right], \tag{11.61}
$$

where $\lambda \equiv b'/b$. The special feature of model (11.61) is that when the $p(t)$-process becomes stationary, the *rate of change* of price is seen to be correlated with the *level* of price for times other than $t = 0$ and $\lim |t| \to \infty$. Also, conversely, the level $p(t)$ and the rate of change $\dot p(t)$, observed at the same instant of time t, are statistically independent. It should also be observed that we may employ (11.61) to obtain the conditional probabilities

$$
\Pr\left[a < \dot p(t_2) \le b \,\middle|\, p(t) = p_0\right], \tag{11.62}
$$

which are of immediate interest to someone speculating in the stock market.

5.3 The purpose of this section is to remove the assumption (11.34), $\alpha > 0$, which made it possible to speak of asymptotic stationarity of sample functions of the price adjustment process

$$
\frac{dp}{dt} = -\alpha p(t) + u(t). \tag{11.63}
$$

In fact, a differential equation will be considered which does not *necessarily* represent the dynamics of prices in a *competitive* market. Thus, one may consider a more general equation:

$$
\frac{dp}{dt} = A[t, p(t)] + B[t, p(t)]u(t), \tag{11.64}
$$

which depicts the hypothesis that the "shocks" are modified by a function $B(., .)$ which is not only time-varying but also depends upon the *level* of the current price. It is only proper to assume certain properties of $A(t)$

and $B[t, p(t)]$; for the discussion to follow, it will be sufficient to assume [20] that the correlation $K(\theta)$ of $p(t)$ and $p(t + \theta)$ has the following properties:

$$K(\theta) = K(-\theta); \lim_{|\theta| \to 0} K(\theta) = 1; \lim_{|\theta| \to 0} \frac{K(\theta) - 1}{\theta} = \text{const},$$

$$(11.65)$$

$$\lim_{|\theta| \to 0} \frac{1}{\theta} [1 - K(\theta)]^2 = \text{const}, \quad \lim_{|\theta| \to 0} \frac{1}{\theta} [1 - K(\theta)^2] = \text{const}.$$

The equation (11.64) as before, will be interpreted as

$$\int_{t_0}^{t} dp(\tau) = \int_{t_0}^{t} A[\tau, p(\tau)] \, d\tau + \int_{t_0}^{t} B[t, p(\tau)]u(\tau) \, d\tau$$

$$(11.66)$$

$$\text{or} \quad p(t) = p(t_0) + \int_{t_0}^{t} A[\tau, p(\tau)] \, d\tau + \int_{t_0}^{t} B[t, p(\tau)]u(\tau) \, d\tau.$$

At the same time $[A_1]$ will be replaced by the following: $u(\tau) \, d\tau \equiv dy(\tau)$ are the independent increments of a stationary Gaussian process and for $t > t_0$,

$$[A_2] \quad E[y(t) - y(t_0)] = c, \quad E[|y(t) - y(t)|^2] - c^2 = b(t - t_0).$$

A reasonable interpretation of (11.64) or (11.66) is that

$$\lim_{\delta t \to 0} E \left[\frac{p(t + \delta t) - p(t)}{\delta t} \,\middle|\, p(t) = \xi \right] = A[t, p(t)],$$

$$(11.67)$$

$$\lim_{\delta t \to 0} E \left[\frac{\{p(t + \delta t) - p(t)\}^2}{\delta t} \,\middle|\, p(t) = \xi \right] = B[t, p(t)],$$

and if, for the sake of illustration only, we assume that

$$A[t, p(t)] = \alpha, \quad B[t, p(t)] = g(t),$$

so that (11.66) is

$$p(t) - p(t_0) - (t - t_0)\alpha = \int_{t_0}^{t} g(\tau) \, dy(\tau),$$

it is easily seen that the interpretation (11.67) leads to

$$\Pr[p(t) \le \eta \mid p(t_0) = \xi] = \frac{1}{\sqrt{2\pi \, \Delta}} \int_{-\infty}^{\eta - \xi} \exp\left[\frac{(z - \mu)^2}{2 \, \Delta} \right] dz,$$

in which $\mu = c + (t - t_0)\alpha$ and

$$\Delta = b \int_{t_0}^{t} [B(\tau)]^2 \, d\tau.$$

Under the assumptions (11.65) and $[A_2]$ it may be shown that when properly normalized $p(t) \equiv p$ and $p(t') \equiv p'$ have a joint Gaussian distribution density

$$f(p, p') = \frac{1}{\sqrt{2\pi}\sqrt{1 - K(\theta)^2}} \exp\left[-\frac{p^2 - 2K(\theta)pp' + p'^2}{2[1 - K(\theta)^2]}\right],$$

in which $K(\theta)$ is of the form

$$K(\theta) = \text{const } e^{-\beta |\theta|}, \qquad \theta \equiv t' - t > 0.$$

Again, the conditional probability

$$\Pr\left[p(t') \leq \eta \mid p(t) = \xi\right] = \frac{1}{\sqrt{2\pi[1 - K(\theta)^2]}} \int_{-\infty}^{\eta} \exp\left\{\frac{y - K(\theta)\xi}{2[1 - K(\theta)^2]}\right\} dy$$

is seen to be of significance to a speculator.

Chapter 12

REINFORCEMENT
OF ANTICIPATIONS

The aim of this chapter is to examine how the attitudes of individual sellers may influence the market price. The attitudes refer to the manner in which price anticipations are formed and the manner in which firms react to these in arriving at the production-inventory decisions. Section 1 describes a simple representation of attitudes, and Section 2 gives a general frame for the description of seller's reaction. In Section 3 a brief analysis is made of computer experiments for determining the market price *via* the equality of aggregate demand and supply functions. Variances of production capacity, aggregate consumer demand, and an anticipation parameter appear as control variables in the design of experiments. There is remarkable agreement of this analysis with ordinary economic intuition; however, the results should not be interpreted as theorems because they were not derived through the usual deductive procedure in a complete system of postulates.

1. ANTICIPATIONS: FORMATION AND REVISION

The anticipations about the product price are assumed to be single-valued unbiased estimates of the actual values corresponding to the mathematical expectations with subjective distributions. A scheme for representing the formation and revision of anticipations is given in this section.

1.1 Suppose that each seller has his own *subjective evaluation* of a distribution[1] of the price p_n in the nth period before it is determined in the market. Whether a seller has various degrees of belief that p_n will take on

[1] This is not to be interpreted as a probability distribution, although it may possess all the formal properties of a probability distribution. The essential point is that a subjective distribution lacks the empirical implications of a probability distribution.

a value in the interval $a(n, i) \le p_n \le b(n, i)$ the bounds $a(n, i)$ and $b(n, i)$ depends upon the period (n) and the individual (i). Without loss of generality, it will be assumed that the degrees of belief are consistent for a given individual, and that they can be represented by an absolutely continuous distribution function, $f(n, i, p)$, such that

$$\int_{a(n,i)}^{b(n,i)} f(n, i, p) \, dp = 1. \tag{12.1}$$

Let $\tilde{p}_n$ be the *commonly held* anticipation about the price p_n. Of the several ways of characterizing this, the following seems to be adequate for most purposes:

$$\tilde{p}_n = E[p_n] = \int_{a(n,i)}^{b(n,i)} p f(n, i, p) \, dp. \tag{12.2}$$

In order to represent the *formation* of individual and group anticipations, the following recursion hypothesis is made:

$$b(n, i) - a(n, i) = \sum_{t=1}^{t(i)} g(t, i) \, |\tilde{p}_{n-t} - \bar{p}_{n-t}|, \qquad g(t, i) \ge 0, \tag{12.3}$$

where $\bar{p}_k$ denotes the *actual* market price of the kth period. According to this hypothesis, the range of the believed price is a weighted sum of the absolute deviations of the commonly shared anticipations from the realized market prices in the past. How far back a firm goes into the past and what weights are employed in (12.3) are specific to the firm. Observe, now, that (12.2) and (12.3) jointly determine the numbers $a(n, i)$ and $b(n, i)$ and, hence, the individual behavior. It remains to complete the scheme by introducing a second hypothesis. This concerns the manner in which the group's commonly shared anticipation $\tilde{p}_n$ changes over time. It will be assumed that $\{\tilde{p}_n, n = 1, 2, \ldots\}$ are updated in each period in the following manner:

$$\tilde{p}_n = \bar{p}_{n-1} + \alpha(\tilde{p}_{n-1} - \bar{p}_{n-2}) + (1 - \alpha)(\bar{p}_{n-1} - \bar{p}_{n-2}). \tag{12.4}$$

In other words, in the process of revising the $\tilde{p}_n$, the sellers take into account the anticipations of the immediate past and the actual market prices of the two preceding periods. Being the same for all the sellers, equation (12.4) is a behavorial characteristic of the *group*. In an extended analysis, however, one may fruitfully consider α to be a distributed variable, varying over the sellers. To sum up: Eqs. (12.3) and (12.4) are a representation of the behavorial characteristics of firms in regard to the formation and revision of price anticipations.

2. SPECULATIVE INVENTORY HOLDING

A wider concept of pure competition is introduced. A situation is considered in which individual firms expect to be able to sell as much as they would like to in each period at whatever price happens to rule in the market in that period. That is, although there is uncertainty about the future price, the quantity to be offered for sale at each *possible* price is a *non*random decision variable. Such expectation on the part of the individual firm should turn out to be correct most often. This requires that price adjust itself in each period so that the plans of the producers (in the aggregate) and consumers (also in the aggregate) become compatible. But the requirement of compatibility does not preclude a speculative holding of inventories. Therefore, express provision is made for a behavorial hypothesis about speculative inventory holding. The principal motivation is to take into account the possibility that relative to the current price the variations of future anticipated prices may have asymmetric effects.

2.1 Consider the product stock-flow identity for the *i*th firm: The product offerings $X_s(n, i)$ during the period equal the initial inventory $I(n - 1, i)$ *plus* the planned production $Z(n, i)$ for the current period, *less* the closing inventory $I(n, i)$;

$$X_s(n, i) = I(n - 1, i) + Z(n, i) - I(n, i). \tag{12.5}$$

The $Z(n, i)$ will be viewed as an *optimally determined number* and the $X_s(n, i)$ and $I(n, i)$, as *random* variables. For the purpose of an explicit theory of speculative inventory-holding, a minimization principle[2] will be employed, first, to determine the optimal level of production $Z(n, i)$, the range of $X_s(n, i)$, and the expected inventory $I(n, i)$ at the end of the period. Thus, the planned availability $A(n, i)$ is defined as the production $Z(n, i)$ *plus* the initial inventory or, alternatively, as the planned supply plus the planned closing inventory. In other words,

$$A(n, i) \equiv Z(n, i) + I(n - 1, i)$$
$$\equiv X_s(n, i; p) + I(n, i), \tag{12.6}$$

where the $Z(n, i)$ is to be determined by an optimization. In pure competition the marginal cost should equal the price (which is yet to be

---

[2] This is not to imply that in reality the firms do minimize costs. The purpose of invoking the optimization assumption is merely to explore the observable consequences of a specific behavior assumption.

determined), so that if $C(.)$ denotes the function relating total production cost to the amount produced, one would have

$$\left(\frac{dC}{dy}\right)_{y=Z(n,i)} = 0 \rightarrow Z(n, i) = Z(n, i; p).$$

Thus (12.6) may be written

$$A(n, i) = A(n, i; p) = I(n - 1, i) + Z(n, i; p), \qquad (12.7)$$

where the planned availability is shown to be explicitly dependent upon the undetermined price. Next, a behavior assumption is made so that one may relate the seller's[3] supply function $X_s(n, p)$ to the availability function $A(n, p)$. This may be stated as follows:

$$X_s(n, p) = A(n, p) = \begin{cases} I(n - 1), & \text{if } p < p^*, \\ I(n - 1) + Z(n, p), & \text{if } p \geq p^*. \end{cases} \qquad (12.8)$$

That is, it is assumed that a production decision is made only if the price were to be at least equal to p^*. Thus, only in this event does the question of an *optimally determined* supply function $[Z(n, p)]$ becomes relevant:

$$Z(n, p) = \begin{cases} X_s(n, p) - I(n - 1), & \text{if } p \geq p^*, \\ 0, & \text{if } p < p^*. \end{cases} \qquad (12.9)$$

Evidently, the critical price p^* will be influenced by the production cost $\Phi[I(n - 1)]$ of $I(n - 1)$.

2.2 In order to facilitate the discussion of inventory speculation (see Figure 12.1), define

$u =$ the level that price must reach in order to make inventory holding profitable.

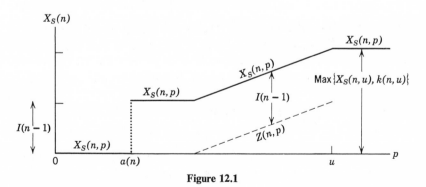

Figure 12.1

---

[3] Until further needed, the index i for the individual firm will be dropped.

The mathematical expectation of the inventory at the *end* of the current period is $\hat{I}(n)$; this is dependent upon u:

$$\hat{I}(n, u) = \int_0^{p^*} [X_s(n, u) - I(n - 1)]f(n, p)\, dp$$

$$+ \int_{p^*}^u [X_s(n, u) - X_s(n, p)]f(n, p)\, dp. \quad (12.10)$$

But the earliest that this quantity can be made available for sale is the $(n + 1)$st period. Therefore, let $\tilde{f}(n + 1, p)$ be the producer's *view* of $f(n + 1, p)$ in the nth period and, similarly, let $\tilde{a}(n + 1)$ and $\tilde{b}(n + 1)$ denote the current view about the lower and upper bounds of price in the following period. Then the expected *revenue* from the production-inventory operations of the current (that is, the nth) period is

$$R(n, u) = \int_0^{p^*} pI(n - 1)f(n, p)\, dp + \int_{p*}^u pX_s(n, p)f(n, p)\, dp$$

$$+ \int_u^{b(n)} X_s(n, u)\, du + \hat{I}(n, u) \int_u^{\tilde{b}(n+1)} p'\tilde{f}(n + 1, p')\, dp'. \quad (12.11)$$

(Note that in the last integral of (12.11), the symbol p' indicates price; it is employed only in order to distinguish it from the present period's price.) The expected *cost* of operation is seen to be

$$K(n, u) = \Phi[Z(n, u)] + \hat{I}(n, u) \int_{\tilde{a}(n+1)}^u p' \cdot \tilde{f}(n + 1, p')\, dp', \quad (12.12)$$

where $Z(n, u) = [Z(n, p)]_{p=u}$. Thus, the optimal inventory holding and, hence, the supply decision are functions of $u^* = u^*(n)$, which is a unique root of the equation

$$\frac{d}{du} [R(n, u) - K(n, u)] = 0. \quad (12.13)$$

2.3 The $u^*(n)$ obtained from (12.13) also determines the optimal supply $X_s(n, u^*) = [X_s(n, p)]_{p=u^*}$, that is, the quantity that can be most advantageously put up for sale, and $Z(n, u^*) = [Z(n, p)]_{p=u^*}$ is the optimal *planned* output. But the *actual output* in the current period is given by

$$Q(n) = \begin{cases} 0, & \text{if } Z(n, u^*) \leq I(n - 1), \\ Z(n, u^*) - I(n - 1) & \text{otherwise.} \end{cases} \quad (12.14)$$

The *aggregate supply function* $X_s(n, p)$ was generated in the computer program as the sum of individual supply functions:

$$X_s(n, p) = \sum_i X_s(n, p, i), \quad (12.15)$$

where in both members the symbol p represents u^*. The *aggregate demand function* was generated as

$$X_d(n, p) = \text{const.} \times [p(n)]^{A_0} \frac{Y(n-1)}{F(n-1)^{A_1}} \frac{\tilde{Y}(n)}{Y(n-1)^{A_2}}, \quad (12.16)$$

appropriate restrictions being imposed on the signs of the parameters. The demand function (12.16) embodies the following hypothesis. The planned volume of purchases depends upon (a) the price to be determined in the market, (b) the level of consumption $F(n-1)$, actually attained in the preceding period, and (c) the current anticipated income $\tilde{Y}(n)$ relative to the actual income in the preceding period. It was additionally assumed that income anticipations are revised according to

$$\tilde{Y}(n) = \beta Y(n-1) + (1 - \beta)\tilde{Y}(n-1), \quad 0 < \beta < 1, \quad (12.17)$$

while the sequence of incomes, $\{Y(n), n = 1, 2, \ldots\}$, was chosen from a uniform distribution on a given range. The market price $\bar{p}(n)$ was obtained as a root of the equation

$$X_d(n, p) = X_s(n, p), \quad n = 1, 2, \ldots. \quad (12.18)$$

It should be observed that the process of individual *bargaining* was not incorporated in the computer program. Also, the *number* of firms was relatively *small*.[4] To sum up: an *effective* reproduction has been ensured for the gross observable characteristics of pure competition, namely, that (a) the market is cleared at a uniform price and (b) buyers and sellers plan their demands and supplies on the basis of a price which is not determined or known in advance.

3. SUMMARY OF OBSERVATIONS

Some of the gross empirical characteristics of the outcome of pure competition are summarized. The observations are empirical implications of the decision rules and environmental conditions that were artificially reproduced in the computer program.

---

[4] As argued in several contexts in the preceding chapters, the question of numbers is irrelevant to the representation of pure competition. The only relevant principle is that the price is to be looked upon as a *parameter*; this, evidently, has been secured at each step described so far. The classical requirement on numbers (of buyers and sellers) serves precisely one purpose: it provides a plausible institutional basis for the more fundamental requirement that no single buyer or seller can alter the market price by his own action.

TABLE 12.1

CORRELATION BETWEEN PRICE AND PRODUCTION
UNDER ALTERNATIVE DISPERSIONS OF CAPACITY

Var [C]: *Lo*			Var [C]: *Hi*		
Var [δ]	Var [Y]	ρ	Var [δ]	Var [Y]	ρ
Lo	*Lo*	+0.39	*Lo*	*Lo*	+0.01
Lo	*Hi*	+0.28	*Lo*	*Hi*	+0.28
Hi	*Lo*	+0.04	*Hi*	*Lo*	+0.17
Hi	*Hi*	+0.22	*Hi*	*Hi*	+0.65

3.1 Given that the sellers speculate in a manner indicated in Section 2, and given that the buyers in the aggregate plan their purchases as in (12.16), it is of interest to inquire about the relationship between the *market price* and the *aggregate output* in a given period. One would ordinarily expect that such a relationship would be influenced, in some fashion, by the states of environment and attitudes (that is, anticipations). Two environmental variables were considered in the computer experiments: (a) the dispersion of production capacity (C) at the disposal of the firms and (b) the dispersion of consumer incomes (Y). In addition, there was a behavorial parameter, the $b(n, i) - a(n, i) \equiv \delta(n, i)$; variance of this parameter was taken as the third control experiments. The product moment correlation ρ between the realized market price $\bar{p}$ and the actual production quantity $Q(\bar{p}) \equiv Q$ are exhibited in Tables 12.1 to 12.3.

There are two cases in which the size of the correlation is negligibly small; in both the variance of consumer income is small and both are excluded from further consideration. Next, observe that with an increase in the diversity of the firms in regard to capacity, there is a reversal in the

TABLE 12.2

CORRELATION BETWEEN PRICE AND PRODUCTION
UNDER ALTERNATIVE DISPERSIONS OF "MOOD"

Var [δ]: *Lo*			Var [δ]: *Hi*		
Var [Y]	Var [C]	ρ	Var [Y]	Var [C]	ρ
Hi	*Lo*	−0.28	*Hi*	*Lo*	−0.22
Lo	*Lo*	−0.39	*Lo*	*Hi*	+0.17
Hi	*Hi*	+0.28	*Hi*	*Hi*	+0.65

TABLE 12.3

CORRELATION BETWEEN PRICE AND PRODUCTION
UNDER ALTERNATIVE DISPERSIONS OF INCOME

Var [Y]: *Hi*			Var [Y]: *Lo*		
Var [δ]	Var [C]	ρ	Var [δ]	Var [C]	ρ
Lo	*Lo*	−0.28	*Lo*	*Lo*	−0.39
Lo	*Hi*	+0.28			
Hi	*Lo*	−0.22			
Hi	*Hi*	+0.65	*Hi*	*Hi*	+0.17

direction of association between market price and aggregate output. In particular, current output tends to increase with the current price, and this increase is sharper when the dispersion of consumer income is higher. This is borne out much more clearly in the following scheme (see Table 12.2) which shows that changes in the dispersion of moods (anticipations) are not uniformly decisive in regard to the correlation. Similarly, one may note (as in Table 12.3) that there is a marked reversal of the direction of association when the dispersions of *both* the moods and the production capacities increase. The effect of an increase in the dispersion of consumer income seems to be more pronounced when the dispersion of *both* capacity and moods are high.

3.2 It is appropriate now to examine the impact (via the withholding of supplies) of speculation upon the behavior of market prices. The influence speculative activity may have on the prices may be examined by comparing the standard deviations of prices under two alternative practices. In order to facilitate frequent reference, use will be made of a catalogue of the experiments in Table 12.4.

TABLE 12.4

ANTICIPATION MODELS

Experiment Number	Variance			Experiment Number	Variance		
	C	δ	Y		C	δ	Y
1	*Lo*	*Lo*	*Hi*	5	*Hi*	*Lo*	*Lo*
2	*Lo*	*Lo*	*Lo*	6	*Lo*	*Hi*	*Hi*
3	*Hi*	*Hi*	*Lo*	7	*Hi*	*Hi*	*Hi*
4	*Lo*	*Hi*	*Lo*	8	*Hi*	*Lo*	*Hi*

The cases of "no anticipations" were rerun on the computer after merging the experiments in Table 12.5; this served to mix the cases of high *and* low variances of the anticipation parameter.

The stage is now set for examining the impact of price speculation on the dispersion of market prices. The basic data are assembled in Table 12.6. The procedure is essentially one of testing for the difference between two empirical standard deviations. The null hypothesis is that the standard deviations of price are not different under the two practices.[5] In each case, the $F_{49,49}(0.05)$ values were significant. Thus the following

TABLE 12.5

"No Anticipations" Models

Experiment Number	Experiments Merged	Var [C]	Var [Y]
I	2, 4	*Lo*	*Lo*
II	3, 5	*Hi*	*Lo*
III	7, 6	*Lo*	*Hi*
IV	7, 8	*Hi*	*Hi*

proposition may be made: *by anticipating prices, the sellers contribute to the uncertainty of prices.* This is one of the aspects of the phenomenon of "reinforcement." The other aspect concerns the uncertainty of sales. Measuring the uncertainty, again, by the standard deviation, a comparison was made between the effects of the two practices in regard to the standard deviation of sales. Except in the case of low variance of capacity (Experiments 1 and 2), the standard deviation of sales was seen to be significantly (at 15% level) different under the two practices. Thus, one may draw a second inference concerning the impact of anticipation: *By anticipating prices, the sellers in the aggregate contribute to the uncertainty of sales.*

3.3 Although the practice of speculative withholding of supplies contributes to the uncertainty of prices and aggregate sales, it also gives rise to a sufficiently *stable pattern* of relationships among certain *aggregate* variables. In particular, the current output is seen to be linearly related to the price-sales-inventories of the previous period (see Table 12.7) in the following manner:

$$Z(n) = \text{const} + b_1 p(n-1) + b_2 S(n-1) + b_3 I(n-1). \quad (12.19)$$

[5] For example, in Experiment I, we would test for the difference between (a) 0.0456 and 0.1157 *and* (b) 0.0456 and 1.3299.

TABLE 12.6
DISPERSION OF SALES WITH AND WITHOUT ANTICIPATIONS

	No Anticipation				Anticipations		
Experiment Number	Standard Deviation of Price	Average Total Sales	Standard Deviation of Sales	Experiment Number	Standard Deviation of Price	Average Total Sales	Standard Deviation of Sales
I	0.0456	648.32	1.4708	2	0.1157	645.68	1.6903
				4	1.3299	630.52	20.3302
II	0.0387	700.34	1.7261	3	0.7610	683.26	25.8243
				5	0.2325	697.06	3.2513
III	0.1674	648.22	5.5032	1	0.4007	639.54	5.2560
				6	1.4367	625.90	18.7782
IV	0.1425	700.26	5.9005	7	2.1390	578.81	47.6452
				8	0.7864	637.38	17.7465

TABLE 12.7
APPARENT PREDICTORS OF CURRENT OUTPUT

Experiment Number	$p(n-1)$	$S(n-1)$	$I(n-1)$	$F_{(3,46)}$	Constant
1	−6.15 (2.85)	−0.23 (0.14)	−0.99 (0.17)	11.23	948.8
3	−44.76 (10.69)	+0.20 (0.06)	—	64.72	679.4
5	−13.06 (6.28)	−2.00 (0.73)	−0.46 (0.15)	9.25	2334.8
7	−27.86 (6.93)	+0.71 (0.93)	−0.08 (0.03)	24.40	873.6
8	−24.17 (9.62)	—	−0.16 (0.05)	9.15	1181.8

Note: Entries in parentheses indicate the standard errors of estimate. The sample size is 50 in each case. The variables are averages over 15 to 20 observations for each period. The three experiments not reported would have been acceptable if a significance level of 10 to 15% were selected.

The linear relationships shown in Table 12.7 are all strongly significant. However, no such relationship was found when the sellers were not supposed to anticipate prices and to speculate. When viewed in the light of the complicated optimization procedure built into the computer program, the stability of patterns under anticipation seems to suggest the following proposition: *If a firm operates in one or another environmental condition*

TABLE 12.8
ANALYSIS OF VARIANCE

Source	d.f.	Price M.S.	Price F	Output M.S.	Output F
Between C	1	276.42	217.32	16084	5.30
Between δ	1	92.97	73.09	110685	36.52
Between Y	1	363.24	285.56	208242	68.71
$Y\delta$	1	5.02	3.94	9513	3.14
δC	1	188.12	147.89	175021	57.75
CY	1	15.42	12.12	21002	6.93
$Y\delta C$	1	7.38	5.79	12023	3.96
Residual	$\dfrac{384}{391}$	1.27	—	3030	—

(*noted in Table* 12.7) *it may, for all practical purposes, replace the entire optimization procedure by determining its output according to the regression equations like* (12.19). In closing this chapter it will be worthwhile to examine the following question: Is there, after all, a significant difference among the principal outcomes—the market price and the aggregate output—generated in the eight experimental conditions? An expedient means of answering this is to set up an analysis of variance for price and for output (see Table 12.8). All the F-values are seen to be significant at 5% or smaller level of significance. Thus, there is a reasonable evidence that *different institutional configurations do have differential effect on prices and aggregate outputs.*

Chapter 13

PURE COMPETITION: INVENTORY-PRODUCTION DECISIONS

In Chapter 11 it was shown that under pure competition the market price would very likely be a Gaussian random variable and that its probability distribution function would not depend on parameters the individual firm could manipulate. Thus, the only decision that is open to the firm is one concerning the quantity and, perhaps, the timing of the sales or purchases. The management of production and inventories under price uncertainty appears to be the key decision problem for a firm in pure competition.

It is such problems that this chapter is concerned with. Although most product markets are not purely competitive from the sellers' viewpoint, there are many—especially those for agricultural and other standardized industrial products—in which the *individual buyers* cannot influence the market price. The analysis of this chapter will be restricted entirely to this type of market situation; *how much and when to acquire* is the decision problem to be investigated under the added *assumption that the buyer has only a limited storage capacity.*

From the viewpoint of inventory theory, this chapter presents some refreshing departures from the existing tradition. Policies and operating rules are explicitly represented as transformations (of the state of inventory) with undetermined parameters. Probability distributions of various functionals or outcomes of the policies are obtained as functions of these parameters; the stage is thus set for the *determination of "good" values of the parameters that will ensure the performance of the system in some desired region of the outcome space.*

The movement of prices will be viewed as a sequence of Gaussian random variables with the special property that the conditional or transition probabilities are Markovian. Given the purchasing rule, the stochastic behavior of the inventories will depend upon these probabilities.

1. THE CASE OF KNOWN PRICE TRANSITION PROBABILITIES

The underlying situation to be considered is one in which future operations are not permitted. The principal input into the inventory model of this section is a set of known transition probabilities of the market price. The storage capacity and the usage rate will be assumed to be constant. Thus opportunities for "good" bargains may be lost; also, an unavoidable purchase may have to be made even though the current price may not be advantageous. These considerations lend some special features to the problem of deciding how much and when to buy.

1.1 Suppose for the sake of definiteness that an inventory η is on hand when a decision to buy is to be made. Since the usage rate is assumed to be a constant (which may be conveniently set equal to one), the quantity η will last η time-periods if no purchases are made until the stock goes down to zero. Define the probability

$$\Phi(a_r, a_k, \eta) = \Pr \text{ [in } \eta \text{ time-periods, the minimum price}$$
$$= a_r \mid \text{current price} = a_k]. \tag{13.1}$$

Let r^* denote the least value of r which makes $\sum_{r=1}^{r^*} \Phi(a_r, a_k, \eta) \geq \alpha$, α being a "confidence coefficient" such that $100\alpha\%$ of the time the least observed price will not exceed a level a_{r*}. If $a_{r*} > a_k$, then let $\eta_*(\alpha)$ denote the least quantity of inventory (or, equivalently, the least duration of time) for which $\sum_{r=1}^{k} \Phi(a_r, a_k, \eta) \geq \alpha$. Note that $\eta_*(\alpha) > \eta$ by construction. Consider a *policy* of the following type:

$$\text{do not purchase if } a_k \geq a_{r*},$$
$$\tag{13.2}$$
$$\text{purchase } X \text{ if } a_k < a_{r*}.$$

Because there is storage limitation, there is an upper bound on inventories; let this be denoted by A. Then the order quantity X is determined by the *rule*:

$$X = \min \left[A - (\eta - 1), \eta_*(\alpha) - (\eta - 1) \right]. \tag{13.3}$$

One may also consider another class of policy in which explicit account is taken of (a) a fixed cost, Y, of placing an order, and (b) a direct unit cost, β, of storage. The relevant signal in this case is the lowest price, $\bar{p}$, in excess of the expected minimum price, $\sum_{r=1}^{N} a_r \Phi(a_r, a_k, \eta)$. If the current price a_k happens to be such that $a_k + Y > \bar{p}$, then, the policy is to avoid frequent purchases. But one may also have $a_k + Y \leq \bar{p}$. In this case if $\xi_*(a_k)$ is the least amount of inventory or least duration of time for which $\sum_{r=1}^{N} a_r \Phi(a_r, a_k, \xi_*(a_k)) \leq a_k$, then, whenever $a_k \leq \bar{p}$, one also has $\xi_*(a_k) > \eta$. In light of this observation, the alternative *policy* may be defined as follows:

$$\text{do not purchase if} \quad a_k + Y > \bar{p},$$

$$\text{purchase } X, \text{ if} \quad a_k + Y \leq \bar{p}. \tag{13.4}$$

In this case the decision variable, X, is to be determined by the *rule*:

$$X = \min \{[\xi_*(a_k) - \eta + 1], A - \eta + 1\}. \tag{13.5}$$

The close resemblance between (13.5)-type rule and the well known (s, S)-rule is worth noting.

1.2   Under either of the two policies (13.2) and (13.4), there will be an *induced movement* of inventory levels and, hence, the "state of the system" will be described by an ordered pair of numbers, say, $(i, j), i = 1, 2, \ldots, A$; $j = 1, \ldots, N$: i denotes the state of inventory and j denotes the state of price. Consider a transition, $(i, j) \rightarrow (i', j')$. Given the pattern of utilization of the inventory, i' depends upon both i and j; also, the probability of occurrence of j' depends upon the initial level of j, and upon the time lapsed. The essential idea is that a decision rule generates a *probability of transition* from (i, j) to (i', j') in one period. For example, due to the decision rule (13.3), i, makes a transition to i', where

$$i' = y(i, j) = \begin{cases} i - 1, & \text{if } a_j > a_{r*}, \\ i + X - 1, & \text{if } a_j \leq a_{r*}. \end{cases}$$

Hence, the probability Ψ of the transition $(i, j) \rightarrow (i', j')$ takes the following form:

$$\Psi_{i,j;i',j'} = \begin{cases} \Psi'_{j,j'}, & \text{if } i' = y(i, j), \\ 0, & \text{otherwise.} \end{cases}$$

Similarly, due to the decision rule (13.5) the dependence of i' on i and j is of the following nature,

$$i' = z(i, j) = \begin{cases} i - 1, & \text{if } \bar{p} > a_j, \\ i + X - 1, & \text{otherwise,} \end{cases}$$

so that the state transition probability is given by

$$\Psi_{i,j;i',j'} = \begin{cases} \Psi'_{j\,j'}, & \text{if } i' = z(i, j), \\ 0, & \text{otherwise.} \end{cases}$$

It should be observed that *given* the decision rule and its parameters, the resulting inventory i' is deterministically dependent upon i and j; that is, the functions like $y(i, j)$ or $z(i, j)$ are *nonrandom*. Thus, the conditional probability of (i', j'), given the entire past history, depends only on (i, j). Put another way, given the knowledge of the present state, future states are all statistically independent of the past states; the pairs $\{(i, j)\}$ form a *simple Markov chain*. Because of the transitions $(i, j) \rightarrow (i', j')$, there will be certain outcomes of direct significance. These may be defined in a number of ways; discussion will, however, be restricted to the following: (a) the cost of purchase, (b) the number of orders per unit of time, and (c) the size of an order. Each of these is a *random* variable and, consequently, some appropriate moment is to be computed. The derivations to be presented will be restricted to means and variances, although the really important issue is one of determining the *stationary distribution* of the inventory level.[1]

1.3 Assuming that inventory level does possess a stationary distribution, it is not difficult to compute the probabilities. Let V_{ij} denote the stationary probability that the system is in state (i, j). Then[1]

$$V_{ij} = \sum_{i',j'} \Psi_{i',j':i,j}, V_{i',j'} \quad (\sum_{ij} V_{ij} = 1, V_{ij} \geq 0), \quad (13.6)$$

and, hence, the probability or the *fraction of "times"* that the inventory will be in state i can be found as

$$b_i = \sum_{j=1}^{N} V_{ij}. \quad (13.7)$$

Next, in order to derive the *average cost of purchase*, consider the probability $B(X, j)$, that in some period a quantity X will be bought at a price, say, p_j. This event occurs when there is a transition from (i', j') to $(i + X - 1, j')$; thus,

$$B(X, j) = \sum_{i'=1}^{i'-X+1} \sum_{j'=1}^{N} V_{i'j'} \Psi_{i',j':i'+X-1,j'}.$$

Note that since $B(X, j)$ is joint density, we would have

$$\sum_{X=0}^{A} \sum_{j=1}^{N} B(X, j) = 1.$$

Therefore, the average cost of a unit purchased is seen to be

$$\left[\sum_{X=0}^{A} \sum_{j=1}^{N} B(X, j) a_j X \right] \div \left[\sum_{X=0}^{A} \sum_{j=1}^{N} B(X, j) X \right].$$

[1] In all cases investigated, Eq. (13.6) was found to possess solutions that satisfied the associated conditions. This, however, is not offered as a proof of the assertion that a stationary distribution of the inventory will always exist. The issue is left open.

A few other performance characteristics can be immediately obtained from $B(X, j)$. For example, the distribution density of an *order quantity* X is $\sum_{j=1}^{N} B(X, j)$; hence the expected order quantity is

$$\sum_{X=0}^{N} X \sum_{j=1}^{N} B(X, j) .$$

Also, the probability that no purchase will be made at any time is $\sum_{j=1}^{N} B(0, j)$ and, therefore, the *average number* of orders per unit of time is $1 - \sum_{j=1}^{N} B(0, j)$.

1.4 It remains to examine how one may obtain the basic probabilities $\Phi(a_r, a_k, \eta)$ in (13.6) whose existence was taken for granted in the derivation of the decision rules. The essential problem here is to derive the probability distribution of the *least element in a given duration, starting with a given observation* $p(0) = x, b \leq x(\tau) \leq a, 0 \leq \tau \leq t$.

In the present context the buying agency would be interested in the conditional distribution of the random variable $T_{ab}(x)$,

$$T_{ab}(x) = \sup \, [\tau : b \leq x \leq a, 0 \leq \tau \leq t],$$

under the condition that the absorption takes place at the lower bound b. Alternatively, one may pose the problem as one of computing the distribution of

$$m[p(0), t] = m(x, t) = \inf_{0 \leq \tau \leq t} [|p(\tau)| \, | \, p(0) = x].$$

There are some elegant methods for solving[2] this class of problems. But something less will suffice if one agrees to consider the special case in which the transition probabilities possess the following *stronger property*:

$$\Pr \, [p_t > p \, | \, p_{t-1} > p, p_{t-2} > p, \ldots] = \Pr \, [p_t > p \, | \, p_{t-1} > p]. \tag{13.8}$$

This necessarily involves implicit assumptions that (a) almost all sample functions of the $\{p(t)\}$-process are continuous and (b) the $\{p(t)\}$-process is separable. The restriction to (13.8) makes it relatively easy to compute the required probabilities. Thus, let

$$\Phi(a_r, a_k, h) = \Pr \, [\min \, \{p_1, \ldots, p_h\} = a_r \, | \, p_0 = a_k],$$

and define the cumulative probability $F(a_r, a_k, h)$:

$$F(a_r, a_k, h) = \sum_{i=1}^{r} \Phi(a_i, a_k, h)$$

$$= 1 - \Pr \, [p_1 > a_r, \ldots, p_h > a_r \, | \, p_0 = a_k]$$

$$\equiv 1 - f(a_r, a_k, h).$$

[2] These are due to Darling-Siegert [7]. The principal difficulty lies in the inversion of certain Laplace transforms.

The probability $f(a_r, a_k, h)$ can be developed as follows:

$$f(a_r, a_k, h) = \Pr\left[p_1 > a_r, \ldots, p_{h-1} > a_r \mid p_0 = a_k\right]$$
$$\times \Pr\left[p_h > a_r \mid p_1 > a_r, \ldots, p_{h-1} > a_r \mid p_0 = a_k\right] \quad (13.9)$$
$$= \Psi(a_r, a_k, h-1)\frac{\Pr\left[p_h > a_r, p_{h-1} > a_r \mid p_0 = a_k\right]}{\Pr\left[p_{h-1} > a_r \mid p_0 = a_k\right]}.$$

Recall, now, the formulas [21] for higher order transition probabilities for stationary Markov chains:

$$\Pr\left[X_n = a_i \mid p_0 = a_k\right] = p_{k,i}^{(n)}$$
$$\Pr\left[X_n = a_i, X_{n+1} = a_j \mid p_0 = a_k\right] = p_{k,i}^{(n)}p_{i,j}.$$

Thus, the probabilities in the numerator of the right member of (13.9) may be written as

$$\Pr\left[p_h > a_r, p_{h-1} > a_r\right] = \sum_{i=r+1}^{N}\sum_{j=r+1}^{N} p_{k,i}^{(h-1)}p_{i,j}. \quad (13.10)$$

Thus one has the following recursive definition of Ψ:

$$\Psi(a_r, a_k, 1) = \sum_{i=r+1}^{N} p_{k,i}$$

$$\Psi(a_r, a_k, n) = \Psi(a_r, a_k, n-1)\frac{\displaystyle\sum_{i=r+1}^{N}\sum_{j=r+1}^{N} p_{k,i}^{(n-1)}p_{i,j}}{\displaystyle\sum_{j=r+1}^{N} p_{k,i}^{(n-1)}}$$

$$= \sum_{i'=r+1}^{N} p_{k,i'}\left[\prod_{s=1}^{n-1}\sum_{i=r+1}^{N}\sum_{i=r+1}^{N} p_{k,i}^{(s)}p_{i,j}\right]$$
$$\div \prod_{s=1}^{n-1}\sum_{i=r+1}^{N} p_{k,i}^{(s)}. \quad (13.11)$$

Therefore, the quantities $\Phi(a_r, a_k, h)$ can be expressed as

$$\Phi(a_r, a_k, h) = F(a_r, a_k, h) - F(a_{r-1}, a_k, h)$$
$$= \frac{\displaystyle\prod_{s=1}^{h-1}\sum_{i=r}^{N}\sum_{j=r}^{N} p_{k,i}^{(s)}p_{i,j}}{\displaystyle\prod_{s=2}^{h-1}\sum_{i=r}^{N} p_{k,i}^{(s)}} - \frac{\displaystyle\prod_{s=1}^{h-1}\sum_{i=1}^{N}\sum_{j=r+1}^{N} p_{k,i}^{(s)}p_{i,j}}{\displaystyle\prod_{s=2}^{h-1}\sum_{i=r+1}^{N} p_{k,i}^{(s)}}. \quad (13.12)$$

2. INVENTORY MANAGEMENT WITH PRICE FORECASTS

When prices are uncertain and all acquisition *has* to be made at spot prices, one may compute the conditional expectations and set up a decision rule that calls for *postponement* of a purchase *unless a good price is observed. The degree to which a price may appear to be good, however, is related to the level of inventory on hand and the usage rate.* The purpose of this section is to explore the use of relatively low order *stable* autoregression schemes as a forecasting device. It is shown that the observed residuals from the predicted levels together with the current levels of inventory may be used as signals to trigger the purchase. The purchase quantity is determined in terms of these variables, but with undetermined weights or parameters. Several measures of performance or outcomes of the system under the decision rule are then analyzed so that the dependence of these on the undetermined parameters may be examined. Thus, it becomes possible to examine the *tradeoffs between the outcomes* and to determine the setting of parameter values required to secure some desired configuration in the performance space.

2.1   The autoregressive schemes to be considered are of the following type:

$$p_t = a + \sum_{r=1}^{k} b_r p_{t-r} + u_t, \qquad (13.13)$$

p_t being the *spot price* at time t and $\{u_t\}$ being an unobservable random disturbance about which the following specifications are made:

$$E[u_t] \equiv 0; \qquad E[\{u_t, u_{t+h}\}] = \sigma^2 \delta(t, t + h),$$
$$u_t \cap N(0, \sigma^2), \qquad t = 1, 2, \dots .$$

For the sake of convenience, the discussion will be restricted to the model

$$p_t = a + b p_{t-1} + c p_{t-2} + u_t. \qquad (13.14)$$

Suppose that an empirical estimate of (13.14) has been obtained and is being used (at the beginning of a period) as a means of computing the conditional expectation of the price in the current period. Consistent with this framework, the *observed deviation* of the actual from the predicted price may be taken as an empirical counterpart $\hat{u}_t$ of the "true" disturbance. To avoid confusion, the variance of the observed residuals will be denoted by s^2; the actual price p_t therefore, can, be expressed as the conditional expectation plus or minus a multiple of s. The purchase decision rules will be based upon $\hat{u}_t$ and the level of inventory I_t on hand. The justification for the former is obvious; that for the latter may be seen from the following consideration: If I_t is high, then a decision to buy can be postponed unless the observed residual happens to be moderately negative. This is the sense in which a price is to be taken as a "good" price. The analysis will be presented under two assumptions. The first will consider the case where the demand upon inventory is a known constant; the second will be devoted to the case where usage rate is random and serially independent.

2.2 Observe, first, that the value of p_t can always be represented in terms of the conditional expectation, plus or minus a certain multiple, say r, of the standard deviation s of the observed residuals. The size of r may be made to reflect the decision-maker's inclination to look upon a price as a "good" price. But that, again, suggests that r should be a diminishing function of the inventory level I_t. Suppose for the sake of simplicity that

$$r = r(I_t) = -kI_t, \quad (k > 0), \quad (13.15)$$

k being otherwise unspecified; the value of k is to be assigned on the basis of the effect it produces on the system performance. Also observe that if the current level of inventory is *just sufficient* to support the current period's usage (assumed to be a *constant*, set equal to one) then a purchase *has to be* made regardless of the current price. If the price is sufficiently "bad," only the current period's requirement will be purchased. To sum up: the critical signal for the purchase decision is the conditional probability $\hat{p}_t$,

$$E[p_t \mid p_{t-1}, p_{t-2}] + rs = \hat{p}_t - k(I_t - 1)s. \quad (13.16)$$

In other words, the policy to be considered is of the form:

Purchase Y if $p_t < p_t - k(I_t - 1)s$,

Purchase nothing (unless $I_t = 1$) if $p_t \geq p_t - k(I_t - 1)s$. $\quad (13.17)$

Subtracting the conditional expectation from both sides of the inequalities, one may write the policy in terms of Y to be defined in (13.20):

Purchase 1 unit, if $I_t = 1$.

Purchase Y, if $\hat{u}_t < -k(I_t - 1)s$,

Do not purchase, if $I_t = 1$ and $\hat{u}_t \geq -k(I_t - 1)s$, $\quad (13.18)$

Now define a normalized quantity λ:

$$\lambda_t = \frac{1}{s} [-k(I_t - 1)s - \hat{u}_t]. \quad (13.19)$$

Evidently, a large positive magnitude of λ will indicate a high degree of "goodness" of an observed price X_t. A rule should now be developed for determining Y itself. Note that when $\hat{u}_t < -k(I_t - 1)s$, the size of purchase is to be determined as a *suitable* function of λ, say $G(\lambda)$. But, in any event, the amount to be purchased cannot exceed $A - (I_t - 1)$, A being the warehouse capacity. Thus, when $Y > 0$, the rule for determining Y is

$$Y = \min [A - I_t + 1, G(\lambda)]. \quad (13.20)$$

Again, for the sake of definiteness, take

$$G(\lambda) = [q\lambda], \qquad (13.21)$$

that is, the integer part of $q\lambda$; $q(>0)$ is, again, *an unspecified parameter.* Similarly, in the event that $\hat{u}_t > -k(I_t - 1)s$ (or, equivalently, where $\lambda \leq 0$), the purchase quantity Y is to be exactly one unit if $I_t = 1$; on the other hand, $Y = 0$ if $I_t > 1$ *and* $\lambda \leq 0$. Thus, the *rule* is the following:

$$Y_t = \begin{cases} \min\{A - I_t + 1, [\lambda q]\} & \text{if } \lambda > 0 \\ 0, & \text{if } \lambda \leq 0 \text{ and } I_t > 1, \\ 1, & \text{if } \lambda \leq 0 \text{ and } I_t = 1. \end{cases} \qquad (13.22)$$

2.3 The next step is to consider the fluctuations or transitions in the state of inventory *due to* the interaction of the decision rule (13.22) and the rate of demand upon the inventory. Now the latter has been assumed to be a known constant ($=1$), and the inventory level has to satisfy the conservation equation,

$$I_t = I_{t-1} + Y_t - 1 \qquad (13.23)$$

(in which Y_t is determined by (13.22)); therefore the changes in the inventory level are random. Now, define

$$L(\alpha, \beta) = \begin{cases} +\infty, & \text{if } \beta < \alpha, \\ -k(\alpha - 1)s - (\beta - \alpha + 1)\dfrac{s}{q}, & \text{if } \beta > \alpha, \\ -\infty, & \text{if } \beta = \alpha, \end{cases} \qquad (13.24)$$

so that one may write

$$\Pr[I_t \leq \alpha \mid I_{t-1} = \beta] = \int_{L(\alpha,\beta)}^{L(\alpha,\beta+1)} N(0, s^2)\, dx. \qquad (13.25)$$

But it is readily seen that this conditional probability is the *same* as that obtained by conditioning upon $I_{t-2}, I_{t-3}, \ldots$, in addition to I_{t-1}. In other words, the transition probabilities of inventory level are Markovian. Since inventory is a discrete-valued variable, the process can be described by a *Markov chain.* Suppose, then, that the states of inventory are denoted by S_i ($i = 1, 2, \ldots, A$). In light of what has been said above, a transition from S_i to S_j occurs in one step if there has been a purchase of $j - i + 1$ units, that is, if given the S_i the size of $\hat{u}_t$ has been sufficient to trigger a purchase of $j - i + 1$ units. Thus the probability of transition may be expressed as follows:

$$P(i, j) = \Pr [I_t = S_j \mid I_{t-1} = S_i]$$

(i) $\qquad = 0, \qquad \text{if } j < i - 1,$

(ii) $\qquad = \displaystyle\int_{[-k(i-1)s-s/q]}^{\infty} N(0, s^2) \, du, \qquad \text{if } j = i - 1$

(iii) $\qquad = \displaystyle\int_{[-2s/q]}^{\infty} N(0, s^2) \, du, \qquad \text{if } i = 1, \;\; j = 1$

(iv) $\qquad = \displaystyle\int_{[-k(i-1)s-(j-i+2)s/q]}^{[-k(i-1)s-(j-i+1)s/q]} N(0, s^2) \, du, \qquad \text{if } 1 \le i \le j < A \;(i, j \ne 1)$

(v) $\qquad = \displaystyle\int_{-\infty}^{[-k(i-1)s-(A-i+1)s/q]} N(0, s^2) \, du, \qquad \text{if } j = A. \qquad (13.26)$

1. Consider, first, the general case $1 \le i \le j < A$. From the rule (13.22), it may be seen that $j - i + 1 = \min \{A - i + 1, [q\lambda]\}$ and, for the case in question, the minimum is at $[q\lambda]$. But, $[q\lambda]$ being an integer, it follows that $j - i + 1 \le q \le j - i + 2$, that is

$$\frac{-k(i - 1)s - (j - i + 2)s}{q} \le \hat{u} \le \frac{-k(i - 1)s - (j - i + 1)s}{q},$$

on account of the definition of λ. This explains formula (13.26), iv.

2. Next consider the case $j = i - 1$, which would occur if no purchases were made ($[q\lambda] = 0$). Here, $0 \le q\lambda \le 1$. But the occurrence of a "no purchase," according to the policy must be due to the fact that $\hat{u}$ was found greater than $-k(i - 1)s$, so that $q\lambda < 1$. Thus, the bounds on the $\hat{u}$ are $-k(i - 1)s - s/q < \hat{u} < \infty$, which explains formula (13.26), ii.

3. Next consider the case $j = A$. Here the critical question is: What is the least price for which $j = A - 1$? The purchase quantity would be $A - i + 1$ for any price below this least price. The magnitude of this price is $-k(i - 1)s - (A - i + 1)s/q$, which is obtained by setting $j = A - 1$ in the lower limit of integration in formula (13.26), iv. Thus, the range of variation of $\hat{u}$ in this case is $-\infty < \hat{u} < -k(i - 1)s - (A - i + 1)s/q$.

4. It remains to consider the case in which exactly one unit has been purchased. This situation can occur only because the price has been greater than the largest price that would call for the purchase of two

units. One can compute the price in question by setting $i = 1, j = 2$ in the upper limit in (13.26), iv. Thus, the event $(i = 1, j = 1)$ corresponds to the case where $-2s/q \leq \hat{u} < \infty$. This explains (13.26), iii. Note, finally, that since the usage rate has been assumed to be one unit per period, $P(i, j) = 0$ only if $j < i - 1$.

2.4.1 Some appropriate characteristics of performance will now be computed in order to evaluate the policy (13.18) and the associated decision rule. Typically, these are functionals of the stationary distribution[3] $V(j)$ of the inventory levels.

$$V(j) = \sum_{i=1}^{A} V(i)P(i, j), \qquad \sum_{j=1}^{A} V(j) = 1, \qquad V(j) \geq 0. \qquad (13.27)$$

The following criteria of performance will be discussed: (a) the mean value and variance of inventory, (b) the expected number of orders per unit period, (c) probabilities of various order-sizes, and (d) the expected cost (when a purchase is made) per expected number of units purchased. Appropriate expressions will be developed for each of these on the basis of stationary distribution given by the solution of Eq. (13.27). The first of the four criteria is easily calculated: the mean value is $\sum_{i=1}^{A} iV(i)$, and the variance is

$$\sum_{i=1}^{A} i^2 V(i) - \left[\sum_{i=1}^{A} iV(i) \right]^2.$$

Now the decision rule says that a purchase is to be made when either $i = 1$ or $\hat{u} < -k(i - 1)s - s/q$. The probability of occurrence of these events is $Q(i)$:

$$Q(i) = \begin{cases} 1, & \text{if } i = 1, \\[2ex] \displaystyle\int_{-\infty}^{[-k(i-1)-s/q]} N(0, s^2)\, du, & \text{if } i > 1. \end{cases} \qquad (13.28)$$

Thus, the probability that at *any* time there be a purchase is given by

$$\Pi = \sum_{i=1}^{A} Q(i)V(i), \qquad (13.29)$$

where the $V(i)$ are given by (13.27). Note that (13.29) can also be interpreted as the expected number of orders or acts of purchase per period.

---

[3] Problems of existence will not be investigated for the reason that it is difficult to develop an analytical expression for the necessary and sufficient condition(s) on the magnitudes of k and q to ensure this. For the realistic range of variations given to these parameters in practical applications and simulation experiments, the existence of stationary probabilities satisfying Eq. (13.27) never presented a problem.

Consider, next, the third criterion of performance: the probabilities of order-sizes. Define

$$D(x) = \text{Pr [a purchase of } x \text{ units will be made]},$$
$$0 \leq x \leq A.$$

This probability is the same as that of the occurrence of a transition of inventory from the state i to the state $i + x - 1$. Thus, $D(x)$ may be computed as

$$D(0) = \sum_{i=2}^{A} V(i)P(i, i - 1),$$

$$D(x) = \sum_{i=1}^{A-x+1} V(i)P(i, i + x - 1), \qquad x = 1, 2, \ldots, A.$$

(13.30)

Given that orders are at all placed, one may verify that the average size and variance of the size of orders are

$$E[\text{size}] = \sum_{i=1}^{A} \frac{iD(i)}{1 - D(0)},$$

$$\text{Var [size]} = \sum_{i=1}^{A} \frac{i^2 D(i)}{1 - D(0)} - \left(\sum_{i=1}^{A} \frac{iD(i)}{1 - D(0)} \right)^2.$$

(13.31)

2.4.2 Now, recall that an act of purchase is triggered by the deviation of the actual price from its expected value, the triggering point being $\hat{u}^* = -k(I_t - 1)s$. The location of u^* is shown in the following diagram:

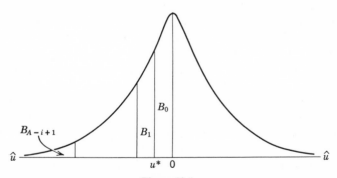

Figure 13.1

The area B_j gives the probability of occurrence of the event that calls for the purchase of j units when the initial inventory is I_t. Thus, when a purchase of j units is made, the associated deviation $(\hat{u})$ of the expected from the actual price must lie between the limits $\hat{u}^* - (j + 1(s/q \leq \hat{u} \leq \hat{u}^* - js/q \, (j \geq 1)$. Consider, then, a *random matrix* $C(i, j)$, the (i, j)th element of which is the random deviation $\hat{u}$, the occurrence of which triggers the purchase of $j - i + 1$ units whenever the initial inventory is i units. Each element of $C(i,j)$ is Gaussian (because each $\hat{u}$ is Gaussian) with zero mean and variance equal to s^2, truncated between $\hat{u}^* - (j - i + 2)s/q$ and $\hat{u}^* - (j - i + 1)s/q$. The mean value of $C(i,j)$ is given by the formula [42]

$$E[C(i,j)] =$$

$$\left\{ \frac{f[-k(i-1)s - (j-i+2)s/q] - f[-k(i-1)s - (j-i+1)s/q]}{F[-k(i-1)s - (j-i+1)s/q] - F[-k(i-1)s - (j-i+2)s/q]} \right\} s^2,$$

where $f(a)$ denotes $1/(s\sqrt{2\pi}) \exp[-\tfrac{1}{2}(a/s)^2]$ and $F(a)$ is an abbreviation for

$$\frac{1}{s\sqrt{2\pi}} \int_{-\infty}^{a} \exp\left[-\frac{1}{2}\left(\frac{x}{s}\right)^2\right] dx.$$

Thus we can define an index of cost as

$$Z = \frac{\sum\limits_{i=1}^{A} \sum\limits_{j=1}^{A-i+1} (j - i + 1)V(i)P(i,j)E[C(i,j)]}{\sum\limits_{i=1}^{A} \sum\limits_{j=1}^{A} (j - i + 1)V(i)P(i,j)}. \tag{13.32}$$

3. A MODEL OF RANDOM WITHDRAWALS

A situation is considered in which the purchase department effectively views the inventory withdrawal rate as a *random* variable. This seems to be appropriate in organizations where the manufacturing activity and the acquisition of raw materials are not under the same decision-maker. In these cases, it is also in place to *assume* that the demands on the purchase department are mutually statistically independent. Although random, the materials usage rate has a natural upper bound, say c, determined by the plant capacity. It is conceivable that a purchase department may aim to provide "enough" raw material for any possible production rate. With a policy like this, the initial inventory in any period is typically required to be no less than the upper bound c. On an average, it will cause a high inventory holding. This suggests that with random usage rate, it may be more profitable to admit possibilities of shortage, that is, to allow the "book" inventories to take on negative values. But if the inventory on the books is allowed to be negative, it is also advisable to wait for a "good" price to make a purchase; on the other hand, if the price is "bad," only the "necessary" amounts will be ordered. The terms "good," "bad" and "necessary" will be defined in detail in the policy to be described below.

3.1 As in the preceding section, let t denote the time a decision is to be made, and let X_t denote the price observed then. Also, let q_n denote the Pr [at any time the usage rate is $= n$], $n = 0, 1, \ldots, c$, and let the greatest integer contained in the expected usage rate be denoted by

$$\left[\sum_{n=0}^{c} n q_n \right] = \rho. \tag{13.33}$$

Define two auxiliary quantities:

$$\lambda = \frac{1}{s} \left[-k(\max \{I_t, 1\} - 1)s - \hat{u}_t \right],$$
$$y = \min \{A - I_t, [q\lambda]\}, \tag{13.34}$$

q being another undetermined parameter. Now consider the following *policy*:

$$\begin{cases} \text{purchase } Y, \text{ if } p_t < \hat{p}_t - k(I_t - 1)s, & (13.35) \\ \text{in addition to } Y, \text{ purchase } y^* = \rho + r - (y + I_t), \text{ if } y + I_t < \rho + r, \\ \text{do nothing, if } p_t \geq -k(I_t - 1)s + p_t. \end{cases}$$

where k and r are the parameters to be determined. Then the actual quantity Y to be ordered (in light of the values of I_t and y) is

$$Y = \begin{cases} y = \min \{A - I_t, [q\lambda]\}, & \text{if } \lambda \geq 0, \text{ and} \\ I_t + \min \{A - I_t, [q\lambda]\} \geq \rho + r, \\ 0, & \text{if } I_t \geq \rho + r, \text{ and } \lambda < 0, \\ y + y^* = \rho + r - I_t, & \text{otherwise.} \end{cases} \tag{13.36}$$

The rule (13.36) will induce certain random movements of the inventory level. These will be characterized by appropriate transition probabilities. Consider, first, the inventory conservation equation

$$I_{t+1} = I_t + Y_t - \alpha_t,$$

$\{\alpha_t\}$ being the family of random variables associated with the number of units required (by the manufacturing department) in the period t. The Y_t is a nonrandom function of I_t and of the random variable $\hat{u}_t$; on the other hand, $\{\alpha_t\}$ is a family of mutually independent, indentically distributed random variables, each independent of $\hat{u}_t$. Thus, the conditional probability of I_{t+1}, *given* the values of $I_t \ldots$, is only a function of the value of I_t. In other words, the inventory process induced by the rule (13.36) is a Markov chain. Define $P(i, j)$:

$$P(i, j) = \Pr \text{ [inventory goes from } i \text{ to } j \text{ in one period]}; \tag{13.37}$$

also, for $i, j = \rho + r - c, \ldots, A$, and $y = 0, 1, \ldots, A - i$, define

$$P^*(i, j) = \text{Pr [purchase} = j \,|\, \text{inventory} = i] \qquad (13.38)$$

for a given decision rule. Expressions for the $P(i, j)$ will be developed first in terms of q_n and $P^*(i, j)$ and then the $P^*(i, j)$ will be derived. The analysis will be made for three possible cases.

3.2   Consider, first, the case where $\rho + r - c \leq i \leq j \leq A$. In this case, $P(i, j)$ may be found as

$$P(i, j) = \sum_{\delta=0}^{\min(A-j,c)} P^*(i, j - i + \delta)q_\delta.$$

The upper limit of summation is determined from the consideration that the purchase quantity is not to exceed $A - i$ *and* the requirement is not to exceed c. Next, consider the case where $\rho - c + r \leq i \leq \rho + r$, $\rho - c + r \leq j \leq \rho + r$, and observe that $\rho + r$ is essentially a buffer stock, so that $\rho + r < A$. The probability $P(i, j)$ appropriate to this case, is

$$P(i, j) = \sum_{\delta=\rho+r-j}^{\delta^*} P^*(i, \rho + r - i + \delta)q_{\rho+r-j+\delta},$$

in which the upper limit δ^* must simultaneously satisfy the inequalities $\rho + r - i + \delta^* \leq A - i$, and $\rho + r - j + \delta^* \leq c$. The δ^* that does so is

$$\delta^* = \min \{A - \rho - r, c + j - \rho - r\}.$$

Finally, consider the case $\rho + r \leq i \leq A$, $i < j \leq \rho + r - c$. There are two possible configurations in this case: (a) $i - j > c$ and (b) $i - j \leq c$. Since the inventory can never jump down by an amount greater than c, the maximum possible requirement, therefore, $P(i, j)$ must be zero in the first of the two configurations. On the other hand, for the latter configuration the expression for $P(i, j)$ is

$$P(i, j) = \sum_{\delta=0}^{\delta^{**}} P^*(i, \delta)q_{i-j+\delta},$$

in which δ^{**} has to satisfy the two inequalities: $\delta^{**} \leq A - i$ and $i - j + \delta^{**} \leq c$. Thus, $\delta^{**} = \min \{A - i, c - i + j\}$.

3.3   The probabilities $P^*(i, j)$ will now be determined. There are several configurations of i and y which have to be carefully distinguished. Consider the situation in which

$$\rho + r - c \leq i < \rho + r, \qquad y < \rho + r - i, \qquad (13.39)$$

that is, the current inventory is strictly less than the buffer stock (hence, the inventory must be brought up to at least $\rho + r$) and the amount ordered is less than $\rho + r - i$. Under the decision rule (13.36), it is clear that

$$P^*(i, y) = 0.$$

Next, consider the situation in which (a) the inventory is lower than the buffer and is brought up to the buffer level and (b) the observed price was not "good" enough to make a bigger purchase. That is to say,

$$\rho + r - c \leq i \leq \rho + r, \quad y = \rho + r - i. \tag{13.40}$$

Therefore, the $P^*(i, y)$ for this case is computed as

$$P^*(i, y) = \Pr\left[[q\lambda] < \rho + r - i\right] \cong \Pr\left[\lambda < \frac{\rho + r - i + 1}{q}\right],$$

which upon substitution of (13.35) for λ, becomes

$$P^*(i, y) = \Pr\left[\hat{u}_t > -k\{\max(i, 1) - 1\}s - \frac{s}{q}(\rho + r - i + 1)\right]$$

$$= \int_{z_1}^{\infty} N(0, s^2)\, du, \tag{13.41}$$

where $z_1 = -k\{\max(i, 1) - 1\}s - (s/q)(\rho + r - i + 1)$. Suppose, now, that all other things remaining the same the price has been good enough for buying more than $y - 1$, but not good enough for $y + 1$; that is,

$$\rho + r - c \leq i < \rho + r, \quad \rho + r < A \tag{13.42}$$

For this situation, it is seen that

$$P^*(i, y) = \Pr\left[y < q\lambda < y + 1\right] = \Pr\left[\frac{y}{q} < \lambda < \frac{y + 1}{q}\right],$$

which, on substitution from (13.35) for λ, gives

$$P^*(i, y) = \int_{-z_2}^{z_3} N(0, s^2)\, du,$$

where $z_2 = -[s(y + 1)/q] - k\{\max(i, 1) - 1\}s$, and $z_3 = z_2 + s/q$. Next suppose that the price were to be better than that required for purchasing $A - i + 1$, so that the maximum amount would be bought. This is the configuration

$$\rho + r - c \leq i < \rho + r, \quad y = A - i. \tag{13.43}$$

Proceeding as before,

$$P^*(i, y) = P^*(i, A - i) = \int_{-\infty}^{z_4} N(0, s^2)\, du,$$

with $z_4 = -[s(A - i)/q] - k\{\max(i, 1) - 1\}s$. In each of the preceding four configurations, (13.39), (13.40), (13.42), and (13.43), the current level of inventory is in the interval $\rho + r - c \leq i < \rho + r$. However, there are other configurations in each of which $A > i > \rho + r$. Thus, suppose that

$$A > i \geq \rho + r, \qquad y = 0. \tag{13.44}$$

For this case, it is seen that

$$P^*(i, 0) = \Pr[q\lambda < 1] = \Pr\left[\hat{u}_t \geq \frac{s}{q} - k\{\max(i, 1) - 1\}s\right]$$

$$= \int_{z_5}^{\infty} N(0, s^2)\, du,$$

with $z_5 = -s/q - k\{\max(i, 1) - 1\}s$. Next, consider y to be in the interval $[1, A - i]$, that is, consider

$$A > i \geq \rho + r, \qquad 1 \leq y < A - i. \tag{13.45}$$

It is readily verified that

$$P^*(i, y) = \int_{z_6}^{z_7} N(0, s^2)\, du,$$

where $z_6 = -(y + 1)s/q - sk\{\max(i, 1) - 1\}$ and $z_7 = z_6 + s/q$. Analogous to the situation (13.43), there is a configuration where

$$A > i \geq \rho + r, \qquad y = A - i. \tag{13.46}$$

For this case, $P^*(i, y) = P^*(i, A - i)$ is given by

$$P^*(i, A - i) = \int_{-\infty}^{z_8} N(0, s^2)\, du,$$

with $z_8 = -(A - i + 1)s/q - k\{\max(i, 1) - 1\}s$. Finally, consider the case where the inventory equals A, the maximum storage capacity; that is,

$$i = A, \qquad y = 0. \tag{13.47}$$

Evidently, the probability $P^*(A, 0)$ is seen to be

$$P^*(A, 0) = 1.$$

3.4 The performance characteristics of the decision rule (13.36) will now be computed on the basis of the stationary distribution $V(i)$ of the "book" inventory:

$$V(i) = \sum_j V(j)P(i, j), \qquad \sum_j V(j) = 1, \qquad V(j) \geq 0. \tag{13.48}$$

Thus, the mean value and variance of the *physical* inventory are, respectively, the following:

$$E[I] = \sum_{i=\rho+r-c}^{A} V(i) \max (i, 0), \quad \text{Var } [I] = \sum_{i=\rho+r-c}^{A} V(i)[\max (i, 0)]^2 - [E(I)]^2.$$

$$(13.49)$$

As in Section 1, it is possible to develop the order-size distribution $D(y)$:

$$D(y) = \sum_{i=\rho+r-c}^{A-y} V(i)P^*(i, y),$$

$$(13.50)$$

$$(y = 0, 1, \ldots, A + c - \rho - r).$$

The probability distribution and the expected number of units that will not be supplied are among the important characteristics of performance. These are readily computable from the $V(i)$; thus,

$$\text{Pr [shortage} = x] = V(-x), \quad x = 1, 2, \ldots, c - \rho - r;$$

and the expected number of unfilled orders is M:

$$M = \begin{cases} \sum_{i=\rho+r=1}^{-1} \{-iV(i)\}, & \text{if } \rho + r - c < 0, \\ 0, & \text{otherwise.} \end{cases}$$

PART FOUR

Chapter 14

SOME EXTENDED MODELS
OF UNCERTAINTY

There are some aspects of uncertainty in sales that may well be ignored in the short-run management of price and/or selling expenses. But there are others that are significant in the context of long-term irreversible decisions, such as the installation of new capacity. The present chapter appropriately modifies the models of sales uncertainty (under oligopolistic forms of competition) and prepares the ground for an analysis of such decisions. The departure from the preceding models is twofold: First, time is allowed to enter explicitly. Second, an explicit consideration is given to the influence of the prices of competing products. The principal content of this chapter is a model of forward and backward transition probabilities of the demand rates for the products of a given firm (*vis-à-vis* its competitors).

1. A SPECIAL BEHAVIOR ASSUMPTION

The (S, M, Y)-complex to be treated here is substantially the same as in the model of differentiated oligopoly (Chapter 4, Section 2). There is, however, an important specialization of customer behavior: If the product has been sold during the period $(t - \Delta t, t]$, then the customer's relative utility for it will decrease in $(t, t + \Delta t)$ as $\Delta t \to 0$. With but a slight strengthening of this behavior assumption, it is shown that the aggregate sales by a firm would be a *superposition* of elementary *renewal processes*. A differential equation is obtained for the transition probabilities of demand.

1.1 A potential customer of a firm will be viewed as an individual (or group of individuals acting together) who purchases the firm's product or one of a specified *set* (Σ) of other products. Firms producing the other

products of the set will be called "competition." The primary characteristics of the customers are assumed to be the following:

M:1 The sale of a product in the period $(t - \Delta t, t]$ decreases the utility
the customer places on the products in Σ in the period $(t, t + \Delta t)$,
as $\Delta t \to 0$;

M:2 If no sale has been made in $(t - \Delta t, t]$, then the utility placed upon
each product in Σ is increased in the period $(t, t + \Delta t)$.

M:3 Customers can and do distinguish between products both on
price and nonprice bases.

The information-communication pattern will be assumed to be the same
as in the models of Chapter 4, Sections 1 and 2. The most important
structural assumption of these models will be restated:

S: The total capacity of the industry exceeds the total sales of the
products (in Σ) in any time period and, thus, all demands are fulfilled.

Since the *market in question is one of durable industrial equipment*, it is
reasonable to assume that a customer seeks to maximize expected utility.
Together with the notion of Σ and (M:1), this implies that a sale from Σ
in $(t - \Delta t, t]$ will, in general, *decrease* the *probability* of a sale from Σ in
$(t, t + \Delta t)$, especially if Δt is small. In other words, if

Pr [a sale occurs in $(t - \Delta t, t] \equiv P(t - \Delta t, t)$,

Pr [a sale occurs in $(t, t + \Delta t) \mid$ the previous sale occurred at t]

$$\equiv P(t, t + \Delta t \mid t),$$

a rigorous statement of the implication is

$$\lim_{\Delta t \to 0} \frac{P(t - \Delta t, t)}{\Delta t} > \lim_{\Delta t \to 0} \frac{P(t, t + \Delta t \mid t)}{\Delta t}.$$

Also, the implication of M:2 is that one would expect the probability of a
sale to increase in $(t, t + \Delta t)$ if the previous sale occurred at t and if Δt
is not small. Thus, $P(t, t + \Delta t \mid t)$ is monotone increasing with increasing
Δt. Thus viewed, the sale (from Σ) over time to a single customer will
appear as a "simple" renewal process [17] and the *aggregate sales* over a
period of time can be represented as a *superposition of a number of independent simple renewal processes*. On account of the stipulation (*S*),
demands not fulfilled by one firm are fulfilled elsewhere; hence, the
transition or conditional probabilities of the sales of an individual firm
remain the *same as if it had made the sale*. The process, therefore, can be
viewed as one of *demand* rather than of sales.[1]

[1] Part of a firm's demand will consist of demands not fulfilled by other firms. The
validity of this view depends largely on (a) the number of firms in the industry and (b)
the institutional mechanism by which unfilled demand is allocated among firms that
fill it.

1.2 Consider the demand for a single product (in Σ) and define its rate of demand at time t as the number of units demanded in $(t - \tau, t)$, τ being a fixed length of time. It is evident from the description of the process that the demand in $(t - \tau, t)$ is *conditional* upon the demand ξ in the period $(t - \tau - \Delta t, t)$. The conditional probabilities may be specified in a number of ways. For the sake of definiteness two assumptions will be made in this regard. *First*, the probability of a transition from ξ to $\xi + 1$ or to $\xi - 1$ during $(t, t + \Delta t)$ depends only upon t, Δt and the state ξ at t.[2] *Second*, v, the total demand (for products in Σ) during $(t - \tau, t)$ is approximately a constant for a given τ, that is, relative to the time scale of the transitions considered, $v(t)$ changes very slowly if at all. Define, then, the following probabilities relating to the product of the firm of interest (labeled 1) and the product of the "competitor" (labeled 2):

$$P_{\xi}(t) = \text{Pr [demand rate for 1 is } \xi, \text{ at } t],$$

$$Q_{\xi}(t) = \text{Pr [demand rate for 2 is } \xi, \text{ at } t]. \tag{14.1}$$

Thus, in view of the first of the two assumptions made, the forward (from ξ to $\xi + 1$) and backward (from ξ to $\xi - 1$) probabilities of transition for 1 and 2 may be written as follows:

	Forward	Backward	Stay
1.	$\lambda(\xi, t)\Delta t + o(\Delta t)$,	$\mu(\xi, t)\Delta t + o(\Delta t)$,	$1 - [\lambda(\xi, t) + \mu(\xi, t)]\Delta t + o(\Delta t)$
2.	$\alpha(\xi, t)\Delta t + o(\Delta t)$,	$\beta(\xi, t)\Delta t + o(\Delta t)$,	$1 - [\alpha(\xi, t) + \beta(\xi, t)]\Delta t + o(\Delta t)^2$

$$\tag{14.2}$$

On account of the specification (S), it follows that if 1 is in state ξ, then 2 must be in state $v - \xi$; thus, a transition $\xi \to \xi + k$ for one implies a transition $v - \xi \to v - \xi - k$ for the other. In other words, the transition probability densities must satisfy

$$\lambda(\xi, t) = \beta(v - \xi, t), \qquad \mu(\xi, t) = \alpha(v - \xi, t). \tag{14.3}$$

Also, since the process is of a "renewal" type, the transition probability densities are to satisfy the following conditions [17],

$$\lambda(\xi, t) \geq \lambda(\xi + 1, t); \qquad \mu(\xi, t) \leq \mu(\xi + 1, t). \tag{14.4}$$

---

[2] Such dependence on t may be due to the influence of "intermediate" variables, such as the level and change of price.

A simple representation of $\lambda(\xi, t)$ and $\mu(\xi, t)$ consistent with conditions (14.3) and (14.4) may be chosen as

$$\lambda(\xi, t) = (\nu - \xi)\lambda(t) = \beta(\nu - \xi, t),$$

$$\mu(\xi, t) = \xi\mu(t) = \alpha(\nu - \xi, t). \tag{14.5}$$

Making use of (14.2) and (14.5), the differential equation for the state probabilities is seen to be

$$\frac{dP_\xi}{dt} = \lambda(t)(\nu - \xi + 1)P_{\xi-1} - [\lambda(t)(\nu - \xi) + \mu(t)\xi]P_\xi$$

$$+ \mu(t)(\xi + 1)P_{\xi+1}, \qquad \xi = 1, 2, \ldots, \nu - 1 \tag{14.6}$$

with the boundary conditions

$$\frac{dP_0}{dt} = -\lambda(t)\nu P_0 + \mu(t)P_1,$$

$$\frac{dP_\nu}{dt} = \lambda(t)P_{\nu-1} - \mu(t)\nu P_\nu. \tag{14.7}$$

2. SOME IMPLICATIONS OF THE RENEWAL MODEL

Equations (14.6) and (14.7) are employed to determine (a) the mean-value and variance of the demand rate and (b) the probability distribution of steady-state demand. A behavior hypothesis is then introduced with immediate consequences upon the forms of $\lambda(\xi, t)$ and $\mu(\xi, t)$: the *transition densities emerge as functions of the level and change of the asking price.*

2.1 Define the power series

$$F(s, t) = \sum_{\xi=0}^{\nu} (s)^\xi P_\xi(t);$$

then the equations (14.6) and the boundary conditions (14.7) can be combined into a single equation:

$$\frac{\partial F}{\partial t} + (s - 1)(\lambda s + \mu)\frac{\partial F}{\partial s} = \nu(s - 1)\lambda F. \tag{14.8}$$

The "characteristic equation" [53b] for this is seen to be

$$\frac{dt}{1} = \frac{ds}{(s - 1)(\lambda s + \mu)} = \frac{dF}{\nu(s - 1)\lambda F}. \tag{14.9}$$

Let θ and Φ be two functions such that $\theta\Phi = s - 1$ but are otherwise arbitrary. Then the first pair in (14.9)

$$\Phi[\dot\theta - (\lambda + \mu)\theta] + \theta[\dot\Phi - \lambda\theta\Phi^2] = 0.$$

Let θ denote the solution of $\dot\theta - (\lambda + \mu)\theta = 0$, that is,

$$\theta = \theta_0 \exp\left\{\int_0^t [\lambda(\tau) + \mu(\tau)]\,d\tau\right\}$$

$$\equiv \theta_0 e^{\gamma(t)}; \tag{14.10}$$

then Φ must satisfy $\dot\Phi - \theta_0\lambda e^{\gamma(t)}\Phi^2 = 0$, so that

$$-\frac{1}{\Phi} + \frac{1}{\Phi_0} = \theta_0 \int_0^t \lambda(\tau)e^{\gamma(\tau)}\,d\tau. \tag{14.11}$$

Using (14.10) and noting the requirement that $\theta\Phi = s - 1$, we may write (14.11) as

$$C_1 \equiv \frac{1}{\theta_0\Phi_0} = \frac{1}{s-1}\,e^{\gamma(t)} + \int_0^t \lambda(\tau)e^{\gamma(\tau)}\,d\tau. \tag{14.12}$$

Employing (14.12) to eliminate $s - 1$ between the equation defined by the first and third ratios of (14.9), we have

$$\frac{dF}{F} = \frac{\nu\lambda e^{\gamma(t)}\,dt}{\left[C_1 - \int_0^t \lambda(\tau)e^{\gamma(\tau)}\,d\tau\right]}. \tag{14.13}$$

Thus it may be verified that

$$F = \text{const}\left[C_1 - \int_0^t \lambda(\tau)e^{\gamma(\tau)}\,d\tau\right]^\nu$$

and another application of (14.12) gives

$$F = [(s-1)^{-1}e^{\gamma(t)}]^\nu f\left[(s-1)^{-1}e^{\gamma(t)} + \int_0^t \lambda(\tau)e^{\gamma(\tau)}\,d\tau\right], \tag{14.14}$$

$f(.)$ being an arbitrary real-valued function.

2.2 It is now possible to obtain the probabilities $P_\xi(t)$ for $\xi = 0, 1, \ldots,$ ν. Let $\xi(0) = \xi_0$; then,

$$P_\xi(0) = \begin{cases} 1, & \text{if } \xi = \xi_0, \\ 0, & \text{otherwise.} \end{cases}$$

This yields an initial condition:

$$F(s, 0) = (s)^{\xi_0} = (s-1)^\nu f\left(\frac{1}{s-1}\right).$$

Define the following:

$$X(t) = (s - 1)^{-1}e^{\gamma(t)} + \int_0^t \lambda(\tau)e^{\gamma(\tau)}\, d\tau,$$

$$w(t) = e^{-\gamma(t)}\left[1 + \int_0^t \mu(\tau)e^{\gamma(\tau)}\, d\tau\right],$$

$$A(t) = 1 - e^{-\gamma(t)}/w(t).$$

Then the solution of (14.14) can be expressed as

$$F(s, t) = [(s - 1)e^{-\gamma(t)}X(t)]^{\nu}\left[\frac{X(t) + 1}{X(t)}\right]^{\xi_0}$$

$$= [(1 - w)s + w]^{\nu - \xi_0}[(1 - wA)s + wA]^{\xi_0}. \qquad (14.15)$$

Hence the state probabilities are seen to be

$$P_n(t) = \Pr\,[\xi = n; t]$$

$$= \binom{\nu}{n}w^{\nu - n}(1 - w)^n \sum_{j=0}^{\xi_0} g_j\left(\frac{1 - wA}{1 - w}\right)^j (A)^{\xi_0 - j}, \qquad (14.16)$$

in which g_j is defined as

$$g_j = \frac{\binom{\xi_0}{j}\binom{\nu - \xi_0}{n - j}}{\binom{\nu}{j}}.$$

It may be readily verified from (14.16) that in the steady state demand has the binomial distribution

$$P_n(t) = \binom{\nu}{n}\left(\frac{\lambda}{\lambda + \mu}\right)^n\left(\frac{\mu}{\lambda + \mu}\right)^{\nu - n}. \qquad (14.17)$$

Some tedious calculation shows that the distribution (14.16) has the following mean value $\bar{\xi}(t)$ and variance $D^2(t)$:

$$\bar{\xi}(t) = \left[\xi_0 + \nu\int_0^t \lambda(\tau)e^{\gamma(\tau)}\, d\tau\right]e^{-\gamma(t)}, \qquad (14.18)$$

$$D^2(t) = \nu\left[1 - e^{-\gamma(t)}\int_0^t \lambda(\tau)e^{\gamma(\tau)}\, d\tau\right]e^{-\gamma(t)}\int_0^t \lambda(\tau)e^{\gamma(\tau)}\, d\tau$$

$$+ \xi_0 e^{-\gamma(t)}\left\{2\left[1 - e^{-\gamma(t)}\int_0^t e^{\gamma(\tau)}\lambda(\tau)\, d\tau\right] - 1 - e^{-\gamma(t)}\right\}. \qquad (14.19)$$

2.3 So far the behavior hypothesis (M:3) has not been taken into account. However, it is clear that an explicit consideration of (M:3) will make the transition densities λ and μ dependent on the price p and its rate of change $\dot{p}$. It appears that, subject only to a few "commonsense" restrictions, the nature of dependence (on p and $\dot{p}$) is arbitrary. Thus, for the sake of illustration, a simplified model is considered. Because typically the firm has *no knowledge* of the asking price of "competition," it seems to be more realistic to suppose that the transition densities will be (observable as) functions *only* of the firm's *own* price. Assuming linearity, the λ and μ may be written

$$\lambda(t) = \bar{a}_\lambda(t) - \bar{b}_\lambda(t)p(t) - \bar{c}_\lambda(t)\dot{p}(t),$$

$$\mu(t) = \bar{a}_\mu(t) + \bar{b}_\mu(t)p(t) + \bar{c}_\mu(t)\dot{p}(t),$$

(14.20)

in which the functions $\bar{a}(.)$, $\bar{b}(.)$ and $\bar{c}(.)$ are all positive valued. The quality of the model prescribed in (14.6) and (14.7) and (14.20) is essentially the same as that of the dynamic or multiperiod models of Chapter 8. *The fact that certain transition probabilities exist and take on specific forms has its origin in the stability of the mode of competition and of the structural properties of the market. For without such stability the demand process would not be measurable (in the sense of probability theory).* Also, without such stability the steady-state probabilities (14.17) would not be defined. Thus, it will be explicitly assumed that the mode of competition and the structure of the market are stable and, thus, the $P_\xi(t)$, $\xi = 0$, $1, \ldots, \nu$ will be *approximated* by (14.17). It should be emphasized that such an approximation *does not preclude* the time-dependence of λ and μ. The "goodness" of this approximation rests on how fast $P_n(t)$ approaches $P_n(\infty)$, that is, on the speed of convergence of the factor

$$\sum_{j=0}^{\xi_0} g_j \left(\frac{1 - wA}{1 - w} \right)^j (A)^{\xi_0 - j}$$

in (14.16) to one. This, again, depends chiefly on the size of $\bar{a}$. Thus in (14.20), if $\bar{a}_\lambda = \bar{a}_\mu = \bar{a}$ is a constant and large relative to $\bar{b}p + \bar{c}\dot{p}$, then $\lambda = \bar{a}$ and $\mu = \bar{a}$, and the expression in question becomes $[(1 - e^{-2\bar{a}t})/(1 + e^{-2\bar{a}t})]^{\xi_0}$.

3. A TEST OF THE MARKOV TRANSITIONS OF SALES

The principal *assertion* of Chapter 8 and of the "renewal" model of Sections 1 and 2 of this chapter have been the following: under certain types of market organization, the demand, seen from the viewpoint of an individual firm, is a Markov process, and its transition probabilities depend on the price asked by the firm. The aim of this section is to test this assertion in the same manner (see Chapter 10) and with the same kind of data employed to test the models of Chapter 4. For obvious practical reasons the stochastic process in question is assumed to be discrete-state and discrete parameter (i.e., price) and the transition densities are replaced by empirical frequencies.

3.1 The sales and price data to be analyzed refer to a very weakly differentiated oligopoly consisting of eight firms with their aggregate capacity approximately twice the industry demand. The "ensemble" consists of 10 runs each covering 100 sales periods; a sample record of the price and sales is presented for two firms in Figures 14.1, 14.2 and Table 14.0. One of the principal characteristics of the *ensemble* is the existence of

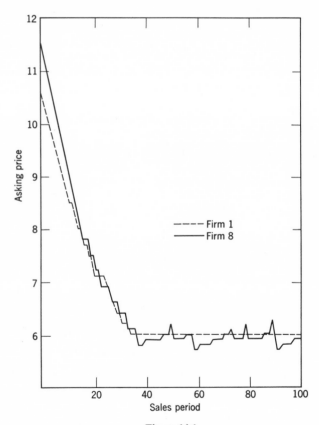

Figure 14.1

TABLE 14.0

COMPARISON OF SALES AND PRICES

Run 1–Firm 1

Periods 1–25		Periods 26–50		Periods 51–75		Periods 76–100	
Price	Sales	Price	Sales	Price	Sales	Price	Sales
10.5	0	6.9	0	6.0	0	6.0	0
.2	←——→	.6	1014	↑	445	↑	563
.0	0	.6	0		0		464
9.8	1090	.4	1014		0		0
.5	0	.4	0		0		0
.3	753	.2	1014		172		116
.1	0	.2	1014		0		0
.0	1330	.2	0		←——→		0
8.8	0	6.0	1014		0		116
.7	1224		1014		336		0
.5	0		455		0		0
.5	0		0		470		258
.2	1114		0		0		644
.0	0		391		0		0
.0	0		0		0		←——→
7.8	1014		←——→		0		0
.8	327		0		561		199
.5	0		444		0		0
.5	0		0		0		0
.3	0		0		0		0
.1	1014		0				631
.1			686				
.1			0				
.1							
6.9	1014	6.0	0	6.0	0	6.0	631

Run 1–Firm 8

11.5	0	6.6	1436	5.9	1436	5.9	408
.2	↔	.6	1436	.9	1436	.9	1436
10.9		.6	0	.9	481	6.2	0
.6		.4	1436	.9	435	5.9	1436
.4		.4	1436	6.0	365	↔	↔
.1		.4	0	.0	354		
9.8	↔	.1	1436	.0	0	5.9	1436
.6		.1	1436	5.7	1436	6.0	199
.3		.1	656	.7	↔	.0	201
.0	0	.1	0	.8		.0	748
8.7	261	5.8	1436	↔		.3	0
.5	0	.8	↔			.0	0
.2	1572	.8		.8	1436	5.7	1436
.0	0	.9		.9	555	.7	↔
7.7	0	↔		↔	647	.8	
.7	1486				219	.8	
.8	0	.9	1436	.9	575	.8	
.5	1436	6.0	409	6.0	0	.8	
.5	0	.0	276	.0	1426	5.9	1436
.2	1436	.0	807	.1	1309	↔	↔
.2	1436	.2	0	5.9	1436		
6.9	1436	5.9	1436	.9		5.9	1436
.9	1436			.9			
.9				.9			
.9							

197

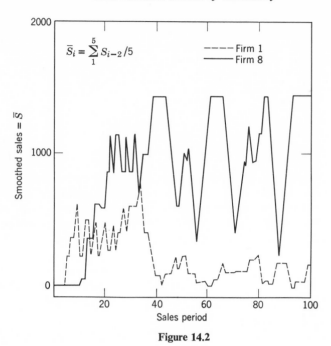

Figure 14.2

a *transient* regime followed by a stable or *equilibrium* regime. The first covers the initial or earlier periods and is characterized by the *downward* adjustment of the asking price in response to an underfulfilment of demand. The equilibrium regime, on the other hand, is a period of stable prices and the price adjustments that do occur are seen to follow a pattern different from that in the transient regime. The initial variations in the asking price are *upward* at a time when the firm's sales are at capacity; the later downward variations represent an adjustment in response to the reduction in sales that is ultimately due to a price-raising action. The characteristic feature of the transient regimes is that one or more firms are operating below their capacity and above their minimum asking price. In the equilibrium regime all firms are operating at one or both of their capacity constraints. In light of these observations, it will be appropriate to assume that the λ and μ in (14.20) *will be different for the two regimes*. In the equilibrium regime the transition frequencies are more likely to depend upon the demand ξ and the asking price p; thus the influence of $\dot{p}$ may be ignored. The transient regime, on the other hand, is more likely to be a period in which $\dot{p}$ will play a more significant role. Thus, for the purposes of empirical analysis, the equations (14.20) will be modified as follows:

Parameters	Equilibrium Regime	Transient Regime
$\lambda =$	$\bar{a}_\lambda - \bar{b}_\lambda p$	$\bar{a}_\lambda - \bar{c}_\lambda \dot{p}$
$\mu =$	$\bar{a}_\mu + \bar{b}_\mu p$	$\bar{a}_\mu + \bar{c}_\mu \dot{p}$

$$(14.21)$$

Finally, it should be observed that one must define the (discrete) states of demand ξ. In view of the (S, M, Y)-specifications of Chapter 4, Section 1, it is natural to expect that the changes in a firm's sales, when they occur, are to be large, for typically a firm operates at capacity or sells almost nothing (see Figure 14.2). Thus it appears that the demand may be described in terms of two states: a high level ξ_u and a low level ξ_f. (For model (14.17), this means that $\xi_u = v$ and $\xi_f = 0$.) To sum up: The Markov hypothesis is to be tested subject to the prior convention that there are only two states ξ_u and ξ_f and that the λ and μ in the transient and equilibrium regimes are as in (14.21).

3.2 Consider the equilibrium regime with two states, $\xi_f : 0 \leq \xi < 800$ and $\xi_u : \xi > 800$, and consider the matrices (see Table 14.1) of frequencies of transitions at various levels of the asking price.

TABLE 14.1

SALES TRANSITION FREQUENCIES DUE TO PRICE VARIATIONS
(EQUILIBRIUM REGIME)

	$p = 5.8$		$p = 5.9$		$p = 6.0$		$p = 6.1$		$p = 6.2$	
From/To	ξ_f	ξ_u	ξ_f	ξ_u	ξ_f	ξ_u	ξ_f	ξ_u	ξ_f	ξ_u
ξ_f	0	0	88	26	444	17	10	0	5	0
ξ_u	0	248	65	662	28	34	4	3	2	2

Note: The number of upward and downward transitions are not equal. This is due to the fact that a transition is recorded as an observation for the equilibrium regime *only if* the price at which the sale took place had not changed since the previous period. Some of the transitions from one sales level to another took place at the time the price changed and thus were not recorded.

Suppose that the transition probabilities, given an asking price p and a present sale ξ, are predicted as

$$\lambda(\xi, t) = (\bar{a}_\lambda - \bar{b}_\lambda p)(\xi_u - \xi),$$

$$\mu(\xi, t) = (\bar{a}_\mu + \bar{b}_\mu p)(\xi - \xi_f). \tag{14.22}$$

The constants $\bar{a}_\lambda$, $\bar{a}_\mu$, $\bar{b}_\lambda$, and $\bar{b}_\mu$ are found by minimizing

$$\sum_{k=1}^{5} \sum_{i=1}^{2} (n_{iik} - n_{ik} P_{iik})^2, \tag{14.23}$$

in which n_{iik} is the number of observations on the diagonal in row i of the kth matrix (that is, the matrix associated with the kth level of price) and n_{ik} is the sum of the observations in that row. Equation (14.23) can also be written as

$$\sum_{k=1}^{5} \sum_{i=1}^{2} W_{ik}[P'_{iik} - P_{iik}]^2, \tag{14.24}$$

in which W_{ik} is the weight n_{ik}^2/n^2, where n^2 is defined as

$$n^2 = \sum_{k=1}^{5} \sum_{i=1}^{2} n_{ik}^2$$

and P'_{iik} and P_{iik} are defined as

$$P'_{iik} = \frac{n_{iik}}{n_{ik}},$$

$$P_{iik} = 1 - (\bar{a}_\lambda - \bar{b}_\lambda p_k)(\xi_u - \xi_i) - (\bar{a}_\mu + \bar{b}_\mu p_k)(\xi_i - \xi_f).$$

The estimates turn out to be the following:

$$a_\lambda = 0.004126, \qquad b_\lambda = 0.000682,$$

$$a_\mu = -0.003143, \qquad b_\mu = 0.000545. \tag{14.25}$$

[If the equations (14.22) are written in the form

$$\lambda(\xi, t) = \bar{a} + \bar{b}_\lambda(\bar{p} - p)(\xi_u - \xi),$$

$$\mu(\xi, t) = \bar{a} - \bar{b}_\mu(\bar{p} - p)(\xi - \xi_f), \tag{14.26}$$

then $\bar{a} = 0.88 \times 10^{-4}$ with $\bar{p} = 5.922$.] To sum up,

$$\lambda(\xi) = \begin{cases} 0.5251 - 0.8866p - 0.0040\xi + 0.0007p\xi, \\ \quad \text{if } 5.76 < p < 6.06, \qquad \xi \le 800, \\ 0, \quad \text{if } p > 6.06. \end{cases} \tag{14.27}$$

$$\mu(\xi) = \begin{cases} 0.0043 - 0.0708p - 0.0032\xi + 0.0005p\xi, \\ \quad \text{if } 5.76 < p < 6.06, \qquad \xi \ge 800, \\ 0, \quad \text{if } p < 5.76. \end{cases} \tag{14.28}$$

The predicted (P_0) and observed (P_0') probabilities of the event "no transition" at $\bar{\xi}_f = 130$ and $\bar{\xi}_u = 1,300$ are shown in Table 14.2 for various levels of the asking price.

TABLE 14.2

COMPARISON OF PREDICTED AND OBSERVED PROBABILITIES
OF "NO TRANSITION" IN THE EQUILIBRIUM REGIME

Mean Level of ξ	Price (p)	Predicted Probability (P_0)	Observed Probability (P_0')	Weight (W)
	5.8	0	0.800	0
130	5.9	0.772	0.879	0.016
	6.0	0.966	0.959	0.259
	6.1	1.000	1.000	0
	5.8	1.0	0.975	0.075
1,300	5.9	0.911	0.911	0.645
	6.0	0.548	0.847	0.005
	6.1	0.429	0.783	0

In conclusion, it is of interest to observe that the *transition* densities are seen to depend upon the *level* from which the transitions occur. This may be tested against the null hypothesis that the transitions are independent of the states from which they occur. There is a criterion [68] for performing this test within the hypothesis that the chain is Markovian: that is

$$\sum_{i=1}^{2} \sum_{j=1}^{2} \frac{n(n_{ij} - n_i n_j/n)^2}{n_i n_j},$$

asymptotically distributed χ^2 with one degree of freedom for each of the matrices of Table 14.1. The null hypothesis is seen to be rejected at the 95% level.

Chapter **15**

AN APPLICATION: INVESTMENT DECISIONS AND PRICE POLICY

Some implications of the model of the preceding chapter will be examined for possible impact on capital investment decisions. In particular, the decisions to expand capacity will be shown to depend upon the price policy a firm is prepared to pursue. This demonstration is an extension of the short-run analysis (Chapter 9), indicating that the firm is never free to pursue arbitrary price policies, because prices determine the transition probabilities of sales of the firm.

The nature and content of this extended application to the long-run depend upon several factors. The more important ones are the following: (a) operational measures of "capacity" and "amount" of capital equipment, (b) technology of production, and (c) costs of changing capacity and of using and owning the equipment.

Section 1 is devoted to a specification of each of these elements. Section 2 is concerned with a situation in which the technology of the production of capital goods is supposed to be constant, while in Section 3, the more general case is considered in which technology undergoes changes.

1. SOME PRIMARY CONCEPTS

The purpose of this section is to set out in detail the operational definitions of (a) capacity and amount of capital goods, (b) production technology, and (c) costs of using and owning capital goods. Comparable viewpoints are also cited.

1.1 Capacity is defined as the *maximum* amount of output that can be produced in a specified time with the aid of the stock of capital equipment possessed by the firm: This stock is taken to be directly proportional to

$x(t)$, the dollars invested in equipment.[1] It will be assumed that equipment can be discarded and when discarded the oldest piece is thrown out first. Capacity however, is regarded as *dependent on the productivity of the equipment which again is assumed to depend on the time it was acquired.* Thus capacity can be represented as the integral of investment, weighted by the productivity of the equipment per dollar spent on it. In other words, if $f(t)$ denotes the capacity[2] of a unit of physical equipment purchased at time t, and if $g(t)$ denotes the price per unit of the equipment the capacity of the firm at time t is given by the integral

$$y(t) = \int_{t-s(t)}^{t} \frac{f(\tau)\dot{x}(\tau)}{g(\tau)} \, d\tau. \tag{15.1}$$

in which $s = s(t)$ is the age of the oldest piece of equipment in stock at time t and $\dot{x}(t)$ is the rate of investment at time t. Associated with $y(t)$, the capacity, we may consider the "worth" of the firm's equipment (at time t) defined as

$$w(t) = \int_{t-s(t)}^{t} \dot{x}(\tau) \, d\tau, \tag{15.2}$$

As in the *ABK* model [4], it is assumed that the firm can produce any quantity that does not exceed its capacity and, because capacity depends on the amount of equipment owned by the firm, there will be no explicit reference to a production function.[3] The economic force that moves the

---

[1] This is also the sense in which Arrow-Beckman-Karlin (ABK) [4] define capacity. If $\dot{x}(t)$ denotes the rate of investment in new equipment (of the same kind as the old ones), and if a denotes the amount of capacity per dollars worth of equipment, then the capacity at time t is defined in the ABK model as

$$y(t) = y(0) + \int_0^t a \, \dot{x}(\tau) \, d\tau,$$

where the derivative $\dot{x}(t)$ is to be understood as the limit:

$$\dot{x}(t) = \lim_{\Delta t \to 0^+} \frac{x(t + \Delta t) - x(t)}{\Delta t}.$$

In the models considered by Smith [52], the conditions of production are such that demand can be satisfied by employing the amount of (continuously variable) current inputs specified by the production function appropriate to the given stock of capital equipment. The concept of "capacity," therefore, does not appear in Smith's models; the motivation for investing in equipment is to reduce the cost of current inputs per unit of output by operating on a more efficient segment of the long-term cost-curve.

[2] To be measured in units of product per unit of equipment per unit of operating time.

[3] A production function is a function that gives the maximum amount of products that *can* be produced from given amounts of the current inputs and a given "amount" of capital goods.

firm to buy equipment is the opportunity to increase revenues by closing the gap between demand and capacity, whenever such a gap exists. The forces that move the firm to scrap equipment are the cost of maintaining the equipment. The only variable cost considered in the *ABK* model is the cost of purchasing the equipment,[4] but again the price per unit of equipment is regarded as a constant. This assumption is an unnecessary restriction and, as seen in (15.1), the price per unit is explicity time-dependent. To enrich this simple generalization, it is supposed that the overhead requirements (i.e., the maintenance man-hours per machine per year) for a piece of equipment are known for the piece of equipment at the time it is purchased.[5] Thus, the total overhead cost at any time is seen to depend on the number of machines purchased in each interval in the past which have not been discarded. So, if $m(t)$ denotes the "operating burden" associated with a unit of equipment purchased at time t, then $m(t)\dot{x}(t)/g(t)$ is the rate at which this burden increases and, thus,

$$v(t) = \int_{t-s(t)}^{t} \frac{m(\tau)\dot{x}(\tau)}{g(\tau)} \, d\tau,$$

will represent the burden on the stock of equipment held by the firm at time t.

1.2 Two major environmental variables affecting the investment decision problem need careful description. These are, first, the possible variation of technology in the capital goods industry and, second, the nature of uncertainty of the product demand. *ABK* assumes that there is no change in the capital goods technology or in its selling price, so that capacity purchased per dollar is the same throughout the planning period. This assumption is quite appropriate if the impact of capital goods technology on the relationship between the price and capacity of the capital goods is small or slowly changing. Under such circumstances, the price per unit of capacity can be looked upon as an *average* taken over the planning period. In the basic model of Smith, the technology of the capital goods industry is of no relevance, for the decision to purchase and the amount to purchase are determined once and for all at the beginning

---

[4] This is charged as a depreciation expense and, for the sake of simplicity, is written off *immediately in full*. The results, however, may be shown to hold if a straightline depreciation and an identical writeoff period are used for all investments.

[5] The ABK models assume that the maintenance costs are directly proportional to output and so they can be absorbed into the gross selling price. Smith (*op. cit.*) makes the same assumption in his basic models, although in a later generalization he assumes that the maintenance outlays are in direct proportion to the cumulative consumption of the current inputs.

of the planning horizon.[6] One of the principal departures of the model to be developed here is that it considers the *effects of technological changes on the productivity and the overhead requirements* of equipment: Both these factors are incorporated in the definitions of capacity and overhead requirement. The second major environmental factor is the nature of demand. The *ABK* and Smith models treat the anticipated demand as a point estimate or mean value of the actual (random) demand available at each point in the planning period. The most outstanding departure of the present model is not only to consider the randomness[7] of demand (sales) but also to characterize such randomness from an analysis of the behavioral and structural characteristics of the market. It only remains to be indicated that the decision criterion to be considered in the following section is the expected discounted profits. This will be optimized by choosing (a) the product selling price, (b) the amount to be invested, and (c) the amount of equipment to be discarded.

2. AN APPLICATION OF THE "RENEWAL" MODEL

The model of Chapter 14 is now applied to the decision situation described in the preceding section. In keeping with the assumption (see Chapter 14, Section 1) that demands not met by the firm will be fulfilled "elsewhere," it will be supposed that *unfilled demands cannot be back-ordered.* Also, it will be assumed that the planning period is finite and that *capacity additions can be continuous.* The problem of optimal expansion is solved first under the assumption of a fixed technology and then the more general situation of a varying technology is considered.

2.1 It should be recalled from Chapter 14 that the transition densities λ and μ were seen to be dependent upon the price and its change. This will now be emphasized by writing

$$P_{\xi}(t) = H[\xi; t, p(t), \dot{p}(t)],$$

where $p(t)$ denotes the firm's price at time t. Also, the expected demand rate $\bar{\xi}(t)$ will be replaced by the symbol $\bar{\delta}(t)$. Next, recall the definition

---

[6] Technological changes are relevant in an n-step investment model, and this generalization of the Smith models was made by Hinomoto [29].

[7] The one exception is the work of Manne [66] where an interesting analysis is made of capacity expansion in response to *growing* demand. The growth of demand is modeled as a Bachelier-Wiener diffusion process, and the *mathematical* development is almost identical with that of Feller [21]. The essence of Manne's model is a description of demand increments as a Gaussian random variable with mean-value μt and variance $\sigma^2 t$.

of plant capacity $y(t)$ and the implicit assumption that unfilled demands cannot be back-ordered. Thus, the expected sales rate at time t is given by

$$\bar{\delta}[y(t)] = \int_0^{y(t)} \xi \cdot H(\xi)\, d\xi + y(t) \int_{y(t)}^\infty H(\xi)\, d\xi$$

$$= y(t) + \int_0^{y(t)} [\xi - y(t)]H(\xi)\, d\xi. \tag{15.3}$$

The assumption that no back-ordering is permitted also means that the rate of *net* revenue is

$$[p(t) - q(t)] \cdot \min\{\xi(t), y(t)\} - b\dot{y}(t), \tag{15.4}$$

where b is the rate of depreciation and $q(t)$ is the unit production cost. Therefore, the expected net revenue discounted over the planning period T is given by $J(T)$:

$$J(T) = \int_0^T \{[p(t) - q(t)]\bar{\delta}(t) - b\dot{y}(t)\} \exp(-\rho t)\, dt \tag{15.5}$$

ρ being the (instantaneous) rate of discount. Optimization of $J(T)$ is considered under the two restrictions; that price is to remain nonnegative and that there is a ceiling to the permissible rate of investment:

$$\text{(i) } p(t) \geq 0, \qquad \text{(ii) } 0 \leq \dot{y} \leq M. \tag{15.6}$$

Thus, the decision problem is mathematically equivalent to seeking *two functions* $p(t)$ *and* $y(t)$ *that satisfy* (15.6) *and render* $J(T)$ *maximum.* Observe that the mathematical problem is one of optimizing an *integral* subject to inequality constraints [8, 58]. Nonnegative functions $a_p(t)$ and $a_y(t)$ are now introduced, and the inequalities are replaced by equality restrictions;

$$\dot{y}(M - \dot{y}) - (a_y)^2 = 0, \qquad p - (a_p)^2 = 0. \tag{15.7}$$

Next, let $\lambda_y(t)$ and $\lambda_p(t)$ be the Lagrange multipliers associated with the equations in (15.7). Then the constrained maximization problem is reduced to an unconstrained maximization of $J(T, \lambda_y, \lambda_p)$:

$$J(T, \lambda_y, \lambda_p) = \int_0^T \{[(p - q)\bar{\delta}(y) - b\dot{y}] \exp(-\rho t)$$

$$+ \lambda_y[\dot{y}(M - \dot{y}) - a_y{}^2] + \lambda_p[p - a_p{}^2]\}\, dt. \tag{15.8}$$

The functions $p(t)$ and $y(t)$ that render this integral stationary with respect to strong variations are given by the Euler-Lagrange equations

$$\frac{d}{dt}\left[\lambda_y(M - 2\dot{y})\right] = \left\{(p - q)\int_y^\infty H(\xi)\,d\xi - b\rho\right\}\exp\left(-\rho t\right), \quad (15.9)$$

$$\frac{d}{dt}\left[(p - q)\exp\left(-\rho t\right)\frac{\partial\bar{\delta}}{\partial p}\right] = \frac{\partial}{\partial p}\left[(p - q)\bar{\delta}\right]\exp\left(-\rho t\right) + \lambda\rho, \quad (15.10)$$

$$\lambda_y[\ddot{y}(M - \dot{y}) - (a_y)^2] = 0, \qquad \lambda_y a_y = 0, \quad (15.11)$$

$$\lambda_p[p - (a_p)^2] = 0, \qquad \lambda_p a_p = 0. \quad (15.12)$$

In order to solve the Eqs. (15.9) to (15.12), let $y(0) = y_0$ and $p(0) = p_0$. With a view to preclude meaningless solutions, *assume* that the firm's initial capacity is such that the expected lost profits (exclusive of the cost of capital) do not exceed the cost of carrying the investment in an additional unit of capacity. In other words, it is assumed that at $t = 0$ the following holds:

$$\omega(0) \equiv [p(0) - q(0)]\int_{y(0)}^\infty H(\xi)\,d\xi \leq b\rho. \quad (15.13)$$

The integral in (15.13) represents the initial probability that sales exceed capacity.

2.2 The solution procedure consists of two steps. *First*, one constructs the set of corner points at which the expansion of capacity is to be initiated. *Second*, one develops a condition signaling the termination of a phase of expansion. Thus, analogous to $\omega(0)$ of (15.13), define $\omega(t)$:

$$\omega(t) = [p(t) - q(t)]u[y(t), t, p(t), \dot{p}(t)]$$
$$\equiv [p(t) - q(t)]\int_{y(t)}^\infty H(\xi)\,d\xi, \quad (15.14)$$

in which $p(t)$ and $\dot{p}(t)$ are the solutions of (15.12). Also, define the set of instants $T^*(\hat{t})$

$$T^*(\hat{t}) = [t \mid \omega(t) = b\rho, \qquad \dot{\omega}(t - 0) > 0, \qquad t > \hat{t} \geq 0] \quad (15.15)$$

and let its elements be denoted by t_i, $i = 1, 2, \ldots, N(\hat{t})$. Note that except for $t = \infty$, $T^*(\hat{t})$ *is* the set of corner points.[8] Suppose now that

---

[8] In order to show that corner points at the beginning of an expansion phase have the properties defining $T^*(\hat{t})$, let t^* be a particular corner point and let ϵ be an arbitrarily small positive number. Now, $\dot{y}(t) = 0$ everywhere on the interval $t^* - \epsilon < t < t^*$. Therefore, by familiar reasoning [8] $\lambda_y(t^* - 0) > 0$. Also, $\dot{y}(t) > 0$ on the interval $t^* < t \leq t^* + \epsilon$; hence, $\lambda_y(t^* + 0) = \lambda_y(t^* + 0) = 0$ and, by (15.9), $\omega(t^* - 0) = b\rho$. But since $\lambda_y(t)$ is continuous, it follows that $\dot{\lambda}_y(t^* - 0) < 0$ and, again, by (15.9), it is seen that $\dot{\omega}(t^* - 0) < b\rho$. Thus, $\dot{\omega}(t^*) > 0$.

$T^*(0)$ contains at least two elements and let $t^*(0)$ be the smaller of the two. Set $y(t) = y(0)$ on $0 \leq t \leq t^*(0)$. Then compute

$$M\lambda_y(t_i) = \int_t^{t_i} [\omega(\tau) - b\rho]e^{-\rho\tau} \, d\tau$$

for $i = 1, 2, \ldots, N(\hat{t})$. Again, let $\hat{t}^*$ be the least $\hat{t} > t^*(0)$ such that $\lambda_y(t_i) = 0$ for some t_i in $T^*(\hat{t}^*)$, and let t^* be the least t_i in $T^*(\hat{t}^*)$ for which $\lambda_y(t_i) = 0$. Then the optimal solution is to set $y(t) = y(\hat{t}^*)$ on $\hat{t}^* \leq t \leq t^*$ and, thereafter, beginning at $t = t^*$, to proceed as above. The assumption implicit in this solution is that the *demand for investment funds* does not exceed the allowable rate M. A stochastic version (not gone into in this work) of this is that for all t and $\tau > t$ the following inequality shall be satisfied:

$$\int_{y(t)}^{\infty} H(\xi) \, d\xi > \int_{y(t)+(\tau-t)M}^{\infty} H(\xi) \, d\xi.$$

2.3   It remains to consider the more general situation in which technological changes in the capital goods may affect the cost of acquiring and maintaining equipment and may even induce the firm to scrap idle equipment with a view toward saving on maintenance costs. This line of generalization calls for a change in the definition (15.3) of expected sales rate. Thus, in terms of the symbols introduced in Section 1, define the following:

$$\theta(t) = \frac{m(t)}{g(t)}, \qquad \Phi(t) = \frac{f(t)}{g(t)},$$

$$\bar{\theta}(t) = \int_{t-s(t)}^{t} \theta(\tau)\dot{x}(\tau) \, d\tau \Big/ \int_{t-s(t)}^{t} \dot{x}(\tau) \, d\tau = \frac{v(t)}{w(t)},$$

$$\bar{\Phi}(t) = \int_{t-s(t)}^{t} \Phi(\tau)\dot{x}(\tau) \, d\tau \Big/ \int_{t-s(t)}^{t} \dot{x}(\tau) \, d\tau = \frac{y(t)}{w(t)}.$$

$\bar{\theta}(t)$ represents the *average* (investments being the "weights" employed) increase in what was defined earlier as the operating burden; similarly, $\bar{\Phi}(t)$ is the *average* increase in capacity per dollar of investment at time t. Writing $y(t) = \bar{\Phi}(t)w(t)$, $v(t) = \bar{\theta}(t)w(t)$ and denoting the maintenance cost by $c(t)v(t)$, we see that the expected aggregate net profits are the following version of (15.5):

$$J(T) = \int_0^T [(p - q)\bar{\delta}(\bar{\Phi}w) - c\bar{\theta}w - b\dot{x}] \exp(-\rho t) \, dt. \tag{15.16}$$

which is to be maximized subject to the constraints

$$0 \leq \dot{x} \leq M, \qquad \dot{x} \geq \dot{w}, \qquad p(t) \geq 0. \tag{15.17}$$

The unknown functions to be determined are $s(t)$ and $x(t)$. As in the preceding paragraph, introduce Lagrange multipliers $\lambda_x(t)$, $\lambda_w(t)$ and $\lambda_p(t)$ and "slack" functions $a_x(t)$, $a_w(t)$ and $a_p(t)$. Then, the Euler-Lagrange equations for the *un*constrained optimization problem gives rise to the following equations for a necessary condition of optimum:

$$\lambda_w = \left[c\bar{\theta} - (p - q)\bar{\Phi} \int_{w\bar{\Phi}}^{\infty} H(\xi)\, d\xi \right] e^{-\rho t}, \qquad (15.18)$$

$$\lambda_w + \lambda_x(M - 2\dot{x}) = b \exp(-\rho t), \qquad (15.19)$$

$$\frac{d}{dt}\left[(p - q)\frac{\partial \bar{\delta}}{\partial p} \exp(-\rho t) \right] = \frac{\partial}{\partial p}\left[(p - q)\bar{\delta} \right] e^{-\rho t} + \lambda p, \qquad (15.20)$$

$$\dot{x}(M - \dot{x}) - a_x{}^2 = 0, \qquad \lambda_x a_x = 0, \qquad (15.21)$$

$$\dot{x} - \dot{w} - a_w{}^2 = 0, \qquad \lambda_w a_w = 0, \qquad (15.22)$$

$$p - a_p{}^2 = 0, \qquad \lambda_p a_p = 0. \qquad (15.23)$$

First, observe that λ_w and λ_x must vanish at the corners of the paths $w(t)$ and $x(t)$. Also, the optimal path will consist of three kinds of subarcs: (a) those on which capacity will be expanded ($\dot{x} > 0, \dot{s} = 1$), (b) those on which capacity will be reduced by scrapping equipment ($\dot{x} = 0, \dot{s} < 1$), and (c) those on which capacity will be held constant ($\dot{x} = 0, \dot{s} = 1$). According to (15.21), $\lambda_x = 0$ on the first kind of subarc and, hence, on account of (15.18) and (15.19) one has

$$-b\rho = c\bar{\theta} - (p - q)\bar{\Phi} \int_{w\Phi}^{\infty} H(\xi)\, d\xi.$$

But since $y = \bar{\Phi}w$ and $v = \bar{\theta}w$, the condition may be written as

$$(p - q)y \int_{y}^{\infty} H(\xi)\, d\xi = cv + b\rho. \qquad (15.24)$$

In other words, along the subarcs of the first kind, capacity is expanded at a rate such that the "burden" and the interest charges on *total* investment is just equal to the profit lost on demands in excess of capacity. Next, observe that according to (15.22), $\lambda_w = 0$ on subarcs of the second kind, and, hence, on account of (15.18), one would have

$$(p - q)\bar{\Phi} \int_{\bar{\Phi}w}^{\infty} H(\xi)\, d\xi = c\bar{\theta},$$

that is,

$$(p - q)y \int_{y}^{\infty} H(\xi)\, d\xi = cv. \qquad (15.25)$$

Thus, on the second kind of subarcs, capacity is allowed to be depleted at a rate such that the "burden" on the total investment just equals the profits lost on demands in excess of capacity.

2.4 In the preceding scheme of calculation, the *optimal selling price* is to be derived as a solution of (15.20). An inspection of (15.20) should make it obvious that if the demand probability density is *independent* of the rate of change of price, that is, if $\partial H(\xi)/\partial \dot{p} = 0$ for all t, then the price must be set such that

$$\frac{\partial \bar{\delta}}{\partial p} = \frac{\bar{\delta}}{p - q}, \qquad \frac{p}{\bar{\delta}} \frac{\partial \bar{\delta}}{\partial p} = \frac{p}{p - q} ; \qquad (15.26)$$

that is, such that the elasticity of expected demand with respect to the asking price is $- p/(p - q)$. Loosely speaking, given the capacity, the price is to be set so as to maximize profits. But again this implies that on an interval (say, $\check{t}^* \leq t \leq t^*$) of constant capacity, the price is to be adjusted so as to hold the expected profits at the level determined by

$$[p(t) - q(t)]\bar{\delta}(t) = [p(\check{t}^*) - q(\check{t}^*)]\bar{\delta}(\check{t}^*). \qquad (15.27)$$

Because $\bar{\delta}$ tends to disappear as price goes up, it follows that on such intervals the asking price may well be *raised* (*cut*) if the market happens to be *expanding* (*contracting*).[9] In conclusion, it will be worthwhile to examine the implications of (15.9) and (15.20) on the optimal price policy when (a) the *binomial* distribution (Chapter 14, Section 16) is approximated by the *uniform* distribution

$$H(\xi) = \begin{cases} 0, & \text{if } \xi < \bar{\xi} - D\sqrt{3}, \\ \dfrac{1}{2D\sqrt{3}}, & \text{if } \bar{\xi} - D\sqrt{3} < \xi < \bar{\xi} + D\sqrt{3}, \\ 0, & \text{if } \xi > \bar{\xi} + D\sqrt{3}, \end{cases}$$

$\bar{\xi}$ and D^2 being the mean-value and variance of the binomial distribution, and (b) the transition densities

$$\lambda = a_\lambda - b_\lambda p - c_\lambda \dot{p}, \qquad \mu = a_\mu + b_\mu p + c_\mu \dot{p}$$

are such that $b_\lambda = b_\mu = b$ and $c_\lambda = c_\mu = c$. Setting $a_\lambda = a + b\bar{p}$, $a_\mu = a - b\bar{p}$, $k_1 = b/a$ and $k_2 = c/a$, the mean-value $\bar{\xi}$ and the variance

---

[9] At the level of the industry, the implication is that rising demand will, in general, cause capacity to increase up to some point beyond which it will be held constant and demand will be allowed to come into line by a general increase in price.

D^2 are seen to be

$$\bar{\xi} = \frac{\nu}{2}\,[1 + k_1(\bar{p} - p) - k_2\dot{p}], \qquad D^2 = \frac{\nu}{4}\,\{1 - [k_1(\bar{p} - p) - k_2\dot{p}]^2\}.$$

(15.28)

It will be assumed that p is sufficiently close to $\bar{p}$ and $\dot{p} \cong 0$ so that $D^2 = \nu/4$. Thus the expected sales are given by

$$\delta = \begin{cases} y, & y < \bar{\xi} - D\sqrt{3}, \\[2mm] \dfrac{2y(\bar{\xi} + D\sqrt{3}) - y^2 - (\bar{\xi} - D\sqrt{3})^2}{4D\sqrt{3}}, & \bar{\xi} - D\sqrt{3} \le y \le \bar{\xi} + D\sqrt{3}, \\[2mm] \bar{\xi}, & y > \bar{\xi} + D\sqrt{3}. \end{cases}$$

(15.29)

(The only region of interest is $y > \bar{\xi} - D\sqrt{3}$, for $y < \bar{\xi} - D\sqrt{3}$ implies that $\bar{\delta}$ is independent of price and price would be raised until $y = \bar{\xi} - D\sqrt{3}$.) Now consider the case in which the initial capacity $y(0)$ exceeds the requirement so that $\omega(0) < b\rho$. If in particular $y(0) > \xi(0) + D(0)\sqrt{3}$, then the optimal price is to be determined as the solution of

$$\frac{d}{dt}\left[(p - q)\exp{(-\rho t)}\frac{\partial\bar{\xi}}{\partial\dot{p}}\right] = \exp{(-\rho t)}\frac{\partial}{\partial p}\,[(p - q)\bar{\xi}]. \quad (15.30)$$

In other words, the optimal price is given by

$$p - q = \frac{1 - k_1(\bar{p} - q) - k_2\dot{q}}{2k_1 + k_2(p - \dot{\nu}/\nu)} \qquad (15.31)$$

on an interval $0 \le t \le t_0$, t_0 being the least value of t for which $\omega(t) = b\rho$. The following are some of the characteristics of the solution: (a) the price moves with the size of the market, rising as the market expands and falling as it shrinks; (b) if $\bar{p}$ is interpreted as an estimate of the "average" price of the competing products, then the price (asked by the firm) moves with $\bar{p}$; and (c) the price moves in a direction opposite to that of the interest rate ρ. If at some stage $y > \bar{\xi} + D\sqrt{3}$, then $\omega(t, y) = 0$, and since $\omega(t, y) = b\rho$ on subarcs along which capacity is expanded, it follows that $\bar{\xi} - D\sqrt{3} \le y \le \bar{\xi} + D\sqrt{3}$ on such subarcs. In this case, however, the solution of (15.30) cannot be obtained in a closed form.

AN ALTERNATIVE DERIVATION OF SALES PROBABILITIES IN A DIFFERENTIATED OLIGOPOLY

The special feature of this approach is a suitable measure-theoretic construction which makes it possible to make a direct transition to a generalization of the dynamic model of Chapter 8, Section 2, without requiring the Gaussian approximation.

1 Suppose that the demand-prices δ of all buyers (or, perhaps a section of them) lie between a and b. Then, the scaled variable

$$\omega = \frac{\delta - a}{b - a}$$

will evidently lie in $\Omega = \{\omega \colon 0 \leq \omega \leq 1\}$. The price p asked by the firm, therefore, can be conceived of as a point in Ω. Under the specifications of (S, M, Y) of Chapter 8, Section 2, given a contact, a sale $X(p)$ occurs according to whether the price p is below or above the (unknown) demand-price of the customer. Let $X(p)$ be the indicator of this event:

$$X(p) = \begin{cases} 1, & \text{if } \omega > p, \\ 0, & \text{if } \omega \leq p. \end{cases}$$

The probability of sale (that is, the mathematical expectation of $X(p)$) naturally depends, among other things, upon the location of p in Ω. The emphasis of the following analysis will be on the dependence of sales volume on the selling efforts c. Also, the assumption that a transaction relates to exactly one unit of the product will be abandoned. Therefore, the phenomenon of sales will be viewed as a *stochastic process*, $X(c, \omega)$, $\omega \in \Omega$, $c \in C$. For any given level of c, $X(., \omega)$ will be supposed measurable with countably additive measure function $\mu(.)$ on Ω, such that

$\mu(\Omega) = 1$. The range space of $X(c, \omega)$ will be denoted by L.

2   Consider n realizations of the process $X(c, \omega)$,

$$X_k(c, \omega_k), \qquad \omega_k \in \Omega_k \qquad (k = 1, 2, \ldots, n), \tag{I.1}$$

each representing the outcome of a contact in the market. Since the customers are *not distinguishable* and the contacts are mutually *independent*.

$$\Omega_1 = \Omega_2 = \cdots = \Omega_n = \Omega. \tag{I.2}$$

Next, consider the *number of times* the sales are seen to be in the interval $B \subset L$; this can be represented as

$$N(B, c) = \sum_{k=1}^{n} I[X_k(c, \omega_k)], \tag{I.3}$$

$I(.)$ being an indicator function defined as follows:

$$I[X_k(c, \omega_k)] = \begin{cases} 1, & \text{if } X_k(c, \omega_k) \in B, \\ 0, & \text{otherwise.} \end{cases} \tag{I.4}$$

Of immediate interest is the following probability:

$$\Pr[N(B, c) = r], \tag{I.5}$$

which will be derived from the observation that the underlying sample-space is $\Omega \times \Omega \times \cdots \times \Omega$, an n-fold Cartesian product.

3   It is well known that $\Pr[N(B, c) = r]$ is the measure of the set in $\Omega \times \cdots \times \Omega$ on which $N(B, c) = r$ which, again, is the mathematical expectation of a suitably defined counting function $I(r, \omega)$. Since r is an integer, $I(r, \omega)$ may be represented as

$$\begin{aligned} I(r, \omega) &= \frac{1}{2\pi} \int_0^{2\pi} \exp\{iu[N(B, c) - r]\} \, du \\ &= \begin{cases} 1, & \text{if } N(B, c) = r, \\ 0, & \text{if otherwise.} \end{cases} \end{aligned} \tag{I.6}$$

Its mathematical expectation is the following integral:

$$\begin{aligned} J &= \int\limits_{\Omega_1 \times \cdots \times \Omega_n} \frac{1}{2\pi} \int_0^{2\pi} \exp\{iu[N(B, c) - r]\} \, du \, d\omega_1 \cdots d\omega_n \\ &= \frac{1}{2\pi} \int_0^{2\pi} e^{-iru} du \int\limits_{\Omega_1 \times \cdots \times \Omega_n} \exp\left[iu \sum_1^n I(X_k)\right] d\omega_1 \cdots d\omega_n. \end{aligned}$$

But since the Ω's are independent and identical, the integral on $\Omega_1 \times \cdots \times \Omega_n$ may be evaluated as

$$\int_{\Omega_1 \times \cdots \times \Omega_n} \exp\left[iu \sum_{k=1}^{n} I(X_k) \right] d\omega_1 \cdots d\omega_n$$

$$= \prod_{1=k}^{n} \int_{\Omega} \exp\left[iuI(X_k) \right] d\omega_k = \left\{ \int_{\Omega} \exp\left[iuI(X) \right] d\omega \right\}^n. \quad (I.7)$$

(The first equality is due to the "independence" and the second follows from "indistinguishability.") But the integrand in (I.7) may be written as

$$\exp\{ iuI[X(\omega, c)] \} = 1 + iuI + \frac{(iu)^2}{2!} I + \cdots$$

$$= 1 + \left[iu + \frac{(iu)^2}{2!} + \cdots \right] I$$

$$= 1 + (e^{iu} - 1) I(X(\omega, c)). \quad (I.8)$$

Therefore the integral of (I.7) is evaluated as

$$\int_{\Omega} \exp\{ iuI[X(\omega, c)] \} d\omega = 1 + (e^{iu} - 1)\mu[\omega : X(\omega, c) \in B]$$

$$= 1 + (e^{iu} - 1) \Pr[X(c) \in B],$$

so that the required probability is

$$\Pr[N(B, c) = r] = \frac{1}{2\pi} \int_0^{2\pi} e^{-iru}[1 + (e^{iu} - 1)\Pr[X(c) \in B]]^n \, du. \quad (I.9)$$

4   The expression (I.9) cannot be evaluated without knowledge of $\Pr[X(c) \in B]$. But note, first, that the "probability" of *an* event (namely, "sale") is to be a function of the price p, say, $\sigma(p)$. In order to treat the $\Pr[X(c) \in B]$, then, it will be sufficient to *assume* that stationary probabilities (corresponding to stable patterns of competition) have been established, so that

$$\Pr[X(c) \in B] = \frac{|B|}{|L|} = \frac{\sigma(p)}{|L|}, \quad (I.10)$$

where $|B|$ and $|L|$ indicate the *lengths* of these intervals. ((I.10) is seen to preserve the definition of a probability: When $|B| = |L|$, the probability is 1). Also, observe that n in (I.9) is likely to be large in cases of practical interest. Therefore, we introduce a second *assumption*:

$$\lim_{n \to \infty, |L| \to \infty} \frac{n}{|L|} = \lambda. \quad (I.11)$$

In light of the argument in Chapter 4, Section 2, one may consider λ (the average number of customers in B) as a function of c:

$$\lambda = \lambda(c), \qquad \frac{d\lambda}{dc} \geq 0.$$

Under the assumptions (I.10) and (I.11), it may be immediately verified in (I.9) that

$$\lim_{n \to \infty} \{1 + (e^{iu} - 1) \Pr [X(c) \in B]\}^n$$

$$= \lim_{n \to \infty} \left[1 + (e^{iu} - 1) \frac{|B|}{n} \frac{n}{|L|}\right]^n$$

$$= \exp [\lambda(c)\sigma(p)(e^{iu} - 1)] = \exp [(e^{iu} - 1)A(p, c)]. \quad (I.12)$$

Therefore, the required probability is

$$\Pr [N(B, c) = r] = \frac{1}{2\pi} \int_0^{2\pi} e^{-iur} \, du \exp [(e^{iu} - 1) A(p, c)] \quad (I.13)$$

$$= e^{-A(p,c)}[A(p, c)]^r/r!.$$

which is what was obtained in Chapter 4, Section 2.

5   The merit of this approach may be seen more clearly in the computation of the joint probability

$$\Pr [N(B, c) = r, N(B, c') = s]. \quad (I.14)$$

Since the general procedure has already been laid out, the derivations will be brief. Consider first their presentation of the *two-dimensional counting function*:

$$I (r \, s; \omega) = \frac{1}{(2\pi)^2} \int_0^{2\pi} \int_0^{2\pi} \exp \{iu[N(B, c) - r] + iv[N(B, c') - s]\}$$

$$\times \, du \, dv = \delta_{r,0} \, \delta_{s,0}, \quad (I.15)$$

the $\delta_{\cdot,\cdot}$ being the Kronecker symbols. The mathematical expectation of $I(r, s, \omega)$ is seen to be

$$E[I(r, s; \omega)] = \mu[(\omega, \ldots, \omega) \mid N(B, c, \omega) = r, N(B, c', \omega) = s]$$

$$= \frac{1}{(2\pi)^2} \int_0^{2\pi} \int_0^{2\pi} \exp (-iru - isv) \left(\int_\Omega \exp \{iuI[X(\omega, c)]\right.$$

$$\left. + ivI[X(\omega, c')]\} \, d\omega\right)^n du \, dv \quad (I.16)$$

which is the two-dimensional analogue of (I.7). Noting, again, that the

$I[X(\omega, c)]$ and $I[X(\omega, c')]$ are indicator functions, it may be seen that

$$\exp\{iuI[X(\omega, c)] + ivI[X(\omega, c')]\}$$
$$= 1 + (e^{iu} - 1) I[X(\omega, c)] + (e^{iv} - 1) I[X(\omega, c')]$$
$$+ (e^{iu} - 1)(e^{iv} - 1) I[X(\omega, c)] I[X(\omega, c')].$$

Thus, the inner integral in (I.16) is evaluated as

$$\int_\Omega \exp\{iuI[X(\omega, c)] + ivI[X(\omega, c')]\} d\omega$$
$$= 1 + (e^{iu} - 1) \mu[\omega \mid X(\omega, c) \in B] + (e^{iv} - 1)\mu[\omega \mid X(\omega, c') \in B]$$
$$+ (e^{iu} - 1)(e^{iv} - 1)\mu[(\omega, \omega) \mid X(\omega, c) \in B, X(\omega, c') \in B] \equiv g(u, v). \quad (I.17)$$

Consequently, the probability in (I.14) is

$$\Pr[N(B, c) = r, N(B, c') = s]$$
$$= \frac{1}{(2\pi)^2} \int_0^{2\pi} \int_0^{2\pi} e^{-iru - isv}[g(u, v)]^n \, du \, dv. \quad (I.18)$$

We may still invoke the aid of assumptions (I.10) and (I.11), but they do not provide sufficient means to compute the measure $\mu[(\omega, \omega) \mid X(c) \in B]$ on $\Omega \times \Omega$. However, because competition has been assumed to be stable, we may *assume* that this measure would depend solely on the magnitude $|c' - c|$ of the difference in selling efforts. (In fact, the assumption (I.10) is another aspect of the phenomenon of stationarity.) Also, suppose that as $n \to \infty$ and $L \to \infty$ there is a limiting *conditional probability* that a customer who was in the sales-bracket B (when the firm was making sales efforts c) also remains in B when the sales efforts are c'. In particular, *assume* that this limiting probability has the form

$$\Psi(c' - c) = \frac{1}{|B|} \int_B \int_B P(x', c' \mid x, c) \, dx \, dx'$$
$$= \frac{1}{\sigma(p)} \int_B \int_B P(x', c' - c \mid x, o) \, dx \, dx', \quad (I.19)$$

in which x and x' are the values taken on by $X(c)$ and $X(c')$. Under assumptions (I.10), (I.11), and (I.19) it is seen that

$$\lim_{n \to \infty, |L| \to \infty} [g(u, v)]^n = \exp[\sigma(p)\lambda(c)\{(e^{iu} - 1) + (e^{iv} - 1)$$
$$+ \Psi(c' - c)(e^{iu} - 1)(e^{iv} - 1)] \equiv G(u, v). \quad (I.20)$$

We write

$$\Pr[N(B, c) = r \mid N(B, c') = s]$$
$$= \lim_{n \to \infty, |L| \to \infty} \frac{1}{(2\pi)^2} \int_0^{2\pi} \int_0^{2\pi} e^{-iru - isv}[g(u, v)]^n \, du \, dv$$
$$= \frac{1}{(2\pi)^2} \int_0^{2\pi} \int_0^{2\pi} e^{-iur - isv} G(u, v) \, du \, dv \equiv M(r, s; c' - c). \quad (I.21)$$

It remains to verify that the marginal distributions associated with the above distribution retain the form derived earlier. This is done by observing that

$$M(r, c) = \sum_{s=0}^{\infty} M(r, c; s, c')$$

$$= \frac{1}{2\pi} \int_0^{2\pi} e^{-iur} G(u, o) \, du$$

$$= e^{-A(p,c)} \frac{[A(p, c)]^r}{r!}. \tag{I.22}$$

6 In view of what appears in the multiperiod model of Chapter 8, Section 2, it will be profitable to investigate whether the stochastic process defined by assumptions (I.10), (I.11), and (I.19) is Markovian. First, observe that in order that the process $X(c, \omega)$ may be Markovian, the *conditional* probabilities must satisfy the Chapman-Kolmogorov equation:

$$P(r_k, c_k; \cdots; r_2, c_2 \mid r_1, c_1) = P(r_2, c_2 \mid r_1, c_1) \cdots P(r_k, c_k \mid r_{k-1}c_{k-1}). \tag{I.23}$$

Let $c' - c = \alpha$ and consider the implication of this property:

$$P(s, \alpha \mid r, 0) = \prod_{s'=0}^{\infty} P(s, \alpha; s', \alpha' \mid r, 0)$$

$$= \prod_{s'=0}^{\infty} P(s', \alpha' \mid r, 0) P(r, \alpha - \alpha' \mid s', 0),$$

which, again, implies that the matrix $Q(\alpha)$ of the probabilities $P(s, \alpha \mid r, 0)$ satisfies the following relationship:

$$Q(\alpha) = Q(\alpha') \cdot Q(\alpha - \alpha'). \tag{I.24}$$

Next, observe that the conditional probabilities $P(s, \alpha \mid r, 0)$ can be developed from the following expansion of $G(u, v)$ in (I.20):

$$G(u, v) = \exp [A(p, c)(e^{iu} - 1)] \exp [A(p, c)(e^{iv} - 1)]$$

$$\times \sum_{j=0}^{\infty} \frac{\Psi^j(\sigma)}{j!} (e^{iu} - 1)^j (e^{iv} - 1)^j. \tag{I.25}$$

Define the following symbols:

$$\Gamma_{rj} = e^{A(p,c)} [A(p, c)]^r (r!) \frac{1}{2\pi} \int_0^{2\pi} \exp [-iurG_1(u)]$$

$$G_1(u) \equiv \exp [A(p, c)(e^{iu} - 1)][e^{iu} - 1)^j$$

$$\Phi_{js} = \frac{1}{j!} \frac{1}{2\pi} \int_0^{2\pi} e^{-ivs} G_2(v) \, dv$$

$$G_2(v) \equiv \exp [A(p, c)(e^{iv} - 1)](e^{iv} - 1)^j .$$

In terms of these symbols, it may be verified that

$$P(s, \alpha \mid r, 0) = \frac{M(s, \alpha; r, 0)}{M(r)} = \sum_{j=0}^{\infty} \Gamma_{rj} [\Psi(\alpha)]^j \Phi_{js}. \tag{I.26}$$

In view of the fact that $\Psi(0) = 1$, the following must hold:

$$P(s, 0 \mid r, 0) = \begin{cases} 1, & \text{if } s = r, \\ 0, & \text{otherwise}; \end{cases}$$

hence Γ_{rj} and Φ_{js} satisfy the following equation:

$$\sum_{j=0}^{\infty} \Gamma_{rj} \Phi_{js} = \begin{cases} 1, & \text{if } s = r, \\ 0, & \text{otherwise}. \end{cases}$$

Therefore $P(s, \alpha \mid r, 0)$ may be interpreted as a restriction of the matrix $Q(\alpha)$ to the diagonal. Finally, observe that for (I.24) to hold it is necessary only to have $\Psi(\alpha) = \Psi(\alpha') \Psi(\alpha - \alpha')$; but because $\Psi(\alpha)$ is to be measurable, this property requires that $\Psi(\alpha)$ have the form

$$\Psi(\alpha) = e^{-\beta |\alpha|}, \qquad \beta > 0. \tag{I.27}$$

It is instructive to compare this form with a similar one *postulated* in Chapter 8. Equations (I.25) and (I.26) relate to *conditional probabilities*, whereas the corresponding forms in Chapter 8 relate to *correlations*. Preliminary analysis of computer experiments appears to substantiate the forms in (I.25) and (I.26), although the fulfillment of this condition is not sufficient to assert that the Markov property holds.

Appendix II

ON THE CONCAVITY OF AVERAGE PROFITS FUNCTION

1 Recall the definition of expected or average net profits:

$$\bar{\pi}(p, c) = (p - c)A(p, c) - E[K(S)], \qquad A(p, c) \equiv \mu(p)\lambda(c), \qquad \text{(II.1)}$$

and introduce the following hypotheses:

1. The partial derivatives $\partial^n A/\partial p^r \partial c^{n-r}$, $(r = 0, 1, \ldots, n; \ n = 1, 2, \ldots, N < \infty)$ exist and are finite on $R = \{(p, c):p_1 < p < p_2, c_1 < c < c_2\}$.

2. For arbitrarily small positive numbers δ_1 and δ_2, and for $n > 1$, the quantities

$$\binom{n}{r} \frac{h^{n-r}k^r}{A(p, c)} \frac{\partial^n A(p, c)}{\partial p^r \partial c^{n-r}}, \qquad r = 0, 1, \ldots, n,$$

are of the order of o(n, k) whenever $|h| < \delta_1$ and $|k| < \delta_2$.

(The symbol o(h, k) signifies

$$\lim_{|h| \to 0, |k| \to 0} \frac{o(h, k)}{|h| + |k|} = 0).$$

The second hypothesis essentially amounts to the statement that, for very small variations of p or c, the function $A(p, c)$ has no points of discontinuity of the first kind and may be approximated very closely by a two-dimensional plane. In particular, observe that for $n = 1$, this hypothesis is equivalent to the one that states that $A(p, c) = \mu(p)\lambda(c)$ satisfies a Lipschitz condition in both of its arguments. The requirement that $(h/A) \partial A/\partial p$ be of the order o(h) for $|h| < \delta_1$, is equivalent to the requirement that $(h/A) \partial A/\partial p < \beta$ (where β is a positive constant), that is, the price elasticity of sales has finite upper and lower bounds. Similarly, the requirement that $(k/A) \partial A/\partial c$ be of the order of o(k) for $|k| < \delta_2$ is equivalent to the requirement that the elasticity of sales with respect to selling efforts should be finite.

2 Also recall that a function $G(x, y)$ of two real variables x and y is said to be *concave* in x and y on $\tilde{R} = \{(x, y) : a_1 < x < a_2, b_1 < y < b_2\}$ if and only if, for $0 \leq \alpha \leq 1$, the inequality

$$G(\alpha x' + (1 - \alpha)x'', \alpha y' + (1 - \alpha)y'') \leq \alpha G(x', y') + (1 - \alpha)G(x'', y''),$$
(II.2)

holds everywhere on $\tilde{R}$. Next, choose a pair of arbitrary points in $\tilde{R}$, $P : (p', c')$ and $Q : (p'', c'')$, and consider the function $\bar{\pi}(p, c)$ for the two arguments $\alpha p' + (1 - \alpha)p''$ and $\alpha c' + (1 - \alpha)c''$:

$$\bar{\pi}(\alpha p' + (1 - \alpha)p'', \alpha c' + (1 - \alpha)c'')$$
$$= [\alpha p' + \bar{\alpha} p'' - \alpha c - \bar{\alpha} c''] \cdot A(\alpha p' + \bar{\alpha} p'', \alpha c' + \bar{\alpha} c'')$$
$$- E[K(S) \mid \alpha p' + \bar{\alpha} p'', \alpha c' + \bar{\alpha} c''], \qquad (\bar{\alpha} \equiv 1 - \alpha). \quad \text{(II.3)}$$

The last term in the right member of (II.3) signifies that, in computing the mathematical expectation of $K(S)$, one should consider the "perturbations" given to p and c which appear as parameters in the probability distribution of S.

3 Define the following symbols:

$$h = \alpha p' + \bar{\alpha}(p'' - p') = \bar{\alpha}(p'' - p'); \qquad h' = p'' - p'; \quad \text{(II.4)}$$
$$k = \alpha c' + \bar{\alpha}(c'' - c') = \bar{\alpha}(c'' - c'); \qquad k' = c'' - c'$$

and expand $A(.\,,\,.)$ and $E[K(S) \mid .\,,\,.]$ of (II.3) in Taylor series up to the linear terms. Thus,

$$A(\alpha p' + \bar{\alpha} p'', \alpha c' + \bar{\alpha} c'')$$
$$= A(p' + h, c' + k) \cong A(p', c') + h\left(\frac{\partial A}{\partial c}\right)_P + k\left(\frac{\partial A}{\partial c}\right)_P; \quad \text{(II.5)}$$

$$E[K(S) \mid \alpha p' + \bar{\alpha} p'', \alpha c' + \alpha c'']$$
$$= E[K(S) \mid p' + h, c' + k]$$
$$\cong E[K(S) \mid p', c'] + h\left(\frac{\partial E[K(S)]}{\partial p}\right)_P + k\left(\frac{\partial E[K(S)]}{\partial c}\right)_P. \quad \text{(II.6)}$$

Similarly, employing the variables h' and k', consider the following expansion:

$$A(p'', c'') = A(p' + h', c' + k')$$
$$\cong A(p', c') + h'\left(\frac{\partial A}{\partial p}\right)_P + k'\left(\frac{\partial A}{\partial c}\right)_P, \quad \text{(II.7)}$$

$$E[K(S) \mid p'', c''] = E[K(S) \mid p' + h', c' + k']$$
$$\cong E[K(S) \mid p', c'] + h'\left(\frac{\partial E[K(S)]}{\partial p}\right)_P + k'\left(\frac{\partial E[K(S)]}{\partial c}\right)_P.$$
(II.8)

In view of (II.4) to (II.8), the condition (II.2) for concavity gives the following: $\bar{\pi}(p, c)$ is concave in both p and c if and only if everywhere on $\tilde{R}$ the following holds:

$$-(p' - p'')^2 \frac{\partial A}{\partial p} + (c' - c'')^2 \frac{\partial A}{\partial c} + (p' - p'')(c'' - c')$$

$$\times \left[\frac{\partial A}{\partial c} - \frac{\partial A}{\partial p}\right] \geq 0. \quad (II.9)$$

On account of the properties postulated for $\partial A/\partial p$ and $\partial A/\partial c$ in Chapter 4, Section 2, the first two terms in the left member of (II.9) are positive. However, there is no a priori reason to suppose that everywhere on $\tilde{R}$ the third term is either nonnegative or, if negative, is less than the sum of the first two terms. This is the reason why concavity is not *assured* on purely a priori grounds.

REFERENCES

[1] Arrow, K. J., S. Karlin, and H. Scarf. *Studies in the Mathematical Theory of Inventory and Production.* Stanford University Press, Stanford, 1958.

[2] ————. *Studies in Applied Probability and Management Science.* Stanford University Press, Stanford, 1961.

[3] Arrow, K. J. "Price-Quantity Adjustments in Multiple Markets" in *Mathematical Methods in the Social Sciences.* Stanford University Press, Stanford, 1960.

[4] Arrow, K. J., M. Beckman, and S. Karlin. "Optimal Expansions of Capacity of a Firm," pp. 92–105, in *Studies in the Mathematical Theory of Inventory and Production.* Stanford University Press, Stanford, 1958.

[5] Bass, F. M. "A Dynamic Model of Market Share and Sales Behavior." *Proc. Winter Conf. Amer. Mktg. Assoc.*, December 1963.

[6] Bellman, R. *Dynamic Programming.* Princeton University Press, Princeton, New Jersey, 1957.

[7] Bendat, J. S. *Principles and Applications of Random Noise Theory.* John Wiley, New York, 1958, pp. 212–217.

[8] Berkowitz, L. "Variational Methods of Control and Programming." *J. Math. Anal. Appl.*, **3**, 145–169, 1961.

[9] Bertrand, J. *Theorie Mathematique de la Richesse Sociale. J. des Sarants*, pp. 499–508, 1883.

[10] Blanc-LaPierre, A., and R. Fortet. *Theorie Des Fonctions Aleatoires.* Masson et Cie, Paris, pp. 329–334, 1953.

[11] Bowley, A. L. *The Mathematical Groundwork of Economics.* Oxford University Press, Oxford, 1924.

[12] Chamberlin, E. H. *The Theory of Monopolistic Competition.* Harvard University Press, Cambridge, 1956.

[13] ————. *Towards a More General Theory of Value.* Harvard University Press, Cambridge, 1957.

[14] Charnes, A., and W. W. Cooper. *Management Models and Industrial Applications of Linear Programming*, **II**, 671–678. John Wiley, New York, 1961.

[15] ————. "Chance Constrained Programming." *Management Science.* **6**(1), 73–79, 1959.

[16] Cournot, A. *Researches into the Mathematical Principles of the Theory of Wealth.* (Eng. Tr. by N. T. Bacon.) Macmillan, New York, 1927.

[17] Cox, D. R. *Renewal Theory.* Methuen and Company, London, 1962.

[18] Cyert, R. M., and J. G. March. *A Behavioral Theory of the Firm.* Prentice-Hall, Englewood Cliffs, New Jersey, 1963.

[19] Darling, D. A., and A. J. F. Siegert. "The First Passage Problem for a Continuous Markov Process." *Annals Math. Stat.*, **24**, (4), 624–639, 1953.

[20] Doob, J. L. *Stochastic Processes.* John Wiley, New York, 1953.

[21] Feller, W. *An Introduction to Probability Theory and Its Applications*, Vol. **I.** John Wiley, New York, 1957.

[22] Fellner, W. *Competition Among the Few.* Augustus M. Kelley, New York, 1960.

[23] Fouraker, L. E., and S. Siegel. *Bargaining Behavior.* McGraw-Hill, New York, 1963.

[24] Hadley, G., and T. M. Whitin. *Analysis of Inventory Systems.* Prentice-Hall, Englewood Cliffs, New Jersey, 1963.

[25] Harrod, Roy F. "Price and Cost in Entrepreneurs' Policy." *Oxford Economic Papers,* No. 2, 1939.

[26] Haynes, W. W. *Pricing Decisions in Small Business.* University of Kentucky Press, Lexington, 1962.

[27] Hicks, J. R. *A Revision of Demand Theory.* Oxford University Press, London, 1959.

[28] ———. *Value and Capital* (2nd ed.). Oxford University Press, London, 1946.

[29] Hinomoto, H. "Capacity Expansion with Facilities Under Technological Improvement." *Management Science,* 581–592, March 1965.

[30] Holt, C. C., F. Modigliam, J. F. Muth, and H. A. Simon. *Planning Production, Inventories and Work Force.* Prentice-Hall, Englewood Cliffs, New Jersey, 1960.

[31] Howard, Ronald A. "Stochastic Process Models of Consumer Behavior." *J. Advertising Res.,* 3(3), 1963.

[32] Kac, M. *Statistical Independence in Probability, Analysis, and Number Theory.* Carus Memorial Lectures, Mathematical Society of America, 1959.

[33] Kahn, R. F. "The Problem of Duopoly." *Eco. J.* Vol. XLVII, 1937.

[34] Kaplan, A. D. H., *et al. Pricing in Big Business: A Case Approach.* The Brookings Institutions, Washington, D.C., 1958.

[35] Kaysen, Carl. "Collusion Under the Sherman Act." *Quart. J. Eco.,* LXV, 267–270, 1951.

[36] Kendall, M. G. *The Advanced Theory of Statistics,* Vol. **II.** Charles Griffin, London, 1952.

[37] Koopmans, T. C., and W. Hood. *Studies in Econometric Method.* Cowles Commission for Research in Economics, Monograph No. 14, 1961.

[38] Koyck, L. M. *Distributed Lags and Investment Analysis.* North-Holland Publishing, Amsterdam, 1954.

[39] Liebhafsky, H. H. *The Nature of Price Theory.* The Dorsey Press, Homewood, Illinois, 1963.

[40] Machlup, F. *The Economics of Sellers' Competition.* Johns Hopkins Press, Baltimore, 1952.

[41] Middleton, D. *An Introduction to Statistical Communication Theory.* McGraw-Hill, New York, 1960.

[42] Mood, A. M. *Introduction to the Theory of Statistics.* McGraw-Hill, New York, 1950.

[43] Price, R. "A Useful Theorem for Nonlinear Devices Having Gaussian Inputs." *IRE Transactions,* PGIT, 4(1), 69 ff, 1958.

[44] Rosenblatt, M. "Independence and Dependence," pp. 431–443 in *Proceedings of the Fourth Berkeley Symposium on Mathematical Statistics and Probability,* Vol. **II.** University of California Press, Berkeley, 1961.

[45] Rozanoff, Ur. A. "An Application of the Central Limit Theorem," pp. 445–454 in *Proceedings of the Fourth Berkeley Symposium on Mathematical Statistics and Probability,* Vol. **II.** University of California Press, Berkeley, 1961.

[46] Samuelson, P. A. *Foundations of Economic Analysis,* pp. 269–276. Harvard University Press, Cambridge, 1947.

[47] Scitovsky, T. *Welfare and Competition.* Unwin University Books, London, 1952.

[48] Shubik, M. *Strategy and Market Structure.* John Wiley, New York, 1959.

[49] Shubik, M., and J. H. Griesmer. "Towards a Study of Bidding Processes." *Naval Res. Logistics Quat.,* 10(1, 2, 3), 11–217, 1963.

[50] Siegel, S. *Nonparametric Statistics for Behavioral Sciences.* McGraw-Hill, New York, 1956.

[51] Silver, E. A. "Markovian Decision Processes with Uncertain Transition Probabilities or Rewards." Technical Report No. 1, Research in Control of Complex Systems. Cambridge, M.I.T., August 1963.

[52] Smith, V. *Investment and Production,* Harvard University Press, Cambridge, 1961.

[53a] Sneddon, I. A. *Fourier Transforms.* McGraw-Hill, New York, 1951.

[53b] *Elements of Partial Differential Equations.* McGraw-Hill, New York, 1957.

[54] Stigler, G. J. "Notes on the Theory of Duopoly." *J. Pol. Eco.,* **XLVIII**, 533 ff, 1940.

[55] Sweezy, P. M. "Demand Under Condition of Oligopoly." *J. Pol. Eco.,* **XLVII**, 568–573, 1939.

[56] Telser, L. G. "Advertising and Cigarettes." *J. Pol. Eco.,* Vol. **LXX**(5), October 1962.

[57] ———. "The Demand for Branded Goods as Estimated from Consumer Panel Data." *Rev. Eco. Stat.* Vol. **XLIV**(3), August 1963.

[58] Valentine, F. A. "The Problem of Lagrange with Differential Inequalities as Added Side Conditions," pp. 407–488 in *Contributions to the Calculus of Variations* (1933–37). University of Chicago Press, Chicago, 1937.

[59] von Neuman, J., and O. Morgenstern. *The Theory of Games and Economic Behavior.* Princeton University Press. Princeton, New Jersey, 1947.

[60] von Stackelberg, H. *The Theory of the Market Economy.* William Hodge, London, 1952.

[61] Wagner, H. M. *Statistical Management of Inventory Systems.* John Wiley, New York, 1962.

[62] Wilks, S. S. *Mathematical Statistics.* John Wiley, New York, 1962.

[63] Edgeworth, F. Y. *Papers Relating to Political Economy,* I, 111–142. Macmillan, London, 1925.

[64] Rothschild, K. W. "Price Theory and Oligopoly." *Eco. J.,* **LVII**, 304 ff., 1947.

[65] Eiteman, W. J. *Price Determination.* Business Report No. 16, School of Business Administration, University of Michigan, Ann Arbor, 1949.

[66] Manne, A. S. "Capacity Expansion and Probabilistic Growth." *Econometrica,* pp. 632–49, October 1961.

[67] Berkowitz, L. D. "Variational Methods in Problems of Control and Programming." *J. Math. Anal. Appl.,* pp. 145–69, 1961.

INDEX

Anticipations, about price, 158–163
  reinforcement of, in pure competition, 158–169
Autocorrelation function, of sales in differentiated oligopoly, 87–89
  of sales in undifferentiated oligopoly, 81–83

Classical theory, conjectural variation in, 11–14
  equilibrium and determinacy in, 8–11
  modification of, 7, 17–19, 24, 25
Collusion, apparent, in differentiated oligopoly, 114, 115
  in undifferentiated oligopoly, 95–98, 107, 108
Competition, descriptors of, 18, 136, 137
  dimensions of, 2–7
  equilibrium and determinacy of, 8–16
  framework of, 17–20
  price–quantity distribution in pure, 141–150
  state of mind or set of acts, 20

Decision, multiperiod, 79–98
  pricing and investment, 202–211
  production and inventories, 99–115, 170–187

Decision, single period, 62–78

Institutions, role of, in analysis, 18
  types of, 27, 33, 34, 38, 39, 53, 54, 158–163, 188–191

Kinked demand curve, 85, 107

Leadership, 14–16

Market share, conflict with other objectives, 75–78
  in differentiated oligopoly, 35, 36
  in undifferentiated oligopoly, 28–30
  related to price and profits, 62–78
  tradeoff with profits, 67–70
Monopolistic competition, brand preference, 55–59
  Chamberlin's tangency condition, 116–118
  interaction among sales, 53–55
  macro distribution of sales, 41–44
  micro distribution of sales, 44–51

Oligopoly, differentiated, derivation of sales probabilities in, 34–36
  descriptors of, 33–34
  in interaction among sales, 53–55
  sales probability in "large group" case of, 37–40

Oligopoly, differentiated, skewness of
    sales distribution, 59-61

Oligopoly, undifferentiated, deriva-
    tion of sales probability,
    28-30, 213-219
    descriptors of, 27

Price rigidity, in differentiated
    oligopoly, 114, 115
    in undifferentiated oligopoly,
    95-98, 107, 108

Optimization, Chamberlin's tangency
    condition, compared with,
    116-118
    of shortrun profits, 99, 100
    structure of optimal decision rules
    under, 99-115, 170-187,
    202-211

Transition probabilities, Markovian
    property of, 92-95, 150-157

Transition probabilities, of prices
    in pure competition, 150-157
    of sales in differentiated oligopoly,
    89-92, 192-201
    of sales in undifferentiated
    oligopoly, 82-86

Uncertainty, in price, 137-141
    in volume of sales, 20-22
    measure of, 21
    nature of, in oligopoly, 27,
    36, 40, 188-191,
    213-219
    nature of, in pure competi-
    tion, 136

Verification, method adopted
    for, 121-124
    nature of, 119-121
    results of, 125-127,
    132-134, 194-201